Communication and Professional Practice

Dearborn™
Home Inspection

This publication is designed to provide accurate and authoritative information in regard to the subject matter covered. It is sold with the understanding that the publisher is not engaged in rendering legal, accounting, or other professional service. If legal advice or other expert assistance is required, the services of a competent professional person should be sought.

President: Roy Lipner
Publisher and Director of Distance Learning: Evan M. Butterfield
Senior Development Editor: Laurie McGuire
Content Consultant: Alan Carson
Acting Editorial Production Manager: Daniel Frey
Creative Director: Lucy Jenkins
Graphic Design: Neglia Design Inc.

INTRODUCTION

Welcome! This home inspection training program has two primary goals:

• To provide you with a sound introduction to the components, materials and mechanics of house systems that you will encounter and evaluate as a home inspector;

• To provide you with a solid understanding of inspection processes, strategies and standards of practice that will help define the scope of your inspections.

We hope you enjoy this training program and develop a good understanding of the various house systems as you proceed. Good luck!

FEATURES OF THIS PROGRAM

This program is structured to help you learn and retain the key concepts of home inspection. It also will help you form a set of best practices for conducting inspections. A number of features are included to help you master the information and put your knowledge into practice:

• Topics are organized into evenly paced Study Sessions. Each Session begins with learning objectives and key words to set up the important concepts you should master by the end of the Session. Each Session concludes with Quick Quizzes to help you test your understanding. Answers to Quick Quizzes are provided so you can check your results.

• Scope and Introduction sections present the ASHI® (American Society of Home Inspectors) Standards of Practice for each major topic. Standards help you define a professional, consistent depth and breadth for your inspections.

• An Inspection Checklist at the end of each section summarizes the important components you will be inspecting and their typical problems. You can use this as a set of field notes during your own inspections.

• The Inspection Tools list will help you build your toolkit of "must have" and optional tools for the job.

• An Inspection Procedures section provides some general guidelines to conducting your inspection of each major house system. This feature will help you develop a methodology to complement your technical knowledge.

• Field Exercises give you an opportunity to turn your knowledge into real world experience.

SUMMARY

The road we have paved for you is designed to be easy and enjoyable to follow. We trust it will lead you quickly to your destination of success in the home inspection profession.

ACKNOWLEDGMENTS

Thanks to Kevin O'Malley for his inspiration, advice and guidance. Thanks also to James Dobney for his invaluable input and encouragement. Special thanks are extended to Dan Friedman for his numerous and significant contributions.

We are grateful for the contributions of: Duncan Hannay, Richard Weldon, Peter Yeates, Tony Wong, Graham Clarke, Ian Cunliffe, Joe Seymour, Charles Gravely, Graham Lobban, Dave Frost, Gerard Gransaull, Jim Stroud, Diana DeSantis, David Ballantyne, Shawn Carr and Steve Liew.

Special thanks are also extended to Susan Bonham, Dearbhla Lynch, Lucia Cardoso-Tavares, Jill Brownlee, Ida Cristello and Rita Minicucci-Colavecchia who have brought everything together. Thanks also to Jim Lingerfelt for his invaluable editing assistance.

► PROFESSIONAL PRACTICE

► COMMUNICATION AND REPORT WRITING

1

PROFESSIONAL PRACTICE

Communication & Professional Practice

MODULE

► TABLE OF CONTENTS

► 1.0 OBJECTIVES

The Practice,
Not The
Business

The goal of this Section is to provide you with an overview of the home inspection practice. We will describe home inspections and home inspectors. This program is not about the **business** of home inspection. We won't be dealing with marketing, operations or finance issues.

Not Technical

It's also not a technical section. We won't be talking about how to identify and inspect specific house components. The other nine Modules in this program are dedicated to these issues.

Who, What,
How And Why

By the end of this Section, you should have a good understanding of what a home inspection is and how and why home inspections are conducted. You'll learn about the characteristics of a good inspector and about typical clients. For some of you this will be review of familiar material. We believe there is enough thought provoking material to make it worth reading even if you've been in home inspection for some time.

Communication & Professional Practice

M O D U L E

STUDY SESSION 1

1. This Study Session covers the general sections of the ASHI® Standards of Practice, the Code of Ethics and a general introduction.

2. At the end of this Study Session, you should be able to –
- describe in one sentence what home inspections must provide for clients
- describe three components of written reports
- describe two general limitations to inspections
- list 10 general exclusions to home inspections
- list 13 things that inspectors are not required to do as part of an inspection
- define the term **technically exhaustive**
- define **home inspector**
- summarize in one sentence each the seven elements of the Code of Ethics

3. This Study Session may take roughly one hour.

4. Quick Quiz 1 is at the end of this Session.

Key Words
- **Scope**
- **Significantly deficient**
- **Observed**
- **Installed systems and components**
- **Technically exhaustive**
- **Life expectancy**
- **Causes**
- **Methods**
- **Specialized use**

- *Compliance*
- *Market value*
- *Advisability of purchase*
- *Pests*
- *Cosmetic items*
- *Underground items*
- *Warranties*
- *Guarantees*
- *Engineering*
- *Strength*
- *Adequacy*
- *Efficiency*
- *Shut down*
- *Normal operating controls*
- *Hazardous substance*
- *Future conditions*
- *Operating costs*
- *Acoustical properties*
- *Inspector*
- *Practical experience*
- *Honest conviction*
- *Good faith*
- *Disclose information*
- *Compensation*
- *Commissions or allowances*
- *Conflict of interest*
- *Professional integrity*

► 2.0 SCOPE AND INTRODUCTION

2.1 SCOPE

We'll start our discussion by looking at the scope of a home inspection as defined by the American Society of Home Inspectors (ASHI®). These are the most broadly accepted Standards of Practice in the profession throughout North America. There are other standards set by other organizations and while there are differences, they are substantially similar.

We'll start by looking at the general parts of the Standards. We won't deal with the specific component inspection details, since they are dealt with in each of the corresponding Modules of this program. We'll then move on to discuss the Code of Ethics.

2.1.1 THE ASHI® STANDARDS OF PRACTICE

The following are the ASHI® Standards of Practice effective January 1, 2000.

1. INTRODUCTION

1.1 The American Society of Home Inspectors® Inc. (ASHI) is a not-for profit professional society established in 1976. Membership in ASHI is voluntary and its members include private, fee-paid *home inspectors.* ASHI's objectives include promotion of excellence within the profession and continual improvement of its members' inspection services to the public.

2. PURPOSE AND SCOPE

2.1 The purpose of these Standards of Practice is to establish a minimum and uniform standard for private, fee-paid home *inspectors* who are members of the American Society of Home Inspectors. *Home Inspections* performed to these Standards of Practice are intended to provide the client with information regarding the condition of the *systems* and *components* of the home as inspected at the time of the *Home Inspection.*

2.2 The *inspector* shall:

    A. *inspect*:

        1. *readily accessible systems* and *components* of homes listed in these Standards of Practice.

        2. installed *systems* and *components* of homes listed in these Standards of Practice.

B. *report:*

1. on those *systems* and *components* inspected which, in the professional opinion of the *inspector,* are *significantly deficient* or are near the end of their service lives.
2. a reason why, if not self-evident, the *system* or *component* is *significantly deficient* or near the end of its service life.
3. the inspector's recommendations to correct or monitor the reported deficiency.
4. on any *systems* and *components* designated for inspection in these Standards of Practice which were present at the time of the *Home Inspection* but were not inspected and a reason they were not inspected.

2.3 These Standards of Practice are not intended to limit *inspectors* from:

A. including other inspection services, *systems* or *components* in addition to those required by these Standards of Practice.

B. specifying repairs, provided the *inspector* is appropriately qualified and willing to do so.

C. excluding *systems* and *components* from the inspection if requested by the client.

3. STRUCTURAL SYSTEM

3.1   The *inspector* shall:

A. *inspect:*

1. the *structural components* including foundation and framing.
2. by probing a *representative number* of structural components where deterioration is suspected or where clear indications of possible deterioration exist. Probing is NOT required when probing would damage any finished surface or where no deterioration is visible.

B. *describe:*

1. the foundation and report the methods used to *inspect* the *under-floor crawl space.*
2. the floor structure.
3. The wall structure.
4. The ceiling structure.
5. The roof structure and *report* the methods used to *inspect* the attic.

3.2 The *inspector* is NOT required to:

A. provide any *engineering service* or *architectural service.*

B. Offer an opinion as to the adequacy of any *structural system* or *component.*

4. EXTERIOR

4.1 The *inspector* shall:

A. *inspect*:

    1. the exterior wall covering, flashing and trim.
    2. all exterior doors.
    3. attached decks, balconies, stoops, steps, porches, and their associated railings.
    4. the eaves, soffits, and fascias where accessible from the ground level.
    5. the vegetation, grading, surface drainage, and retaining walls on the property when any of these are likely to adversely affect the building.
    6. walkways, patios, and driveways leading to dwelling entrances.

B. *describe* the exterior wall covering.

4.2 The *inspector* is NOT required to:

A. *inspect*:

    1. screening, shutters, awnings, and similar seasonal accessories.
    2. fences.
    3. geological, geotechnical or hydrological conditions.
    4. *recreational facilities*.
    5. outbuildings.
    6. seawalls, break-walls, and docks.
    7. erosion control and earth stabilization measures.

5. ROOF SYSTEM

5.1 The *inspector* shall:

A. *inspect*:

    1. the roof covering.
    2. the *roof drainage systems.*
    3. the flashings.
    4. the skylights, chimneys, and roof penetrations.

B. describe the roof covering and *report* the methods used to *inspect* the roof.

5.2 The *inspector* is NOT required to:

A. *inspect:*

    1. antennae.
    2. interiors of flues or chimneys which are not *readily accessible.*
    3. other *installed* accessories.

6. PLUMBING SYSTEM

6.1 The *inspector* shall:

A. *inspect*:

1. the interior water supply and distribution systems including all fixtures and faucets.
2. the drain, waste and vent *systems* including all fixtures.
3. the water heating equipment.
4. the vent systems, flues and chimneys.
5. the fuel storage and fuel distribution *systems*.
6. the drainage sumps, sump pumps, and related piping.

B. *describe*:

1. the water supply, drain, waste, and vent piping materials.
2. the water heating equipment including the energy source.
3. The location of main water and main fuel shut-off valves.

6.2 The *inspector* is NOT required to:

A. *inspect:*

1. the clothes washing machine connections.
2. the interiors of flues or chimneys which are not *readily accessible*.
3. wells, well pumps, or water storage related equipment.
4. water conditioning *systems*.
5. solar water heating *systems*.
6. fire and lawn sprinkler *systems*.
7. private waste disposal *systems*.

B. determine:

1. whether water supply and waste disposal systems are public or private.
2. the quantity or quality of the water supply.

C. operate safety valves or shut-off valves.

7. ELECTRICAL SYSTEM

7.1 The *inspector* shall:

A. *inspect*:

1. the service drop.
2. the service entrance conductors, cables, and raceways.
3. the service equipment and main disconnects.
4. the service grounding.
5. the interior components of service panels and sub panels.
6. the conductors.
7. the overcurrent protection devices.
8. *a representative number of installed* lighting fixtures, switches and receptacles.
9. the ground fault circuit interrupters.

B. *describe*:

1. the amperage and voltage rating of the service.
2. the location of main disconnect(s) and sub panels.
3. the *wiring methods*.

C. *report*:

1. on the presence of solid conductor aluminum branch circuit wiring.
2. on the absence of smoke detectors.

7.2 The *inspector* is NOT required to:

A. *inspect:*

1. the remote control devices unless the device is the only control device.
2. the *alarm systems* and *components*.
3. the low voltage wiring, *systems* and *components*.
4. the ancillary wiring, *systems* and *components* not a part of the primary electrical power distribution *system*.

B. measure amperage, voltage, or impedance.

8. HEATING SYSTEM

8.1 The *inspector* shall:

A. *inspect*:

1. the installed heating equipment.
2. the vent systems, flues, and chimneys.

B. *describe:*

1. the energy source.
2. the heating method by its distinguishing characteristics.

8.2 The *inspector* **is NOT required to:**

  A. *inspect*:

    1. the interiors or flues or chimneys which are not *readily accessible*.
    2. the heat exchanger.
    3. the humidifier or dehumidifier.
    4. the electronic air filter.
    5. the solar space heating *system*.

  B. determine heat supply adequacy or distribution balance.

9. AIR CONDITIONING SYSTEMS

9.1 The *inspector* **shall:**

  A. *inspect* the *installed* central and through-wall cooling equipment.

  B. *describe*:
    1. the energy source
    2. the cooling method by its distinguishing characteristics.

9.2 The *inspector* **is NOT required to:**

  A. *inspect* electronic air filters.
  B. determine cooling supply adequacy or distribution balance.

10. INTERIOR

10.1 The *inspector* **shall:**

  A. *inspect*:
    1. the walls, ceilings, and floors.
    2. the steps, stairways, and railings.
    3. the countertops and a *representative number of installed cabinets*.
    4. *a representative number* of doors and windows.
    5. garage doors and garage door operators.

10.2 The *inspector* **is NOT required to:**

  A. *inspect:*

    1. the paint, wallpaper and other finish treatments.
    2. the carpeting.
    3. the window treatments.
    4. the central vacuum *systems*.
    5. the *household appliances*.
    6. *recreational facilities*.

11. INSULATION AND VENTILATION

11.1 The *inspector* shall:

A. *inspect*:

    1. the insulation and vapor retarders in unfinished spaces.
    2. the ventilation of attics and foundation areas.
    3. the mechanical ventilation *systems*.

B. *describe:*

    1. the insulation and vapor retarders in unfinished spaces.
    2. the absence of insulation in unfinished spaces at conditioned surfaces.

11.2 The *inspector* is NOT required to:

A. disturb insulation or vapor retarders.

B. determine indoor air quality.

12. FIREPLACES AND SOLID FUEL BURNING APPLIANCES

12.1 The *inspector* shall:

A. *inspect:*

    1. the *system components*.
    2. the vent systems, flues, and chimneys.

B. *describe*:

    1. the fireplaces and *solid fuel burning appliances*.
    2. the chimneys.

12.2 The *inspector* is NOT required to:

A. *inspect*:

    1. the interiors of flues or chimneys.
    2. the firescreens and doors.
    3. the seals and gaskets.
    4. the automatic fuel feed devices.
    5. the mantles and fireplace surrounds.
    6. the combustion make-up air devices.
    7. the heat distribution assists whether gravity controlled or fan assisted.

B. ignite or extinguish fires.

C. determine draft characteristics.

D. move fireplace inserts or stoves or firebox contents.

13. GENERAL LIMITATIONS AND EXCLUSIONS

13.1 General limitations:

A. Inspections performed in accordance with these Standards of Practice

    1. are not *technically exhaustive*.
    2. will not identify concealed conditions or latent defects.

B. These Standards of Practice are applicable to buildings with four or fewer dwelling units and their garages or carports.

13.2 General exclusions:

A. The *inspector* is not required to perform any action or make any determination unless specifically stated in these Standards of Practice, except as may be required by lawful authority.

B. *Inspectors* are NOT required to determine:

    1. the condition of *systems* or *components* which are not *readily accessible*.
    2. the remaining life of any *system* or *component*.
    3. the strength, adequacy, effectiveness, or efficiency of any *system* or *component*.
    4. the causes of any condition or deficiency.
    5. the methods, materials, or costs of corrections.
    6. future conditions including, but not limited to, failure of *systems* and *components*.
    7. the suitability of the property for any specialized use.
    8. compliance with regulatory requirements (codes, regulations, laws, ordinances, etc.).
    9. the market value of the property or its marketability.
    10. the advisability of the purchase of the property.
    11. the presence of potentially hazardous plants or animals including, but not limited to wood destroying organisms or diseases harmful to humans.
    12. the presence of any environmental hazards including, but not limited to toxins, carcinogens, noise, and contaminants in soil, water and air.
    13. the effectiveness of any *system installed* or methods utilized to control or remove suspected hazardous substances.
    14. the operating costs of *systems* or *components*.
    15. the acoustical properties of any system or component.

C. *Inspectors* are NOT required to offer:

    1. or perform any act or service contrary to law.
    2. or perform *engineering services*.
    3. or perform work in any trade or any professional service other than *home inspection*.
    4. warranties or guarantees of any kind.

D. *Inspectors* are NOT required to operate:

1. any *system* or *component* which is *shut down* or otherwise inoperable.
2. any *system* or *component* which does not respond to *normal operating controls*.
3. shut-off valves.

E. *Inspectors* are NOT required to enter:

1. any area which will, in the opinion of the *inspector*, likely be dangerous to the *inspector* or other persons or damage the property or its *systems* or *components*.
2. The *under-floor crawl spaces* or attics which are not *readily accessible*.

F. *Inspectors* are NOT required to *inspect*:

1. underground items including, but not limited to underground storage tanks or other underground indications of their presence, whether abandoned or active.
2. *systems* or *components* which are not *installed*.
3. *decorative* items
4. *systems* or *components* located in areas that are not entered in accordance with these Standards of Practice.
5. detached structures other than garages and carports.
6. common elements or common areas in multi-unit housing, such as condominium properties or cooperative housing.

G. *Inspectors* are NOT required to:

1. perform any procedure or operation which will, in the opinion of the *inspector*, likely be dangerous to the *inspector* or other persons or damage the property or its *systems* or *components*.
2. move suspended ceiling tiles, personal property, furniture, equipment, plants, soil, snow, ice, or debris.
3. *dismantle* any *system* or *component*, except as explicitly required by these Standards of Practice.

GLOSSARY OF ITALICIZED TERMS

Alarm Systems
Warning devices, installed or free-standing, including but not limited to; carbon monoxide detectors, flue gas and other spillage detectors, security equipment, ejector pumps and smoke alarms

Architectural Service
Any practice involving the art and science of building design for construction of any structure or grouping of structures and the use of space within and surrounding the structures or the design for construction, including but not specifically limited to, schematic design, design development, preparation of construction contract documents, and administration of the construction contract

Automatic Safety Controls

Devices designed and installed to protect *systems* and *components* from unsafe conditions

Component

A part of a *system*

Decorative

Ornamental; not required for the operation of the essential systems and components of a home

Describe

To *report* a system or *component* by its type or other observed, significant characteristics to distinguish it from other *systems* or *components*

Dismantle

To take apart or remove any *component*, device or piece of equipment that would not be taken apart or removed by a homeowner in the course of normal and routine *homeowner* maintenance

Engineering Service

Any professional service or creative work requiring engineering education, training, and experience and the application of special knowledge of the mathematical, physical and engineering sciences to such professional service or creative work as consultation, investigation, evaluation, planning, design and supervision of construction for the purpose of assuring compliance with the specifications and design, in conjunction with structures, buildings, machines, equipment, works or processes

Further Evaluation

Examination and analysis by a qualified professional, tradesman or service technician beyond that provided by the *home inspection*

Home Inspection

The process by which an inspector *visually* examines the *readily accessible systems* and *components* of a home and which *describes* those *systems* and *components* in accordance with these Standards of Practice

Household Appliances

Kitchen, laundry, and similar appliances, whether *installed* or free-standing

Inspect

To examine *readily accessible systems* and *components* of a building in accordance with these Standards of Practice, using *normal operating controls* and opening *readily openable access panels*

Inspector

A person hired to examine any system or component of a building in accordance with these Standards of Practice

Installed
Attached such that removal requires tools

Normal Operating Controls
Devices such as thermostats, switches or valves intended to be operated by the homeowner

Readily Accessible
Available for visual inspection without requiring moving of personal property, dismantling, destructive measures, or any action which will likely involve risk to persons or property

Readily Openable Access Panel
A panel provided for homeowner inspection and maintenance that is within normal reach, can be removed by one person, and is not sealed in place

Recreational Facilities
Spas, saunas, steam baths, swimming pools, exercise, entertainment, athletic, playground or other similar equipment and associated accessories

Report
To communicate in writing

Representative Number
One *component* per room for multiple similar interior *components* such as windows and electric outlets; one *component* on each side of the building for multiple similar exterior *components*

Roof Drainage Systems
Components used to carry water off a roof and away from a building

Significantly Deficient
Unsafe or not functioning

Shut Down
A state in which a *system* or *component* cannot be operated by *normal operating controls*

Solid Fuel Burning Appliances
A hearth and fire chamber or similar prepared place in which a fire may be built and which is built in conjunction with a chimney; or a listed assembly of a fire chamber, its chimney and related factory-made parts designed for unit assembly without requiring field construction

Structural Component
A *component* that supports non-variable forces or weights (dead loads) and variable forces or weights (live loads)

System
A combination of interacting or interdependent *components*, assembled to carry out one or more functions

Technically Exhaustive

An investigation that involves dismantling, the extensive use of advanced techniques, measurements, instruments, testing, calculations, or other means

Under-floor Crawl Space

The area within the confines of the foundation and between the ground and the underside of the floor

Unsafe

A condition in a *readily accessible*, *installed system* or *component* which is judged to be a significant risk of personal injury during normal, day-to-day use. The risk may be due to damage, deterioration, improper installation or a change in accepted residential construction standards

Wiring Methods

Identification of electrical conductors or wires by their general type, such as "non-metallic sheathed cable" ("Romex), "armored cable" ("bx") or "knob and tube," etc.

► NOTES ON THE STANDARDS

Inspect	The Standards are clear on the meaning of **inspect.** When we inspect we have to look at and test the components listed in the Standards. We look at them if they are **readily accessible** or if we can get at them through **readily openable access panels**. These are panels designed for the homeowner to remove. They are within normal reach, can be removed by one person, and are not sealed in place.
Testing	We test components and systems by using their **normal operating controls**, but not the safety controls. We turn thermostats up or down, open and close doors and windows, turn light switches and water faucets on and off, flush toilets, etc. We do not test heating systems on high limit switches, test pressure relief valves on water heaters and boilers, overload electrical circuits to trip breakers, etc.
Systems Shut Down	We do not start up systems that are shut down. If the furnace pilot is off, we don't light it. If the electricity, water or gas is shut off in the home, we don't turn it on. If the disconnect for the air conditioner is off, we don't turn it on.
Accessible	We have to inspect house components that are **readily accessible**. That means we don't have to move furniture, lift carpets or ceiling tiles, **dismantle components,** damage things or do something dangerous. The exception is covers that would normally be **removed by homeowners during routine maintenance**. The furnace fan cover is a good example because homeowners remove this to change the furnace filter. Many inspectors use tools as the threshold. If tools are required to open or dismantle the component, it is not considered **readily accessible.**
Installed	We only have to inspect things that are **installed** in homes. This means we don't have to inspect window air conditioners or portable heaters, for example.

Deficiencies

We have to report on systems that are **significantly deficient**. This means they are unsafe or not performing their intended function. Although the Standards are not explicit, we are not required to identify every minor defect in a home. Failing to report a sticking door latch or cracked pane of glass would not be a meaningful breach of the Standards. Some common sense is needed here, determining the effect the issue will have on the safety, usability and durability of the home.

End Of Life

We are required to report on any system or component that in our professional opinion is **near the end of its service life**. This is tricky since we don't know whether inspectors will be held accountable for failed components on the basis that they should have known the component was near the end of its life. With the wisdom of hindsight, it may be hard to argue that the component could not have been expected to fail, when in fact, it did. Time will tell. The situation is also tricky because it includes not only **systems** but individual **components** as well. For many systems there are broadly accepted life expectancy ranges, but these aren't available for some individual components. A reasonable criteria may also be the apparent condition of the component.

Remaining Life

We are not required to determine the remaining life of systems or components. This is related to, but different than, the end of service life issue. If the item is new or in the middle part of its life, we don't have to predict service life, even though the same broadly accepted life expectancy ranges would apply. It's only when the item is near the end, in your opinion, that you have to report it.

Reporting Implications

We have to tell people in writing the **implications** of conditions or problems unless they are self-evident. A cracked heat exchanger on a furnace has a very different implication for a homeowner than a cracked windowpane, for example. It's not enough to tell a client that they have aluminum wiring. We have to tell them of the potential fire risk.

Describe The Implications

It's much better to tell someone to fix a loose railing because someone may fall down the stairs than to quote a specific code requirement. People will only take your recommendations seriously if they understand the implications of making the improvement. *"What will happen if I don't?"* is a fair question from a client about any of your recommendations. You don't need codes or bylaws to advise people on how to make house components perform their intended functions.

Tell Client What To Do

We have to tell the client in the report what to do about any conditions we found. We might recommend they repair, replace, service or clean the component. We might advise them to have a specialist further investigate the condition. It's all right to tell the client to monitor a situation, but we can't tell them that their roof shingles are curled and leave it at that. We have to tell them what to do about the aluminum wire to reduce the fire risk.

What We Left Out

We have to report anything that we would usually inspect but didn't. We also have to include in our report why we didn't inspect it. The reasons may be that the component was inaccessible, unsafe to inspect or was shut down. It may also be that the occupant or the client asked us not to inspect it.

Can It Do The Job?   Our approach is to look at each functional component in the home and evaluate whether it is able to perform its intended function. Roofs are supposed to shed water, gutters are supposed to collect water, chimneys are supposed to vent exhaust products, furnaces are supposed to heat homes, plumbing systems are supposed to carry supply and waste water, etc. We use our knowledge and expereience to form a professional opinion.

Can Go Further   The Standards allow you to deal with other systems and conditions beyond those covered by the Standards. For example, you may want to include inspections of water quality, septic systems, radon and termites. We can also specify repairs if we are qualified and choose to.

Can Do Less   The Standards also suggest that you do not have to inspect everything that is included in the Standards **if requested by the client**. Clients can hire you to simply look at the roof, for example. However, if a client hires you to do a home inspection, you can't choose to omit the electrical system. Clients sometimes, during the course of a home inspection, ask us not to look at the furnace, for example, because their brother-in-law is going to replace it for them. This is acceptable, but document it in your report.

Not Technically Exhaustive   The Standards indicate that home inspections are not technically exhaustive. This means that we are not taking measurements, using instruments, doing testing or performing calculations. Another way to think of it is to say that we are doing a visual field performance evaluation.

We are looking at things that are installed in homes and determining whether they are doing their jobs, to the extent we can by looking at them.

- We do not have to measure framing lumber size, spans or spacing.
- We don't have to measure duct size and runs.
- We don't have to test the quality of the grounding electrodes on electrical systems.
- We don't have to do smoke tests on furnaces to look for cracked heat exchangers.
- We don't have to use manometers to evaluate airflow through duct systems.
- We don't have to use pitot tubes or pressure gauges to analyze water supplies.
- We don't have to trip circuit breakers or measure the current flow through individual branch circuits.
- We don't have to evaluate the design of roof trusses.
- We don't have to perform heat loss calculations.

Four Dwelling Units   The Standards cover buildings that include up to four dwelling units. The Standards also include garages and carports for these buildings. This includes detached garages. We don't have to inspect common elements or areas in condominiums and cooperatives.

The Causes Of Problems

We don't have to indicate the cause of a problem. In many cases, it won't matter. If the window is broken, we don't have to speculate what the cause was. In some cases, it's helpful to identify the cause so the problem won't recur. If we find the furnace is badly rusted around the bottom, we might recommend replacement of the furnace. However, it would be helpful to point out to the client that the furnace is rusting because there is a chronic foundation leakage problem. Similarly, you may tell someone to replace the stained and sagging drywall on a part of a ceiling. It's important, however, to let people know that the shower stall above that ceiling leaks every time it is used.

Don't Say How To Fix

Home inspectors should not be writing repair specifications. The Standards say that we don't have to report on the methods, materials and costs of corrections. Most home inspectors give some general advice on improvements, but stay away from specifics. There is usually more than one way to approach a problem and unless you have specific expertise, you shouldn't be telling contractors how to go about fixing things.

Costs

The Standards don't require you to give ballpark costs for improvements. You don't have to be an estimator. On the other hand, the market reality in many areas is that home inspectors do typically give ballpark costs for improvements. This adds another dimension to a home inspection. There are many cost estimating books available and some of the premium reporting systems include cost estimate numbers for many house components.

Special Use

Home inspectors don't have to tell clients whether the basement can be set up as a hairdressing salon, for example. There are often special physical issues and usually bylaw and code issues involved in specialized uses of homes. Evaluating whether a home is suitable for this kind of thing is well beyond the scope of a home inspection.

Code Compliance

A home inspection is not a code compliance inspection. Nor is it a bylaw inspection. Most existing homes will not meet all current codes. There are several codes that apply to each house. There is typically a building code, electrical code, gas code, plumbing code and so on. No one person can be comprehensively knowledgeable about all current codes. Further, codes change on a regular basis. It's simply not realistic to expect anyone to know all current code requirements on all aspects of a home.

Performance-based Inspection

Since we're not doing code inspections, what are we using as a yardstick? All codes are written for specific reasons. A good home inspector has a strong background in codes and knows what constitutes good practice. Every well written code item boils down to common sense. For example, you may not know exactly how tall railings have to be, but you can get a sense standing beside a railing whether or not you're likely to fall over it if you stumble. With very little experience, you'll also get very good at knowing what average railing heights and stair rises are, for example.

Market Value   Home inspectors should not offer any comment on the price of the home or its value. We are commonly asked at the end of the inspection if the house is good value or if it's priced right. This is a question that you need to defer to a real estate professional. Home inspectors hate it when real estate agents question the inspector's findings or offer technical advice to homeowners during an inspection. In the same sense, real estate agents hate it when inspectors wander into the world of real estate. The world works better all around if everyone stays within their scope of work.

What You Can't See   The Standards tell us in several different ways that if you can't see it, you don't have to inspect it.

Insects, Rodents Or Wood Destroying Organisms   We don't have to identify termites, rats or even rot causing fungi. However, you do have to report on any damage to the structure or other components. You can think of insects, rodents and wood damaging organisms as **causes** of the problems that you do have to identify.

Cosmetics   We don't have to comment on anything subjective. Home inspectors should not comment on architectural or decorating issues. Again, you don't want to be outside of your scope. This is a very dangerous place to be.

Breaking The Law   The Standards say you don't have to do anything that's against the law. This is common sense, of course.

Warranties Or Guarantees   The Standards say that you don't have to offer warranties or guarantees. Most home inspectors do not. There are warranty programs that people can purchase on homes, but they are, in effect, insurance policies.

Licensed Work   Inspectors shouldn't do anything that requires an occupational license including engineering or architectural services, unless they have such a license. For example, in some areas, a license is required to comment on wood-destroying organisms. In these areas, home inspectors should not offer comment. In other areas, only licensed technicians can dismantle and evaluate heating systems. Again, stay within your scope. You are performing a visual inspection of the performance of installed house components.

Danger And Damage   You don't have to go anywhere that is dangerous for you. We recommend that you don't walk on steeply sloped roofs, for example. You also don't have to do anything that may damage the property. You don't have to use a crowbar to force open access hatches.

Don't Turn Utilities On   The inspector does not have to inspect components that have been shut off. If the gas, water or electricity to the house is not on at the time of the inspection, home inspectors are not required to turn them on. As a matter of fact, you should avoid turning them on. Things are usually turned off for a reason. There may be a safety issue. In most cases, you won't know and you risk causing serious damage or injury by activating systems that are shut down.

Disturbing Things

We don't have to move insulation, furniture, suspended ceiling tiles, storage, tree branches, earth, snow or ice to get a better look. This can be an important point. We recommend that you document limitations caused by any of these things. When someone calls you in six months to complain that you didn't identify a crack in a foundation wall, it's helpful if your report says that part of the foundation wall was not visible because of storage. You may not remember what was there at the time of the inspection and it's almost certain that your client won't remember. Many complaints about home inspectors' work are the result of things that only become obvious after the inspection.

Hazardous Substance

We don't have to look for poisons, cancer-causing agents or noise contamination. Indoor air quality and environmental inspections have become a separate profession.

Operating Costs

We are often asked how much it will cost to heat the house or what the electrical bills will be. Home inspectors should not speculate about these. There are so many variables to this question, that your best guess is just going to be a stab in the dark. In some cases, historical information is available that will help people with this issue.

2.1.2 THE *ASHI*® CODE OF ETHICS

The following are the ASHI® Code of Ethics effective June 1, 1992.

Code of Ethics

Honesty, justice, and courtesy form a moral philosophy which, associated with mutual interest among people constitutes the foundation of ethics. The members should recognize such a standard, not in passive observance, but as a set of dynamic principles guiding their conduct. It is their duty to practice the profession according to this code of ethics.

As the keystone of professional conduct is integrity, the members will discharge their duties with fidelity to the public, their clients, and with fairness and impartiality to all. They should uphold the honor and dignity of their profession and avoid association with any enterprise of questionable character, or apparent conflict of interest.

1. The member will express an opinion only when it is based on practical experience and honest conviction.
2. The member will always act in good faith toward each client.
3. The member will not disclose any information concerning the results of the inspection without the approval of the clients or their representatives.
4. The member will not accept compensation, financial or otherwise, from more than one interested party for the same service without the consent of all interested parties.

5. The member will not accept nor offer commissions or allowances, directly or indirectly, from other parties dealing with their client in connection with work for which the member is responsible.

6. The member will promptly disclose to his client any interest in a business which may affect the client. The member will not allow any interest in any business to affect the quality or results of their inspection work which they may be called upon to perform. The inspection work may not be used as a vehicle by the home inspector to deliberately obtain additional work in another field.

7. An inspector shall make every effort to uphold, maintain and improve the professional integrity, reputation and practice of the home inspection industry. He will report all such relevant information, including violations of this Code by other members, to the Association for possible remedial action.

► NOTES ON THE CODE OF ETHICS

The Code of Ethics contains a number of motherhood statements that are intended to protect the public. There are also some specific and important issues addressed in the Code of Ethics.

Motherhood Words

The Code of Ethics is sprinkled with words like **honesty, justice, courtesy, moral philosophy, guiding principles, integrity, fidelity, fairness, impartiality, honor, dignity, honest conviction**, and **good faith**. These are commendable concepts, and this document requires home inspectors to adhere to them. Let's look at some of the specific requirements.

1. Don't Guess

We should only offer opinions when they are based on experience and conviction. We shouldn't be bluffing our way through inspections or guessing at things we don't know. We also shouldn't be telling people what they want to hear, rather than what you know to be true.

2. Don't Lie Or Cheat

This is a motherhood statement which says you must act in good faith toward each client. It doesn't require this in our actions toward others.

3. Confidentiality

The inspection results belong to your clients. They bought them. The inspection results don't belong to you. You are entitled to keep a copy as the producer, but the actual product belongs to your client. As a result, you cannot discuss the inspection results with real estate agents, sellers or other interested parties without the client's permission. This is important and will come back to haunt you if you break this rule.

4. Can't Get Paid Twice

This says that we can't accept compensation from more than one party for the same service unless everyone agrees. You can't do an inspection for Client A and then sell the report to Client B. Remember, the report doesn't belong to you, it belongs to Client A.

Sensitivity Of Real Estate

There is a considerable ethical dilemma that often crops up for home inspectors. We work for the prospective buyer of a property. There is often more than one prospective buyer looking at a property. If you are asked to inspect a house for Client A, life is simple. You perform the inspection, provide the report and accept your fee. If Client B calls and asks you to inspect the same house, you have a number of options:

a. Inspect the house for Client B as a separate service and say nothing.
b. Indicate that you have a potential conflict of interest and decline to do the inspection for Client B.
c. Explain to Client B that you have recently inspected the property for someone else but are willing to do the inspection for Client B.
d. Explain to Client B that you have recently done an inspection of the property for someone else and they may be willing to release the report to Client B with or without a fee. You offer to contact Client A.
e. This is the same as the last one except you give Client A's name and number to Client B.
f. Explain to Client B that you have recently inspected the property for someone else and offer to sell Client B the report.
g. Offer to give Client B the report.

Over the years, we have tried many of these options (but not e., f. or g.) and have concluded that no matter what you do, you expose yourself to criticism. If we say nothing and do the inspection a second time, the seller or real estate agent may consider us unethical for trying to get paid twice for the same work. If you indicate a conflict of interest and decline to do the inspection, you have made Client B aware that there may be competition for the home. This can put Client A at a disadvantage. If you tell Client B that you have done an inspection for someone else, that gives him information that Client A does not have. If you contact Client A about whether they are willing to release the report to someone else before talking to Client B, you have given Client A an advantage over Client B.

Putting one client in touch with another can cause problems too. Client B may ask Client A why they didn't buy the property. The seller and real estate agents are likely to be unhappy with you if Client B changes his or her mind based on the conversation. You don't own the report, so you don't have the right to give it or sell it to client B. These options should not be considered.

No matter what you do, someone may be unhappy. You may want to evaluate these possibilities and make a decision before the situation comes up. At least then you will have given it some thought and understand the possible backlash.

5. Getting Or Giving Kickbacks

Inspectors cannot accept or offer commissions from other parties dealing with **their client** in connection with work for which the member is responsible. This is worded fairly carefully, but is intended to require inspectors to maintain an arm's length from real estate professionals. You should not be accepting kickbacks in any form from real estate agents for inspections. This can obviously expose you to pressure about how your inspections are performed and how your reports are presented. Similarly, you can't pay real estate agents when they send clients to you. Again, the protection of the client is at the heart of this issue and home inspectors must not only be ethical, but must be perceived as ethical. Appearances are everything.

Client Benefits In some cases, benefits are passed on directly to the client. Home inspectors may offer discounted fees to clients of certain real estate agents, for example. This issue is not specifically addressed in the Standards and is a gray one. You can make the argument that the client's interests are well served in this arrangement. Cynics wonder what other components there are to the relationship between the real estate professional and the home inspector.

6. Conflict Of Interest

There are two issues in this item. It's helpful to understand that many people in the home inspection business come from the building trades. While there are several interests that home inspectors might have that would cause a conflict, one of the most common is the fact that they have done some work on this house. It's obviously not appropriate for inspectors to inspect houses that they built. How could they possibly be impartial?

Don't Fix The House The second point in this item is that you cannot use the home inspection to get work in another field. As you step off the ladder and tell the client that the roof is worn out, you shouldn't be handing them a business card with a quotation for a new roof. People will wonder whether the house really needs a new roof and whether the purpose of the inspection is to create work for a contracting or remodeling business. Many home inspectors are involved in construction-related businesses, but the two roles must be kept distinct.

Consulting Not Contracting The Standards say we are permitted to provide other inspection services and specifying repairs. The distinction seems to be that consulting work is acceptable, but contracting work is not.

To sum up our interpretation, if you are a mechanical engineer, you can offer to do a design analysis of the heating and ductwork system for an additional fee, but you cannot offer to replace the furnace.

7. Report Code Violations

The inspector is asked to report any violations of the Code of Ethics by other members to the Association. While the intent is clear and commendable, this is a difficult issue in practice. Will members ever report other members for competitive or personal reasons, rather than professional integrity reasons? Hmm …

Summary

So now you have a sense of the rules of the game. Without getting into the specifics of home inspection details, you should have a good sense of what constitutes an inspection and what your important obligations are.

2.2 INTRODUCTION

Throughout the rest of this Section, we'll talk about—

• what home inspections look like
• what characteristics home inspectors need
• who hires home inspectors and why
• the inspection process

Our Opinion We offer lots of advice on the practice of home inspection in this Section that is not written down anywhere. Much of the commentary is not authoritative because we cannot quote sources for it. We believe in what we are saying and, in many cases, we believe it to be generally accepted good practice within the profession. It is based on our 20 years experience in the home inspection business, but it is only our opinion. It's safe to say that you will find some home inspectors who will disagree with some of the material in this Section. That's healthy and we encourage you to read this material with an open but questioning mind.

Note: We have used the word **agent** to describe a real estate sales professional. We do so, recognizing that some people object to the term. However, it is widely understood throughout North America to mean a real estate salesperson. Throughout this program we try to use words that are understood by the layperson and we use the word **agent,** with apologies to those who object. The word **REALTOR** is a registered service mark of the National Association of Realtors (NAR) in the United States and is used in Canada by agreement between the NAR and the Canadian Real Estate Association. In some jurisdictions, the real estate salesperson is not an agent as defined by law. Only the broker who employs the salesperson can act as an "agent." The word "agent" is commonly used to mean either the broker or salesperson. You'll need to become familiar with how terms are commonly used in your area.

Communication &
Professional Practice

MODULE

QUICK QUIZ 1

☑ INSTRUCTIONS

- You should finish Study Session 1 before doing this Quiz.
- Write your answers in the spaces provided.
- Check your answers against ours at the end of this section.
- If you have trouble with the Quiz, re-read the Study Session and try the Quiz again.
- If you did well, it's time for Study Session 2.

1. Describe in one sentence what home inspections must provide for clients.

   _____

2. List three components of written reports.

   _____

   _____

   _____

3. List two general limitations to home inspections.

   _____

   _____

4. List 10 general exclusions to home inspections.

_____

_____

_____

_____

_____

_____

_____

_____

_____

_____

5. List 13 things inspectors are not required to do as part of an inspection.

_____

_____

_____

_____

_____

_____

_____

_____

_____

_____

_____

_____

_____

_____

6. Define **technically exhaustive** within the scope of a home inspection.

_____

7. Define **inspector** within the context of the Standards of Practice.

_____

8. Summarize in one sentence each, of the seven elements of the Code of Ethics.

_____

_____

_____

_____

_____

_____

_____

If you had no trouble with the Quiz, it's time for Study Session 2.

Key Words

- *Scope*
- *Significantly deficient*
- *Observed*
- *Installed systems and components*
- *Technically exhaustive*
- *Life expectancy*
- *Causes*
- *Methods*
- *Specialized use*
- *Compliance*
- *Market value*
- *Advisability of purchase*
- *Pests*
- *Cosmetic items*
- *Underground items*
- *Warranties*
- *Guarantees*
- *Engineering*

- *Strength*
- *Adequacy*
- *Efficiency*
- *Shut down*
- *Normal operating controls*
- *Hazardous substance*
- *Future conditions*
- *Operating costs*
- *Acoustical properties*
- *Inspector*
- *Practical experience*
- *Honest conviction*
- *Good faith*
- *Disclose information*
- *Compensation*
- *Commissions or allowances*
- *Conflict of interest*
- *Professional integrity*

Communication & Professional Practice

MODULE

STUDY SESSION 2

1. You should have completed Study Session 1 and Quick Quiz 1 before starting this Session.

2. This section covers an overview of the home inspection profession, the characteristics of a good home inspector, typical vehicles, clothes and tools issues, and a description of typical clients.

3. At the end of this Session, you should be able to –
   • describe how the home inspection profession is generally regulated throughout North America
   • indicate the range of estimated number of home inspectors in North America
   • indicate the average fee of a home inspection in North America
   • list eight types of residential inspections
   • describe in one sentence the difference between a home inspection and an appraisal
   • list six people or things to whom home inspectors have obligations during a home inspection
   • indicate the average time required to complete a home inspection
   • list four advantages of having clients attend the inspection
   • list seven attributes of a good home inspector
   • describe in one sentence a suitable home inspector's vehicle
   • describe in one sentence the thing that home inspector's clothing should reflect
   • list 10 basic tools that home inspectors typically use
   • list eight reasons home inspectors may be hired to perform a pre-purchase inspection
   • list 10 thoughts or feelings clients typically have during home inspections
   • list 10 things, other than the client, that commonly distract home inspectors during an inspection

4. This Session may take you roughly an hour and a half to complete.

5. Quick Quiz 2 is included at the end of this Session.

Key Words
- ***Young profession***
- ***Unregulated***
- ***Prepurchase home inspection***
- ***Field review of performance***
- ***Visual inspection***
- ***Non-destructive and non-invasive***
- ***Sampling type inspection***
- ***Conditional offer***
- ***Neutral and unbiased***
- ***Adjust expectations***
- ***Technical wizard***
- ***Great communicator***
- ***Actor***
- ***Diplomat***
- ***Investigator***
- ***Detective***
- ***Communication barriers***
- ***Distractions***

► 3.0 INSPECTIONS AND INSPECTORS

3.1 A BRIEF HISTORY

Formalized In Mid 1970s

The home inspection profession is relatively young. The first professional associations were formed in the mid 1970s. Home inspection got its roots as contractors, engineers, architects and other building specialists were asked by prospective home buyers to comment on the home under consideration.

Borrowed From The Automobile Industry

Cautious home buyers reasoned that if it made sense to check out a used car before buying one, it made even more sense to have someone check out a home, which is a much larger purchase.

East, West, Then Middle

The home inspection business started in the Eastern United States and moved to the West Coast, starting in California. In the 25 years since the early 1970s, home inspection has expanded in from both coasts and has become popular throughout North America.

25 Years Of Change

The home inspection profession has evolved from a rare service to one that is routinely used by prospective home buyers. In many of the mature markets in North America, more than 50 percent of resale homes are inspected. In some markets, the number approaches 100 percent.

Still A Child

The profession is still very young and has a great deal of maturing to do. There has been very little education and training available in the home inspection profession until the last ten years.

Unregulated

The home inspection profession is unregulated in most of North America. Anyone can hang out a shingle and call themselves a home inspector. Licensing is coming and many states in the U.S.A. have instituted licensing of one form or another or are looking at it. In Canada as of year 2000, there is no regulation of the home inspection profession. In many cases, government agencies are shying away from regulating professions. It's costly, it can involve large bureaucracies, and government simply doesn't have the expertise. Many governments prefer self-regulation, but the direction taken by governments is often steered by politics or consumer demand or both.

Time will tell how widespread and restrictive the licensing issue becomes. Many practitioners fear licensing with very low levels of qualification. This may result in the profession being diluted and fees dropping dramatically. This was experienced in Texas in the early days of licensing there. Licensing in Texas has evolved considerably since then, although we understand there are some problems in Texas as well, as of year 2000.

Overly Strict Licensing

If licensing becomes overly strict, and the credentials become all but unattainable, the profession would suffer of course, unless there was a long phasing-in period.

Post Secondary   We believe that over time the home inspection profession will be taught in
Level Education   colleges and, perhaps, universities. It is a complex and important consumer-
oriented profession.

Size Of The   There were more than five thousand people in ASHI® as of year 2000. Although
Profession   firm numbers are not available, it is estimated that there are 20,000 to 25,000 home
inspectors in North America, although many are part-time. Somewhere between
4,000,000 and 5,000,000 homes are sold every year in North America. The theo-
retical capacity of a home inspector is approximately 500 inspections per year. We
know of home inspectors who do more than this, but a rate much higher than 500
cannot be sustained without considerable lifestyle sacrifice and risk of burnout.

Market   Again, there are no good numbers available, but we estimate that the average home
Saturation   inspector in North America performs roughly 200 inspections per year. If there
Level   were 10,000 inspectors performing 200 inspections a year, they would perform a
total of 2,000,000 inspections annually. If there are 4,000,000 houses sold in North
America, one could say that the market is roughly 50 percent saturated.

A Growth   While there is considerable room for error in these numbers, the reality is that
Profession   home inspection is not a mature profession. Even when the market matures, there
will always be room for new practitioners due to competition and attrition.

Home   A recent study by ASHI® suggested that the average home inspection fee across
Inspection Fees   North America is roughly $250. We are aware of home inspection fees as low as
$125, and fees in excess of $1,000.

Who Are The   Home inspectors traditionally have come from other trades and professions. Many
Inspectors?   have gotten into home inspection as a part-time business, supplementing work in
construction, design or other inspection fields. Since there is no formal training,
people have brought various and diverse backgrounds, knowledge and experience
to the world of home inspection.

Diversification   Many home inspectors diversify into other fields as well, many of them peripheral
to the home inspection itself. Lead and radon testing, well water quality testing,
septic tank inspections, indoor air quality testing and environmental audits are
some of the common peripheral services offered by home inspectors during or
separate from home inspection activity.

Types Of   Many home inspection companies are sole proprietorships. Owners may work at
Companies   the business part-time or full-time, as we mentioned. There are some multi-inspector
firms, and there are some relatively large franchises or licensing arrangements.
The largest franchise groups have roughly 300 franchisees, as of year 2000.

Public   Many consumers are not aware of the home inspection profession, and very few
Awareness   consumers have a clear understanding of the profession. Real estate sales
organizations generally have a good understanding of the profession, since their
work is often closely linked with that of the home inspector.

Home
Inspection
And The Real
Estate Sales
Transaction

Over the last 25 years, the home inspection has become an additional step in the real estate transaction. To sales people working on commission, the home inspection can be an unwelcome step because it slows down the process, may result in renegotiation and can stop the transaction process altogether. We'll talk about real estate issues later in this Module.

The State of Home Inspection – 1997

In 1997, a study of the home inspection profession in the United States and Canada conducted by the American Society of Home Inspectors indicated the following:

• More than 75 percent of home inspectors are between ages 34 and 57.
• More than 80 percent have a background in general construction.
• More than 75 percent have been in the business 10 years or less.
• More than 70percent work on a full-time, rather than part-time, basis.
• Sole inspectors represent almost half of the home inspectors and roughly a third are corporations.
• More than 75 percent of home inspectors are one or two person operations.
• Most home inspectors work according to the Standards.
• Roughly 70 percent offer radon services.
• Roughly 40 percent offer lead inspection services.
• Roughly 35 percent offer septic system inspection services.
• Roughly 30 percent offer well flow inspections.
• Roughly 30 percent offer swimming pool inspections.
• Roughly 25 percent offer spa inspections.
• Roughly 25 percent offer termite inspections.
• Roughly 15 percent offer UFFI inspections.
• Roughly 10 percent offer sea wall inspections.
• More than 50 percent of home inspectors also perform commercial inspections.
• The average fee for a residential inspection in 1996 was roughly $240.
• Roughly 40 percent of home inspectors base their fees on the property size.
• Roughly 25 percent have a flat fee.
• Ten percent base their fees on property value.
• Sixteen percent used a combination of criteria.
• Roughly 50 percent of home inspectors use reports that are combination narrative and checklist.
• About 30 percent use narrative reports.
• About 10 percent use checklists.
• Sixty-eight percent of inspectors performed 300 inspections or less in 1996.
• For most home inspectors, the spring is busiest time of year with the summer next, fall third and winter the slowest.
• Over 90 percent of inspectors used an inspection contract or agreement.
• Over 85 percent of those contracts included a limit of liability clause.
• More than 55 percent of home inspectors carry errors and omission insurance.
• Over 80 percent of home inspectors have gross revenues of $100,000 or less.

3.2 PRE-PURCHASE HOME INSPECTION – A LOOK FROM THE OUTSIDE

Types of Inspection

The focus of our discussion will be on the pre-purchase home inspection since it is far and away the most common. Other types of inspection include –

• prelisting or presale inspections
• prerenovation inspections
• problem-solving inspections
• maintenance inspections
• course of construction or progress inspections
• legal dispute inspections
• inspection of relatively new homes as warranties are about to expire

These may provide diversification opportunities for home inspectors.

Home Inspections Defined

We have defined the home inspection according to the Standards of Practice. The following descriptive terms all apply to a pre-purchase home inspection:

• Field performance review
• Evaluation of physical condition
• Visual inspection of readily accessible, installed components
• Not technically exhaustive
• Non-destructive
• Non-invasive
• Sampling type inspection

A home inspection is designed to determine whether all of the essential components of a house are present and doing their job, as evidenced by a visual inspection.

Form Versus Function

The home inspection concentrates on the function of the home, rather than the form. Architectural and decorating considerations are not included.

Not An Appraisal

Some people confuse home inspection and appraisal. An appraisal may involve an inspection of a property, but the goal of an appraisal is to determine the fair **market value** of a property, rather than establish its physical condition. Appraisers will often find house problems and may call upon home inspectors to investigate situations that are unclear to appraisers.

Ethics

We talked about the Code of Ethics. Home inspectors get pulled a number of ways. They have obligations to all of the following:

• The home buyer, who is typically the client
• The home seller
• The listing agent (the agent working with the seller)
• The selling agent (the agent working with the buyer)
• The home itself
• The home inspector himself or herself

*Good Faith
To All*

The Code of Ethics requires members to act in good faith toward clients. We extrapolate that to suggest that home inspectors should operate in good faith toward everyone. We believe that we owe every person honesty and courtesy. It's not just the right thing to do, it's good business. Those who operate less than honestly and professionally are generally haunted by their actions eventually.

*Home
Inspectors Get
Pulled*

Home inspectors are often subjected to several different pressures. We'll talk about this more when we talk about typical clients and the real estate transaction, but we'll give you a few examples:

• A home buyer has had trouble getting financing for a home, and asks you to write a favorable report because the lender wants to see a copy. The buyer wants the lender to make the loan.

• The buyers have had second thoughts about the house and want out of the transaction. The only condition in their offer is the home inspection condition. The buyers ask you to write a negative report to help them get out of the deal.

• The buyers have a conditional offer (agreeing to buy the home for the agreed price if the results of the inspection are satisfactory) on home inspection and want the house but think they have paid too much. They ask you to write a harsh report so they can renegotiate based on your findings.

• The real estate salesperson indicates there are several good home inspectors that he or she typically recommends (many recommend at least three). A home inspector who causes a transaction to fall apart may not be on the list, let alone at the top.

• The seller of the home you are inspecting has already purchased another home and is desperate to have the deal go through, challenging every comment you make about the home that may be considered negative. (Sellers typically have a pride of ownership, as well as a strong motivation to see a favorable report so that the transaction will go through.)

• A young couple is buying the house. The husband has fallen in love with the house but the wife is not sure that it's the right home for them. The husband wants you to produce a very positive report while the wife is looking for an excuse to back out of the purchase. Each speaks to you privately at different times during the inspection, giving you direction as to how your report should be slanted.

*What's The
Right Thing
To Do?*

Many home inspectors believe that their obligation is to the buyer. As you can see from some of the examples above, the wishes of the buyer are not always consistent with the Code of Ethics or with professional business practices. We have adopted the position that our highest obligation is to the home. Regardless of the pressures that we feel, we strive to provide reports that realistically describe the condition of the house in our opinion. We make no attempt to minimize or magnify conditions we identify.

It's A Bumpy Road	There are often people who are unhappy with the results because of this approach, but, since people in a real estate transaction have diverse interests, this is to be expected. We have long since stopped trying to make everyone happy and, although it's not our goal to make anyone unhappy, we feel compelled to report the house exactly as we see it. In our opinion, that's the only kind of report that will consistently stand up to long-term scrutiny.
Neutral And Unbiased	It's one of the joys of the home inspection profession that we are truly unbiased. We have no particular interest in whether or not the transaction goes through. The seller obviously has a strong motivation. The real estate sales people have a similar but slightly different motivation. The seller wants to get as much money as he or she can for the house. The real estate salespeople would like to see the sale at the highest possible price, but are more concerned that a sale does take place. Buyers are trying to get the best price they can, and often have misgivings about the transaction they are entering.
Inspectors Get Paid Either Way	Home inspectors charge a fee for their work, and often don't even know whether the transaction was completed. We provide our report, collect our fee and move on. We sometimes hear when transactions aren't completed in the form of a complaint from a real estate agent or a seller, but, other than that, are not usually aware of the outcome.
Can't Operate In A Vacuum	While it's nice to think that home inspectors can be insulated from all the real world pressures, it's a stretch to think that that's the case. There are many forces outside of the real estate transaction itself. The marketplace can drive you to change your way of doing business. Competition can affect your pricing, and so on. In short, the home inspection profession is also a business and subject to the same outside influences as any other business.
Harder Than It Looks	Home inspection looks deceivingly simple. In reality, it's extremely complex. A good analogy would be a medical doctor who was a general practitioner. While they don't have an area of specialization, they are expected to have broad knowledge of a large number of issues. The medical analogy is a good one in the sense that just as doctors can cure some conditions but sends patients to specialists for others, home inspectors can offer advice on many issues but sometimes have to recommend further investigation by specialists.
It's A Performance	A home inspection is performed in front of an audience. The audience may simply be a buyer, but it's often the buyers and their family, a selling agent, a listing agent and a seller. Just as a good actor can make a performance seem very simple and natural, a good home inspection can look deceptively easy and natural. It's true in business, in the arts and in the sports world. People who are very good at what they do make it look easy.

The Reality

Home inspection is hard work. It requires comprehensive technical knowledge, a keen eye, good powers of deductive reasoning, an ability to focus and think quickly, an ability to read people and put them at ease, and good communication skills to successfully transfer the home inspector's observations and conclusions to the client. There is pressure to perform, little time to think, considerable liability, and lots of ways to destroy your credibility instantly. We'll talk more about the characteristics of a home inspector shortly.

Poorly Understood Profession

We touched on this earlier. Home inspection is not well understood by most people. It's one of the great dangers of the field. People tend to put an inordinate amount of faith in a home inspection report. Unrealistic expectations are often fueled by glowing recommendations by real estate salespeople about this wonderful home inspector who will tell you **everything** about the home. Marketing efforts often foster this **complete peace of mind** perception. It's easy to see how the risks are high if the unrealistic expectations are not adjusted. The home inspection profession has considerable work ahead to better educate the consumer as to the scope and limitations of a professional home inspection. One of the great risks to the profession is new practitioners who do not understand the liabilities and the importance of creating realistic expectations among clients.

How Long Does A Home Inspection Take?

Some people claim they can do a home inspection in as little as an hour or an hour and a half. Other people say that the process should take eight hours. In most parts of North America, a typical home inspection might run two and a half hours.

Should It Be Longer?

Would we be able to tell people more about the house if we had longer to do the inspection? Of course. What's magic about two and a half hours? There's nothing magic, but a number of factors have lead to this average number.

• The fees charged by home inspectors make it tough to justify spending much longer at a home.
• The patience of sellers and real estate agents is limited.
• It's hard for anyone to focus for more than two and a half hours on any task. Home inspectors are effectively on stage for two and a half hours and that's plenty for most people.

Note: This discussion assumes that a single inspector performs the inspection.

Law Of Diminishing Returns

There's another way to look at the home inspection. A great deal can be learned about a home during a single tour around and through it. The faster you tour the house, the less you will see. However, as you start to slow the tour or repeat the tour, there comes a point where the additional amount of information picked up is smaller and smaller. The data collection process operates at a very high rate for the first couple of hours and then diminishes. While you will discover more and more things the longer you inspect a home, the rate at which you pick up valuable new information drops dramatically after the first couple of hours.

Can I Do
Shorter
Inspections?

You could do shorter inspections and still provide a good deal of information to clients. If your fees were less than your competition, this could be a valuable service. However, the perception might be that you are not doing a comprehensive job. Perhaps more importantly, it's very difficult to meet the Standards of Practice in much less than two and a half hours. Since the Standards have been broadly accepted as a minimum standard of home inspection, there is a significant barrier to doing shorter, more cursory inspections.

Greater
Liability

Many people believe that the shorter the inspection, the higher the liability. Clients may be willing to pay less for a slightly shorter inspection, but are not likely to reduce their expectations accordingly. It may not be a convincing argument to explain to a judge that you didn't meet the Standards of Practice because you charged a fee that only allowed you stay in the house for an hour.

Could I Do
Longer
Inspections?

Inspections may run longer than two and a half hours and there may be very little problem with this. Depending on the complexity of the house, and the demands of the client, this happens to all inspectors. Some use long inspection times as a marketing tool. The business decision that has to be made is whether or not people are willing to pay more money for longer inspections and whether the negative effects on sellers, real estate agents, your ability to concentrate and the client's ability to focus make it worthwhile. When our inspections on a typical house run much longer than two and half to three hours, it's common for the real estate salespeople to let us know that we did not perform well. Whether the criticism is fair may not be the real issue.

Can Clients Attend?

We **encourage** clients to attend the inspection for several reasons:

- **Better communication**. It's easier to communicate with someone face to face than over the telephone or, worse still, only in writing. You're going to communicate in writing no matter what; however, the communication is much enhanced if you can speak to the person and get their feedback. Later in the Module, we'll talk about some verbal communication skills. You probably already have a sense of the value of one-on-one communication.
- **Showing is better than telling**. When you find a significant problem or condition, it's much easier to make clients understand by showing them as you tell them about it.
- **Lowered liability**. A properly done home inspection generally leaves a very favorable impression with a buyer. The buyer sees how hard you are working on their behalf. Studies have shown and our experience has reinforced the reality that people are less likely to complain or to take legal action against people they have met and established rapport with. If your client works with you at the house for two and a half hours and then has an unexpected event after moving into the house, you're more likely to get a phone call asking for help than a lawyer's letter demanding money.

• **Opportunity to adjust expectations**. During the inspection, you can help the client understand the scope of a home inspection and describe the things you are able to do and not able to do during the course of the inspection. This again helps to reduce liability.

Clients Slow You Down

Some inspectors complain that the inspection process takes longer if clients tag along. While this is true to a point, there is a control issue at play. Good home You inspectors can control the pace of an inspection, even with clients attending. In our experience, while the inspection may be slightly faster without the client, there is also a telephone call to the client after the inspection that can be quite lengthy. The total time for the inspection and phone call often exceeds the average inspection time with a client attending.

Complaints More Likely

Further, the risk of receiving a complaint in the future is higher if the client doesn't come. Handling complaints takes up huge amounts of time, making the extra few minutes spent on site with the client seem trivial indeed.

Fees

We talked about fees ranging from $100 to over $1,000 with averages in the $250 range. How do home inspectors set their fees? There are several approaches. Fees may be based on –

• the square footage of the house
• the selling price of the house
• the number of rooms in the house
• the amount of time the inspector spends
• the level and number of services provided (additional fees are often charged for radon, termite, lead, water quality, septic inspections)

Some inspectors offer a basic inspection and a premium level inspection that goes into more depth. Some inspectors offer inspections with fees in the thousands of dollars that involve a whole team of specialists. The reasons for this usually have more to do with liability control than good value.

Home Inspection Is Great Value

We believe that home inspections are typically underpriced relative to their value in the real estate transaction. The amount of information provided to clients is amazing, irrespective of cost. When considered against real estate commissions, legal fees, the cost of land surveys, appraisals, etc., the $250 spent on a home inspection is wonderful value. One of the unfortunate realities is that by the time the buyer gets to the home inspection process, he or she is worn down by stress and the large number of hidden costs in a real estate transaction. An inspection that costs a few hundred dollars more seems anything but great value. Nonetheless, a well-performed home inspection usually generates feedback like this:

• *"That's the best money I've ever spent!"*
• *"I've learned more about this house in two and a half hours than I know about the house I've lived in for the last ten years."*

When Are Inspections Performed?

Again, there are several choices for inspection schedules. Our choice is to set up inspections at nine, twelve and three o'clock. This allows for performing three inspections per day, assuming the houses are all typical sizes and the travel distance between them is no more than half an hour. Inspectors just beginning will usually have trouble completing their inspection within two and a half hours, and a two-inspections-per-day pace is recommended for new practitioners.

Three Inspections Per Day

Some inspectors perform four inspections per day. In our experience that leads to tired people making mistakes and burning themselves out. As we've said, a home inspection is a performance. The actor that has to do three two and a half hour performances in a day will tell you how that tiring that is, mentally and physically. In our experience, that's the limit.

Seven Days A Week?

Some home inspectors work five days a week, others work six and some work seven. In a multi-inspector firm, inspections are often available six or seven days a week, but individual inspectors only work five days. Some inspectors may work Saturday and Sunday and take Monday and Tuesday off, for example.

The Hungrier Your Are, The More You Work

Generally speaking, people who are not as busy as they'd like to be are much more flexible and will work any day of the week. As people become busier, they often have to pull back from the seven-day-a-week service so that they can have a life. There is no right or wrong answer to this, although we do believe that people who work relentlessly may make more money in the short term, but generally make more mistakes and, over the long term, may not be ahead of the game.

Inspections At Night

Some home inspectors will start inspections just before it gets dark. They do the exterior of the home first and then move inside. While this is possible, we try to avoid this. Home inspections are tricky enough without the additional problem of not being able to see very well. If dusk falls quickly and you haven't finished your outside work, you have a serious problem. We also find that we often go back outside after being in the home for a while to follow up on clues. If it's gotten dark outside, you may not be able to do this. Another issue is that the lighting inside the house may not be good. While this can be overcome with strong flashlights and trouble lights, it doesn't make the inspection any easier.

3.3 THE CHARACTERISTICS OF A GOOD HOME INSPECTOR

We've talked about some of the home inspection realities. Let's try to build the perfect home inspector.

Technical Wizard

The perfect home inspector knows everything about homes. He or she is familiar with every building material, every mechanical and electrical system that's ever been used, and every modification that homeowners have ever made to any of these. He is completely up to date on every new housing related product and method that comes onto the market and is able to anticipate the failure modes of every building material and component. He also knows how to evaluate these systems almost instantly and determine whether they are functioning properly.

Enjoys People   Don't get the idea that the perfect inspector is one-dimensional. Because the inspection is an interpersonal process, the perfect inspector has to enjoy people. He must be able to get along with all sorts of people, including clients, sellers and agents who have relatively high levels of stress because of the nature of the real estate transaction.

Great Communicator   The perfect home inspector must be able to transfer her observations and conclusions into the head of every client, overcoming all of the natural barriers that exist to both verbal and written communications. He must be a skilled listener and reader of body language, knowing exactly when to repeat a point using different words to enhance understanding. The perfect inspector uses exactly the right words in exactly the right number at exactly the right time.

Adjust Expectations   While providing tremendous insights, the perfect home inspector also radically changes the expectations of the client, and perhaps the agents and seller, clearly defining the limitations and scope of a home inspection without diminishing the perceived value of the process.

Actor Or Performer   The perfect home inspector must perform high-level intellectual activity (observing, evaluating, analyzing and drawing conclusions about systems based on only a one-time visual examination) while at the same time building rapport and credibility with an audience. For the most part, there is no set script and the inspector has to improvise his presentation, gearing it to the specific audience without sacrificing any of the technical work.

Diplomat   The home inspector must report his findings in a way that makes the client understand the physical condition of the house. At the same time, the inspector gains nothing by intentionally offending the real estate agents or the seller. The goal is not to make enemies of some while befriending others. The perception of the inspector developed by each audience member must be similarly positive, even though the message may be more palatable to some.

Investigator/ Detective   The perfect home inspector relies on clues and indirect evidence to form opinions and draw conclusions. Since the house is already built and usually furnished, there's a great deal that cannot be seen. Since we are limited to a one-time visit, we can't usually tell if cracks are still moving. If it hasn't rained for weeks, it's hard to know whether the roof will leak. If it's 100°F outside, it's hard to know whether the heating system will keep the house warm. If it's 25°F outside, it's hard to know whether the air conditioning will do its job. The list of limitations is virtually endless. Nonetheless, the perfect home inspector derives accurate conclusions from the tiniest shreds of evidence.

Organized But Flexible   The perfect home inspector has a routine that he follows meticulously. However, when the seller has a sick child in a bedroom and a vicious dog in the backyard, the inspector finds a way to adjust the routine without diminishing the thoroughness and effectiveness of the inspection.

Physical Challenges	The perfect home inspector does not have to be an Olympic athlete, but she has to be able to carry ladders and tools, climb ladders, crawl through attics and subgrade areas. The perfect inspector has to be able to use hand tools with dexterity and to be able to write, use a keyboard and/or dictate with speed and accuracy.
Constantly In The Field	The perfect inspector is comfortable operating out of his vehicle and spending little or no time in the office. The perfect inspector makes time to research, managing to stay current with each building material and system innovation that comes onto the market, as we mentioned earlier.
A Business Person Too?	The perfect home inspector is an amazing individual, but let's make it even more challenging. The perfect home inspector may also be the sole proprietor of a business. Not only does the perfect home inspector perform the inspections, she does the marketing to bring the business in, handles the administration side of the business, including booking the inspections, managing the telephones, providing supplies and all the services that any business needs and handles the financial side of the business, both from a bookkeeping and accounting sense and also an information systems standpoint.
Medical Analogy	We said earlier that the doctor who is a general practitioner is a good analogy to the home inspector. Does this discussion reinforce or diminish that thought?

3.4 VEHICLES, CLOTHES AND TOOLS

3.4.1 VEHICLES

Presentable	It doesn't matter what kind of vehicle you drive, as long as it is clean and presentable. The home inspector's vehicle should not be notable because it is so run-down, dirty, flashy or extravagant. The goal of a home inspection is effective communication. People are more relaxed and communicate better with people they have things in common with. If clients see you driving a car they wouldn't be caught dead in, this creates a small but real barrier to good communication and a first impression that may be hard to overcome.
Put Yourself In Their Shoes	If you traded places with your client, what would you like to see from the home inspector? Most people are hoping the home inspector will be professional, sensible, organized and competent. What kind of cars or trucks do sensible professional people drive? There are lots of possible answers to this, and a wide range of acceptable vehicles. If you insist on driving a vehicle that tells the world you are different from the rest, you've created a hurdle to overcome. In our opinion, home inspection is tough enough without creating any unnecessary hurdles.
Marketing Tool?	Some people put logos and advertising on their vehicles. This is a business decision and has little to do with the practice of home inspection. In terms of a client's perception of the inspector, we see nothing negative about it.

Big Enough?   The vehicle should be big enough to accommodate your tools and ladder. Some inspectors carry one ladder. Others carry more. Step ladders, extension ladders and collapsible ladders are all options. You'll also want to have room for reports, business cards, any reference materials and, if you use a computer and printer on site, you'll need a vehicle big enough to set these up. Cars, vans and trucks are all choices of home inspectors.

Can Client   Your vehicle may become a meeting room at the end of the inspection if your
Join You?   closing discussion has to take place outside the house. This may be the case if the agent has to leave the home and lock up, or if the inspection is obviously inconveniencing the seller. The buyers may also want the closing discussion to take place in your vehicle because they don't want the seller or agents to listen in on the discussion. It may be too hot, cold or wet to have the closing discussion outdoors comfortably. There is often money to change hands and receipts to be signed. This is easier to do in a closed vehicle where wind won't be a problem.

You don't want a half-eaten lunch on the front seat or, worse still, five or six half-eaten lunches. You also don't want confidential materials, such as other clients' reports or payments, lying around in the vehicle where they can be seen from outside through the window.

Summary

In short, your vehicle should be tidy and unremarkable.

3.4.2 CLOTHES

Clothing is a topic of some discussion among home inspectors. We wear ties and dress shirts because we want to be perceived as professionals. Many home inspectors are successful wearing more casual clothes, including golf shirts. Some even wear jeans and shorts. You will have to make a decision about the kind of image you present and, perhaps, what is typical and acceptable in your market.

Look The Part   Again, your clothes should reflect your client's expectation of a home inspector. If you are convinced that home inspectors should wear tweed jackets with patches on the elbows and smoke a pipe, maybe that's the best dress. You don't want to shock the client or draw undue attention to your clothing. Some home inspectors believe the perfect clothing is exactly the clothing that your client is wearing. This can create an instant connection between you and your client. Obviously you're not going to know in advance, so you're going to have to take a stab.

Use The   Some home inspectors dress differently, depending on the neighborhood they'll
Address   be inspecting and the purchase price of the home. If the house is in a fixer-upper neighborhood, you might dress differently than on a street where the average house price is over $2,000,000. Your expectation of your typical client will be different.

Don't
Overdress

If you think your client is likely to be wearing a three-piece suit, that doesn't mean you should be wearing a three-piece suit. That would not fit the image most clients would have of an inspector. You don't want to look like you are dressed so well that you won't roll up your sleeves and get dirty on your client's behalf.

Dress For
Comfort

Dressing for success is important, but you have to be comfortable too. Loose-fitting clothes are better than restrictive clothing. You will be reaching, climbing and sometimes crawling. We recommend coveralls for entering areas where you may get quite dirty. This isn't because we're worried about your laundry or dry cleaning bills; it's rude to walk through a house tracking dirt everywhere.

Indoor Shoes

Speaking of tracking dirt everywhere, many home inspectors carry a pair of slippers or indoor shoes to put on inside homes. Their outdoor footwear is left at the door. Sellers appreciate this gesture. We always take off our shoes at the door unless the house has some very unusual conditions.

Outdoor
Shoe Types

We recommend rubber soled non-slip lace-up shoes for outdoor work. If you are going to be climbing ladders and walking roofs, leather soles are not what you're after. Stocking feet are also not safe. We prefer lace-up shoes because you may accidentally step out of slip-ons.

Many inspectors carry at least one clean shirt in the car with them, as well as wet wipes, breath mints and deodorant.

Gloves, Mask
And Goggles

In addition to coveralls and slip-on shoe covers for crawlspaces and attics, many inspectors carry gloves, masks and goggles for working in insulated attics. Attic insulation can irritate skin, eyes and nasal passages. Gloves are also helpful when crawling onto dark-colored roofs on a hot summer day.

What If It
Rains?

We recommend carrying rain gear and an umbrella. It's a nice touch to carry an extra umbrella for your client. Some inspectors even carry spare rain gear for a client.

3.4.3 TOOLS

In each of the Modules, we list the appropriate tools and their purpose. This list is a summary of the lists in the other Modules. We've broken it down into a basic list and an optional list. There are many tools that you could carry that we don't list here. We are trying to stay within the scope of a home inspection that meets the Standards of Practice and includes the common optional tools.

BASIC TOOLS

• **Binoculars**
To look at parts of the home you can't get to.
• **Flashlight**
To look at poorly lit parts of the house and to scan along interior surfaces looking for irregularities. Flashlights can also be used to tap on siding to determine the substrate. Some inspectors use the end of their flashlight to push open attic access hatches to avoid getting fingerprints on them.

- **Spare Flashlight Batteries and Bulbs**

- **Ladder – step, extension and/or foldable**
  To get to roofs, attics, etc.

- **Screwdrivers – an assortment**
  To open electrical panels and remove access hatches.

- **Carpenter's Awl**
  To probe wood for rot or insect damage.

- **Telescopic Mirror – small**
  To inspect furnace heat exchangers and other confined areas difficult to access.

- **Measuring Tape – 25 feet long, one-inch-wide blade**
  To measure structural members, roof areas, chimney heights, window sizes, stair risers, etc.

- **Electrical Circuit Testers**
  To check that receptacles are wired correctly.

- **Knife**
  To probe wood for damage, scrape paint off labels, break paint seals on access hatches, dig paint out of screw slots, etc.

- **Gloves**
  To protect hands from hot roofs and insulation.

- **Coveralls**
  To keep clothing clean in attics and crawlspaces. A plastic bag for soiled coveralls is a good idea.

- **Mask**
  To avoid inhaling insulation fibers in attics.

- **Pliers – we like channel lock or slip joint**
  To turn screws where slots are worn or where nuts have been used instead of screws.

- **Briefcase or Tool Kit**
  To carry your tools.

OPTIONAL TOOLS

- **Tool Belt**
  To carry tools and keep hands free.

- **Flashlight Belt Loops**
  This is a loop that attaches to your belt that you can hang your flashlight from.

- **Trouble Light – plug in light with extension cord**
  To illuminate crawlspaces and other poorly lit areas where a flashlight may not be adequate.

- **Drop Sheet**

  To put over clothes in closets and below attic hatches to protect the home from dirt and insulation.

- **Large Mirror – six inches by ten inches, for example**

  To look behind water heaters, furnaces, oil tanks and other spaces that are too small to get into, but not as confined as a furnace heat exchanger.

- **Wet Wipes or Paper Towels**

  To clean your hands during and/or after an inspection. We prefer not to use the seller's washroom facilities and hand towels.

- **Moisture Meter or Moisture Scanner**

  To look for elevated moisture levels in suspect areas and to check stains for evidence of moisture.

- **Voltage Detector**

  To determine whether wiring is energized.

- **Ampmeter**

  To verify correct operation of electric furnace, for example.

- **Plumb Bob**

  To measure the amount by which columns or walls are out of plumb.

- **Mason's Level – four-foot spirit level**

  To measure amount by which walls or columns are out of plumb and floors, ceilings or roofs are out of level, or slope of gutters, water plumbing pipes or appliance vents.

- **Extendable Probe**

  To check for rot in places that cannot be reached from the ground or floor level.

- **Nut Driver**

  To remove nuts that may have been used in electrical panels, access covers, etc.

- **Power Screwdriver**

  To facilitate removal of screws from panels and access hatches.

- **Crescent Wrench**

  To remove and replace bolts.

- **Hammer**

  To pull out and replace nails sealing access hatches, etc.

- **Goggles**

  To avoid getting insulation and other irritants in your eyes.

- **Camera – Polaroid, 35mm, digital, Video, etc.**

  To record your findings. Note: some home inspectors include photographs of the home in their reports. Some give copies of videotapes to clients.

• **Carbon Monoxide Sensor**

To check for holes in heat exchangers and possible backdraft problems.

• **Combustible Gas Analyzer**

To check for gas leaks, backdraft and holes in heat exchangers.

• **Compass**

To determine which way the house faces. This can be helpful in order to know where prevailing winds or wind driven rain comes from. Also, if you use the compass points to describe areas of the house, this helps to ensure that you describe the house correctly.

• **Samples of Various Sizes of Electrical Wire**

To help identify wire sizes in the field.

• **Wire Gauge**

To help identify wire sizes in the field.

• **Samples of Various Sizes and Materials of Plumbing Pipes**

To help identify plumbing pipes in the field.

• **Magnet**

To help differentiate between galvanized steel and copper gutters, galvanized steel and brass piping, etc.

• **Latex Gloves (Surgical Gloves)**

To keep hands clean and avoid getting fingerprints on house components.

• **Electrical Tape**

To make temporary repairs to problems (not recommended by writers, but done by some inspectors).

• **Thermometer**

To check temperature rise and temperature drop across furnace heat exchangers and air conditioning and heat pump coils.

Again, there are other instruments that could be used during home inspections. These, however, are the majority of the common tools.

► 4.0 TYPICAL CLIENTS

Who Hires Inspectors? — We are going to focus on the prospective home buyer, although we have talked about several types of inspections, in which the typical clients may be different.

When Are We Hired? — Home inspectors are often engaged after a prospective buyer has negotiated a conditional purchase of a property with a seller. The offer may be conditional on the home inspection or on home inspection and financing, for example. The condition may be waived as a result of the inspection or the condition may be exercised, and the transaction may be aborted. The transaction may also be renegotiated based on the inspection report.

Before The Offer — Although it's not as common in many markets, some buyers engage inspectors to check out properties before putting in an offer. The inspection report may be used to explain to a seller why the offer is at a certain level. There are advantages and disadvantages to each of these approaches, but we don't want to get beyond the scope of this program. Circumstances that led to us being engaged are only of peripheral interest, at least at this stage.

Why Are We Hired?

This may seem like a trivial question, but let's look at some of the possibilities:

• The clients want to make the most informed buying decision possible.
• The clients want a positive reinforcement of their decision.
• The clients are looking for leverage to get out of the deal. They have gotten cold feet.
• The clients are looking for leverage to renegotiate the purchase price. They think they overpaid.
• A husband and wife have strong and very different feelings about a house. Both are looking for the home inspector to support their opposite opinions of the home.
• Real estate agents have insisted on the home inspection to protect their clients and minimize the agent's liability.
• The lender may have insisted on an inspection to protect their investment. The lender can be a bank, but it may also be a family member.
• The mortgage insurer may insist on an inspection to protect their interests.
• The client's employer pays for a home inspection anyway.

*Beware The
Oversell*

Many clients are led to believe that a home inspection provides absolute protection for their purchase. We sometimes hear –

- complete peace of mind
- it's guaranteed protection
- it's good insurance
- it's better than a warranty
- you are covered
- you are protected
- their insurance will cover anything they miss

As you can imagine, home inspectors hate to hear these phrases. Most will stop what they are doing and set about to adjust the client's expectations. Experienced home inspectors know that these dangerous misconceptions often lead to unhappy customers over the long term.

*Ask Them
To Attend*

Although we've touched on it before, it is worth repeating: You want your clients to attend the inspection. They'll be better served and you'll be better protected.

*Client's State
Of Mind*

Good home inspectors are able to empathize with clients. Let's look for a moment at some of the things that your clients may be thinking about during the inspection:

- They are worried, nervous, tense and stressed out about the decision to buy any house.
- They are doubting the wisdom of having chosen this house.
- They are wondering whether they can afford the house.
- They are wondering if they have considered all of the issues, including neighborhood, schools, shopping, recreation, commuting, yard size, house size, house style, etc.

They may be saying to themselves:

- Is this thing a money pit?
- I wish it was over.
- Do we really need a home inspector? If so, is this the right inspector?
- How will we know if he or she is any good?
- Who picked this inspector?
- Do the home inspector and the agent have a relationship I should know about?
- Am I paying too much for the inspection?
- Will the inspector make me feel stupid?
- How should I act? Do I have to do anything?
- Should I ask questions or let the inspector do his or her work?
- Will the inspector think we're idiots for choosing this house and tell us we paid too much for it?

- I wish it was over.
- What will the sellers think? They must think I don't trust them.
- Will the seller be rude? The negotiations have been pretty tough.
- This is just one more step in this whole process that I don't understand.
- Why does everything about buying a house include so much paperwork and cost so much?
- I wish it was over.

Communication Barriers

These are only a sample of the things that might be on your client's mind. A client's state of mind is just one of the barriers to good communication. We'll talk more about this later, but just to give you a flavor, here are some of the other client communication issues you may encounter:

- The clients want to know absolutely **everything** about the house.
- The clients arrive with 27 pages of questions, typed, single-spaced.
- The clients don't want you to talk to them about the house, they just want you to tell them it's okay to buy.
- The clients keep asking you if they should buy the home.
- The clients keep asking you if the price is right.
- The clients ask you to stop so they can write down **everything** you say.
- The clients are a couple who are clearly in the middle of a disagreement.
- The clients want to audiotape or videotape the whole inspection.

There are many other issues you'll have to address, and while we'll talk about many in this Module, you're going to have to rely on your common sense and professionalism to handle the unexpected.

Inspectors Can Be Distracted Too

It's critical that you stay focused and in control of the inspection. The client's communication skills are not likely to be good because of the things we've mentioned. Your communication skills have to be outstanding. They won't be if you are distracted by such things as:

- **The opulence of the house.** Almost every inspector eventually inspects a house that is so expensive and so beautifully furnished and decorated that it is hard to look past these features.
- **Loud arguments** between sellers, and buyers, buyers and agents, agents and sellers, etc.
- **Erotic art** on every wall.
- **Vicious dogs or other pets**.
- **Rats, mice, insects, snakes, bats and other pests** in, under and around the house.

- **Extremely high or low temperatures.**
- **A full bladder.**
- **A flashlight with failing batteries.**
- **Missing critical papers**, including report forms.
- **The next appointment** clear across town that is supposed to start in 15 minutes.
- **A lack of sleep, a hangover or illness.**
- **A recent dispute with a family member, co-worker or boss.**

All of these can reduce your ability to focus. Some of these circumstances are within your control. Some are not. You will need to be able to fight through these distractions and focus, or have the wisdom to stop the inspection and make other arrangements.

Summary

So Is It Worth It?

Sometimes it's not easy being in a performance business. While all of the things that we've talked about can be challenges, the rewards are similarly great. The gratitude expressed by most clients at the end of the inspection is worth more to some inspectors than the fee. The knowledge that you have genuinely helped someone make a significant decision in their life is a great feeling. Home inspectors can alter people's lives dramatically in a positive way. There are very few professions where, over the course of two to three hours, a practitioner can develop rapport, earn respect and deliver a complete product with immediate recognizable value. Driving away from a house knowing that you have used your skills to help someone is a wonderful feeling.

Communication &
Professional Practice

MODULE

QUICK QUIZ 2

☑ INSTRUCTIONS

• You should finish Study Session 2 before doing this Quiz.
• Write your answers in the spaces provided.
• Check your answers against ours at the end of this section.
• If you have trouble with the Quiz, re-read the Study Session and try the Quiz again.
• If you did well, it's time for Study Session 3.

1. Describe how the home inspection profession is regulated in most parts of North America.

2. Indicate the estimated number of home inspectors in North America (a range is fine).

3. Indicate the average home inspection fee in North America.

4. List eight types of residential inspections that home inspectors may be asked to perform.

_____

_____

_____

_____

_____

_____

_____

_____

5. Describe in one sentence the difference between a home inspection and an appraisal.

_____

6. List six people or things to whom home inspectors have an obligation during an inspection.

_____

_____

_____

_____

_____

_____

7. Indicate the average duration of a home inspection.

_____

8. List four advantages of having clients attend the inspection.

_____

_____

_____

_____

9. List seven attributes of a good home inspector.

_____

_____

_____

_____

_____

_____

_____

10. Describe in one sentence a typical home inspector's vehicle.

_____

11. Describe in one sentence how a home inspector should dress. (Hint: should you be dressing to express your tastes?)

_____

12. List 10 basic tools that home inspectors use.

_____

_____

_____

_____

_____

_____

_____

_____

_____

_____

13. List eight reasons home inspectors may be hired to perform a prepurchase inspection.

_____

_____

_____

_____

_____

_____

_____

_____

14. List 10 thoughts or feelings clients typically have during a home inspection.

_____

_____

_____

_____

_____

_____

_____

_____

_____

_____

15. List 10 things, other than the client, that commonly distract home inspectors during an inspection.

_____

_____

_____

_____

_____

_____

_____

_____

_____

_____

If you had no trouble with the Quiz, it's time for Study Session 3.

Key Words

- *Young profession*
- *Unregulated*
- *Prepurchase home inspection*
- *Field review of performance*
- *Visual inspection*
- *Non-destructive and non-invasive*
- *Sampling type inspection*
- *Conditional offer*
- *Neutral and unbiased*
- *Adjust expectations*
- *Technical wizard*
- *Great communicator*
- *Actor*
- *Diplomat*
- *Investigator*
- *Detective*
- *Communication barriers*
- *Distractions*

Communication & Professional Practice

MODULE

STUDY SESSION 3

1. You should have complete Study Sessions 1 and 2 before starting this Session.

2. This Session covers the first three components of the home inspection process, including –
   • the pre-inspection routine
   • the introductory discussion
   • the inspection itself

3. At the end of this Session, you should be able to –
   • list the four parts of a home inspection
   • list the amount of time typically spent on various parts of an inspection
   • list a typical routine or flow of an inspection
   • list four elements of the seller introduction
   • write a script for an introductory discussion, covering all of the main items (eight to 15 sentences)
   • explain in one sentence how improvement recommendations should be presented during the inspection itself
   • describe in two sentences the **macro/micro** approach to home inspection
   • list 10 things inspectors commonly fail to put back the way they found
   • describe in one sentence what you should do when you see something you don't understand during a home inspection

4. This Session may take you roughly an hour and a half to complete.

5. Quick Quiz 3 is at the end of this Session.

Key Words

- *Pre-inspection routine*
- *Introductory discussion*
- *The inspection itself*
- *Closing discussion*
- *Time goals*
- *Vehicle check*
- *Personal check*
- *Arriving early*
- *Knowing the players*
- *Seller introduction*
- *Using names*
- *Taking control*
- *Macro/micro approach*
- *Contract*
- *Perspective*
- *Consistent depth*

► 5.0 THE INSPECTION PROCESS

We're going to break this section down into four segments –

1. The Pre-inspection Routine
2. The Introductory Discussion
3. The Inspection Itself
4. The Closing Discussion

Our Method

Again, this discussion is not technical, but addresses method. The procedures and advice in this section are based on the tens of thousands of inspections we have performed, but we should make it clear that our way is not the only successful way. These approaches work for us. Others may work better for you. However, we believe that the comments in this section make a very strong starting point.

5.1 PRE-INSPECTION ROUTINE

The pre-inspection routine takes place before leaving your home or office. There are number of checks that some inspectors do when parked outside the home that don't really help. If you're at the house and the inspection starts in two minutes, it's too late to realize you have no business cards or report forms and your flashlight battery is dead.

Set Time Goals

You should know before you get to the house how long you plan to be there. An average inspection is two and a half hours. You may want to adjust this time based on what you know about the size of the house, the location, or the condition. You may have been told when the appointment was booked that the house has seven additions. This should be a clue that you may need more than two and a half hours.

Budgeting Your Time

We set goals not only for the total inspection time, but also for the amount of time spent on each phase of the inspection. This allows you to track your progress and avoid finding out after two and a half hours you've only done a third of the inspection. Our typical time goals look like this:

- Introductory discussion – 10 minutes
- Roof and exterior – 30 minutes
- Mechanical, electrical, basement (if applicable) and structure – 30 minutes
- Interior inspection (the house living spaces) – 30 minutes
- The attic and/or crawlspace – 15 minutes
- Recording the inspection results – 20 minutes
- Closing discussion – 15 minutes
- Total – 150 minutes

We intentionally make the last two items on the list a little longer than may appear necessary. This provides us with a little bit of slack in case we fall behind during the earlier segments of the inspection. Successful inspectors always know how long they've been in the house and where they should be at that particular time. There are several things that can be done to adjust the pace of the inspection as necessary. If done properly, these are invisible to the audience.

Know Your Routine

Every successful inspector has a routine. You should never depart from your routine, if possible. Circumstances will occasionally make it necessary, and in those cases you'll have to increase your focus level to compensate. You should know before you leave the office the exact order in which you are going to approach the inspection. This is one sequence that is used by many inspectors:

- Introductory discussion
- Exterior inspection
- Roof
- Heating plant
- Electrical panel
- Water service entry and water heater
- Structure
- Interior rooms
- Attic
- Crawlspace
- Closing discussion

We are more interested in you having a routine than exactly what it looks like. Is it consistent? Is it repeatable on each and every inspection?

Vehicle Check

Is your vehicle presentable? Do you have enough gas? Do you have a map? Do you know exactly where you're going? Do you have an agent's telephone number (most agents have mobile phones or pagers and can be reached by their office)? If you get lost or are delayed, you'll want to call ahead.

Room For A Client?

If you need to have the closing discussion in your car, will that be a problem? Keep the interior of your vehicle tidy and keep at least the front seat passenger side clear. Your clients will often be a couple and there may be at least three of you in the vehicle.

Do You Have Everything You Need?

Do you have all your tools and your ladders? Is everything in good order? Do you have all of your field checklists, report forms, invoices, receipts, business cards, brochures, computer printer paper, etc. If you have a letter you leave with sellers, do you have copies? Do you have spare forms in case something gets spoiled? If you are asked on the spot to perform ancillary services such as radon or septic testing, do you have the necessary materials to do that?

Summary

Your vehicle checklist might look something like this:

1. Clean inside
2. Clean outside
3. Gas
4. Map
5. Directions and route
6. Agents' phone numbers
7. Room for a passenger or two
8. Tools and ladders
9. Papers
10. Coveralls
11. Indoor shoes
12. Spare shirt
13. Rain gear
14. Umbrella

Personal Check

Are You Presentable? Do you look like someone you'd want to do your home inspection? Are your clothes relatively clean? Many inspectors carry a comb or brush, deodorant and breath mints. Most inspectors avoid spicy food, hamburgers with raw onion and food with garlic between inspections as a courtesy to their audience. Will you stop at a washroom before you leave or on the way?

Summary

Your personal checklist may look something like this:

1. Clothes clean
2. Hair combed
3. Deodorant
4. Breath mints
5. Washroom stop

Learn The Neighborhood Leave your office in time to arrive early at the inspection, allowing for unexpected traffic difficulties. Once you find the house, you should drive around the immediate neighborhood to get a sense of the general topography and the size and style of homes in the neighborhood. Is the home you're going to inspect typical? Does it have an addition? Is it the only house in the neighborhood with an old roof or a new roof? Does every other house but this one have new retaining walls? There's a lot you can learn about the house before you walk up to the front door.

Other Homes For Sale Make a mental note of other homes that have a For Sale sign. The odds are good that your clients will have looked closely at these houses and chosen not to buy them. Any visible differences between other houses for sale and the house you're about to inspect may give you some insights into the clients' minds.

Park On The Street	We recommend that you not park on the driveway. If the seller wants to go out during the inspection and you are blocking them in, it's frustrating for the seller and disruptive for you. If you park in the driveway and your client or the agent parks behind you, you may be blocked in when you want to leave. Agents and clients often stay after you leave to discuss the report and perhaps sign a waiver of the home inspection condition. If you have to come back in and interrupt the discussion to ask someone to move a vehicle, no one is very happy.
Don't Park Illegally	Assuming that you arrive early, you may be able to get a good parking spot. If not, you may be tempted to park illegally. Your clients and agents who arrive shortly after you may well notice that you have parked illegally. This may send the wrong message to your audience before you even meet them.
Don't Complain About The Parking	During one of our early inspections, we could not find a parking spot near the home and had to park several blocks away. By the time we found a parking spot and arrived at the front of the house with our ladder and tools, we were a couple of minutes late, we were hot, tired and slightly frustrated. As we introduced ourselves, we said, *"I'm sorry I'm late, but there's just no place to park around here."* The client was silent for a moment and then said, *"You know, I hadn't noticed that but it's true. That's a real problem for me."* While the comment was innocent and may have been accurate, it was unprofessional because it was outside of our scope. In our opinion, this kind of comment is inappropriate.
The Psychological Advantage	Arriving early is always a psychological advantage. If you have already parked and gotten out of the car, you have a slight advantage over the people who arrive after you. When you are the last one there, you are often self-conscious about keeping others waiting and tend to rush gathering your tools and ladder. If you are even slightly disorganized, you may create a very poor impression before opening your mouth. Poor first impressions are powerful and difficult to overcome.
Cell Phone Off	We recommend that you not carry a cell phone that may ring during an inspection. Similarly, we recommend that you not wear a pager that has an audible signal during the inspection. It shows a lack of respect for the client to pause during your inspection to answer a phone or respond to a page. It may appear to your client that the next inspection is more important than this one. There may be circumstances where you have to leave a cell phone or a pager on (a spouse that is nine months pregnant, for example) and if this is the case, we recommend that you explain this to your clients at the beginning of the inspection so that if there is an interruption, they will not be offended.
Know The Players	We strongly recommend that you memorize the clients' names and real estate agents' names, if you have them, before getting out of your vehicle. It's critical that you know who your clients are during the introductory discussion. In many cases, people will only introduce themselves by name and it will be unclear who is the agent and who is the client. Clients also often bring friends or relatives. Unless you know your client's name before the introductions, you may not know which of these people is the client.

So far, we've gotten from the office to the house. Now, let's get out of the vehicle and start the inspection. Here's a Pre-inspection Checklist you might use.

Pre-inspection Checklist

A. Before leaving the office

Vehicle check

• clean outside
• clean inside
• room for a visitor or two
• fuel
• map
• directions and address
• route planned
• agent's phone number
• tools (including spare batteries, bulbs, etc.)
• ladders
• paperwork (spare report forms, field checklists, sellers' letters, contracts, invoices, business cards, brochures, reference materials, computer, printer paper, and peripherals)
• coveralls
• indoor shoes or slippers
• spare shirt
• rain gear
• umbrella (extra for client?)

Personal check

• comb or brush
• breath mints, deodorant
• washroom stop needed?
• memorize clients' and agent's names

B. After leaving the office

• find home
• learn neighborhood
• arrive early
• park on street, legally
• cell phone and pager off
• check that you know clients' and agent's names

So, we've managed to get to the house 15 minutes before the appointment time, we've got our vehicle and ourselves presentable and we've got all of the tools, paperwork and accessories we need. We know the neighborhood and we have a first impression of the house. We've cleared our mind of distractions and we know the name of our client and the agents. Let's begin the performance.

5.2 INTRODUCTORY DISCUSSION

Seller Introduction

If you have arrived early, the clients and agents may not be there yet. Many inspectors take this opportunity to knock on the front door and introduce themselves to the seller. Comments to the seller may include an explanation of how long the inspection will be and where in the house you will be going. You may want to reassure them that the inspection is not destructive and not invasive. You may ask whether there are any pets or people who may be sleeping in the house that you should not disturb.

Seller Letter

We use a letter that explains the inspection to sellers. It looks like this:

To The Homeowner:

Thank you for allowing Carson Dunlop & Associates to visit your home today. As the owner of the house, you are entitled to know the details of the process.

The practice of home inspection has become very popular. Carson Dunlop professionals have examined well over 50,000 houses. We are sensitive to the privacy of homeowners and we respect your property. We strive to leave things exactly as we find them, and yes, we take off our shoes at the front door.

A typical inspection takes two to three hours. The exterior of the house is our normal starting point. We go up on the roof, and then proceed around the outside of the house. From there, we go into the basement and/or crawlspace to examine the major systems of the house. Included are the structure, the heating and air conditioning systems, the electrical service and plumbing system.

After completing our work in the basement, we go through the rest of the house. We test all of the plumbing fixtures, operate windows and doors, look under sinks, in closets and go up in the attic. Carson Dunlop does no destructive testing. We consider alarms and security systems to be a private matter and do not test these.

Our goal is to fairly and accurately report on the condition of the home. Our intention is not to "nitpick," nor do we feel compelled to find problems to justify our existence. At Carson Dunlop we strive to keep our findings in perspective for our clients. If a recommendation we make is typical for homes of that age, or for homes in the area, the buyer will be told that.

While some owners prefer to be home when we do our inspections, others find it easier to leave the house. Either situation is fine with us. We cannot discuss our findings or release a report to anyone without the our client's permission.

Again, thank you for allowing us to visit your home. Should you have any questions about our services, please do not hesitate to call.

Anything I Should Know? — Some inspectors ask the seller whether there is anything they should know about the home before starting. Sometimes there is valuable information offered about problems you would not otherwise know about. If sellers are confused or distressed by the question, inspectors may rescue the seller by saying, *"Is there a dog in the backyard or anyone sleeping in the home, for example?"*

Waiting For Your Audience — After you have introduced yourself to the seller, remain outside, waiting for your clients and the agent to arrive. You may do preliminary macro (big picture) and micro (close up) tours around the exterior of the home and, perhaps, set up your ladder to get onto the roof. If your first tour around the house is clockwise, your second tour with the clients should be counterclockwise.

On The Roof — Some inspectors like to be on the roof when the clients and agents arrive. This shows the clients right at the beginning that you are willing to take risks on their behalf and that you are purposeful and enthusiastic about your work.

The Audience Arrives — Your clients often arrive with the agent, although this isn't always the case. As you meet them, you are courteous, pleasant, relaxed, professional, in control and enthusiastic.

Introductions — Greet everyone as they arrive with a handshake and a business card. Acknowledge the presence of everyone there, even if there are children. You don't have to shake hands with children, but you can say something like, *"And these are your children?"* or *"And these are your assistants?"*

Don't Be Physical — We recommend no physical contact beyond a handshake, such as putting your hand on people's arms or shoulders. People may find this uncomfortable or may view you as overly familiar.

Use Names So You'll Remember Them — We recommend that as you are introduced to people you use their name. You might say, *"Good morning, I'm John Smith from Smith Home Inspections."*

They might reply, *"Hello, I'm Peter Brown."*

You might say, *"It's good to meet you, Mr. Brown, and thank you for choosing us to perform your home inspection."*

You'll have to instantly decide whether you're going to address clients as "Mr. Brown" or "Peter," for example. There are number of factors that might give you some clues as to what is appropriate, but when in doubt, "Mr. Brown" is appropriate. As the inspection goes on, you may change that to "Peter," depending on such things as –

• the person's age
• how they are dressed
• their demeanor
• how others address them (If the agent says "Mr. Brown," so do you.)
• how they address you

What If You Miss The Name?	Sometimes you won't catch the name as people introduce themselves. It may be a difficult name, the person may speak softly or there may be background noise. Now is the time to say, *"I'm sorry, I missed that."* If you gloss over this, you're going to spend the next two and a half hours referring to the person as, *"Hey you."* This makes you look inconsiderate because the people did introduce themselves to you and it looks like you chose not to use their name.
People Appreciate It	You may think it slightly embarrassing to ask someone to repeat their name. Most people appreciate the fact that you are interested enough to ask again. People with unusual names will be used to having them mispronounced. The fact that you are asking so that you can use their name correctly is a courtesy and should not be cause for embarrassment.
Who's Who?	It's important to know who the buyer is. Sometimes you can't tell the buyer from the agent, although in most cases, the agent will give you a card. Clients who arrive in groups are often difficult to sort out. Who is the buyer? Who is the father-in-law who's lending the money? Who is Uncle Charlie, the cousin in the construction business who's the family expert?
Good Thing You Memorized The Name	If you've done your homework, you've already memorized the buyer's name and you'll be able to pick her out. If people just give you their names, and you don't know who the buyer is, you can find out by asking, *"Are you buying the home together?"* That will usually result in the buyer stepping forward and explaining the relationship of the others.
Professional Relationship With Agent	If you've been in home inspection for a while, you'll often recognize the real estate agent or agents. Don't be overly familiar with the agents, even if you attended their charity golf tournament the night before and sat with them at dinner. The appearance of a close relationship between real estate agents and home inspectors may make clients uncomfortable or even question your impartiality.
Don't Be Rude	While you don't want to be too familiar with real estate agents, don't ignore them either. Even if they arrive late or stay in the background, introduce yourself and give them a business card.
Take Control	After the introductions, the agent and the buyers who have been working together will often speak to each other. If they are talking about something important, you should wait patiently. If they're talking about when they are going to get together to sign papers or the agent is relating some piece of information about the home, you should stand back. However, if the conversation is clearly social or as soon as the business conversation is completed, you should take charge of the situation. You can say something like, *"Let's get started, shall we?"*

Start With Questions

Many inspectors start with a couple of questions such as:

• *"Have you bought a home before?"*
• *"Have you ever had a home inspection?"*

If they haven't bought a home before, you don't need to ask whether they've ever had a home inspection. If they have bought a home, you can say, *"So, you've been through this before."* When you ask them if they've had a home inspection, if they say *"No"* you can start to explain the inspection process. If they say *"Yes"* you can respond, *"So, you have a good sense of what this is all about."*

A Reason For These Questions

These questions are not idle. They are intended to do a couple of things:

• They give you a chance to get a sense of your client by listening to him speak. The questions do not put a lot of pressure on the client and should not make him feel uncomfortable. They are questions that can be answered with a simple yes or no, or if the client chooses to, they can expand on the answer. This will tell you something about your client.
• These questions send a message that the inspection will be interactive, not a lecture.
• The questions also display your interest in the client's situation and background without probing.

These are not the only appropriate questions, but they work for us.

Set The Goals

The next thing you want to do is make the client understand the goal of the home inspection from your perspective. You might say, *"Our goal over the next two and a half hours is to give you a clear picture of the condition of the major systems in the house."*

This is a positive sentence telling the client that you're going to give him a clear picture. The words are simple and not intimidating. This sentence also builds in some expectation adjustment messages. We've set the time frame for the inspection, which is valuable to all the parties. We've also focused the discussion on the major systems of the house.

Major And Minor Issues

"As we look for significant issues that may affect your buying decision, we'll come across a number of smaller items. We'll discuss those and include them in our report as a courtesy, but our goal isn't to create a detailed maintenance or repair list."

You've now set the parameters that you're going to be looking for big problems, not little ones. You've also told the client that just because you report on some of the little problems, you're not going to find them all.

Describe The Inspection Flow

"We'll start outside and then move indoors where we'll work from the bottom to the top, finishing with the attic."

You've discussed how the inspection will progress. This gives the client some understanding of what to expect. Just as importantly, you've told her that you do have a specific routine. This lets the client know that you're organized and you've done this before.

We Rather Than I

It's our preference to use the word "we" rather than "I" in describing the actions of the inspector. This creates a team concept and puts you and the client on the same side. This is a valuable relationship to develop during the course of the inspection. The "we" also suggests to the client that you expect him to participate in the inspection. The client gets better value and you can do a better job if your client is available to communicate with you as you go through the home.

Explain Report Delivery

Let your client know when the finished product will be available. You might say:

- *"We'll complete our report at the end of the inspection and by the time we're done, you'll have everything you need to make your decision,"* or
- *"We'll have the report prepared and delivered to you tomorrow by 5:00 p.m."*

Plans And Concerns

You've spoken long enough. Now it's time to ask the client two more questions. The first is, *"Do you have any plans for changes to the house?"*

This gives you another chance to understand your client's frame of reference. It also lets you know whether there are parts of the home that you should not be inspecting. If clients tell you they want to tear off and replace the horrible rear addition, the inspection just got simpler. There are many other insights you may gain depending on their answers to this question. Your role here is to listen very carefully to what they say and react accordingly.

The next question is, *"Do you have any specific concerns about the home or are you looking for a general overview?"*

This question allows you to identify any burning issues that clients may have. Clients may have big issues they want you to address and wait through the whole inspection for you to cover it. If you don't touch on it, it will frustrate the clients. Clients may be so busy waiting for you to cover their issues, that they listen to virtually nothing else you say. It's better to know about that issue before the fact.

One Or Two Issues

If clients express one or two concerns, assure them that these will be addressed and ask them to mention those issues again at the end of the inspection if they still have questions about them. This acknowledges the validity of the issues and puts the responsibility for their satisfactory resolution back in the clients' hands.

Client's Response

The second half of the question allows clients to say that they are just looking for a general overview. If you simply ask whether there are any concerns, clients often feel compelled to come up with some, or feel foolish if they can't. This isn't the response you are looking for, so give them an easy out.

Issues Outside Our Scope

Some concerns raised by clients will be outside the scope of a standard home inspection. This can create an awkward situation. Your response might go like this, *"The issue of soil contamination is not within the scope of a home inspection. We can refer you to some environmental testing companies who can provide answers to those issues."*

You have let the clients know that there is a scope of work that is yours and you have clearly defined their concern as outside the scope.

It's critical that you don't use words like, *"I don't do soils work."*

This makes the client think she's hired the wrong home inspector and if she had hired another one, she would have gotten the information she was looking for. When something is outside of your scope, make it clear that it's outside the scope of the profession, not a failing on your part.

Provide Direction

The second half of the response is to avoid frustrating the client. We try to avoid saying "No" or giving people dead end answers. We try to steer people in the right direction on issues outside of the scope. This focuses the clients' attention in another direction and they will start thinking about taking that step, rather than staring at you in frustration. They will see you as helpful and won't feel foolish for asking an inappropriate question. Inspectors who belittle clients for asking dumb questions usually don't get many more questions. They often don't get many more clients, either.

Multiple Concerns

Clients who have a long list of concerns can consume considerable time. We recommend that you do not take pages of concerns from clients', even if they try to put them into your hands. We generally say something like, *"Let's go through the inspection process and review your list at the end of the inspection to see if there is anything that we haven't addressed."* If you do your job correctly, the only issues that you won't have addressed will be those outside of the scope of a home inspection.

The Next Step

You want to get the inspection going, but there are a couple of things you need to do first. You want to let the client know exactly what her role is going to be. You might say something like, *"Please join me as we go through the home. I won't ask you to get up on the roof or go in the attic or crawlspace, but otherwise we can work together and discuss our findings along the way."*

This makes it clear why your client should follow you.

The Rules About Questions

Clients don't yet know whether they are allowed to ask questions during the inspection. We try to give them direction like this, *"Please feel free to ask questions as we go. We may not get answers until we get the whole picture, but that's okay."*

You have opened the lines of communication, but retained control. Clients who pepper you with questions that pop into their head as you go through the inspection will usually stop doing it if you defer all of their questions. Most people will catch on quickly that if they wait until you get to the appropriate parts of the inspection, most questions will be answered without being asked.

The Contract   You've just spent some time establishing the roles of the people in the inspection process and trying to establish the concept of working together. The client should be developing a comfort level with you. It's time to get the contract signed. In some cases, it may have been signed before the inspection, but in most cases it is not. We won't discuss whether or not you should have an inspection contract. That's a business decision and beyond the scope of our program. We'll assume that you do.

Authorization Form   Ours is called an **Authorization Form**. We think it sound a little less intimidating than **contract**. We say something like, *"This is our Authorization Form that sets out the rules of the game. Please read it carefully while I get started with the roof. Please check that we have your name, address and phone number correctly and if everything is in order, sign the form here (indicating where to sign)."*

They Read While You Check Roof   This explains the purpose of the contract and makes it clear that you expect them to read it carefully. By stepping away to inspect the roof, you give them the opportunity to read the contract in relative privacy and discuss it among themselves if they choose. You don't want the clients up on the roof, in any case, for safety reasons. You've already told them that you don't expect them to come up with you. If you arrived early, you've also had a preliminary exterior tour of the home and know exactly where your ladder should be placed to get up on the roof.

Report Review   If your contract is in your report, this is also an opportunity for a client to familiarize himself with the report they will receive at the end of the inspection. If your report follows this format, you can add a sentence to the contract instructions that says, *"You might want to have a look at the report layout. We'll complete this and give it to you at the end of the inspection."*

Check For Signature   When you come back from the roof, you can ask, *"Was everything in order?"*

You will also want to check for a signature, although if the client has closed the report, now is not the time to open it and check that she has signed it. You'll have several opportunities to do that during the inspection, and you can revisit the issue at the end of the inspection. A verbal acknowledgment that everything was in order is adequate.

What If Client Objects?   We have found that it is extremely rare for clients to object to our contract. If there is an objection, now is the time to find out. If there is a problem with the contract, this does not need to be a confrontational situation. If the client objects to something in the contract, you'll have to decide whether it is a substantial issue or not. If it is a trivial issue, you may agree to change the contract. (You may need to clear this with your employer.) This may mean that your contract is poorly worded since trivial issues should not be included.

Major Issue   If the issue is substantive, you may not be prepared to go ahead with the inspection. At this point, you may want to say something like, *"It seems that a standard home inspection is not what you need. We're happy to waive our fee and let you get on with getting the answers or assurances you need. I'm sorry for the misunderstanding."*

This makes it clear that the client's expectations are outside the scope of a home inspection. It does not send a message that you are not able to do the job. You should think of it as though someone accidentally hired a plumber to wire a house. The conversation can be positive, and while the client will undoubtedly be frustrated, you have expressed a willingness to shoulder responsibility for part of the communication breakdown. This is clearly the extent of the responsibility you are willing to accept. Incidentally, never say, *"Our office should have told you this."*

Blaming someone else in your organization for any problem is not professional and not helpful. You should take responsibility for the organization, since you are representing the firm.

Waive Fee   You've also made the gesture of waiving the fee, although you've obviously wasted your time and perhaps turned down another inspection so that you could attend this one. Complaining about the lost revenue or trying to bill for part of your time, in our opinion, detracts from your professionalism.

Clients Press   Once you have decided that you can't meet the client's expectations, it's usually
The Issue   best to stick to your decision not to do the inspection. In some cases, the clients will try to pressure you to do the inspection and provide the opinions that they are looking for beyond your scope. In some cases, they'll offer to pay you more. There is usually a time sensitivity to the real estate transaction. You have to make your client understand that it's not an issue of additional money. It would not be a favor to your client to do work for which you are not trained. Occasionally, the client will relent and ask you to do a Standard home inspection. If so, be warned. This is a client who is likely to be unhappy with your performance, no matter how good it is.

Summary

So, now we've met the players, established a relationship with them, learned a little about their plans for the house, gotten our contract signed and are ready to move forward.

Here's a sample introductory discussion script:

Sample Introductory Discussion Script

A: To Seller

"Good morning! I'm Ralph Stevens from Best Home Inspections. I understand we have an appointment to look at the home today." Pause.

"Great. We'll start outside and come inside in half an hour or so. We'll be about two hours altogether, and will finish up in the attic. Here's a letter that explains things in more detail." Pause and give them the letter.

"Before I start, is there anything I should know about the home?" Pause. If confused or distressed, continue: *"Is there a dog I shouldn't let out, or someone sleeping, for example?"*

B: To Buyer

"Good morning! I'm Ralph Stevens from Best Home Inspections." Pause.

"I'm sorry, I missed your last name." Pause.

"It's good to meet you, Mr. Brown, and thank you for choosing us to perform your home inspection."

"Have you bought a home before?" – or – *"Is this your first home?"* Pause.

If yes: *"Have you ever had a home inspection?"* Pause.

If yes: *"So you have a good sense of what this is all about."*

If no: *"Okay, I think you'll find it valuable and enjoyable."*

"Our goal over the next $2^1/_2$ hours is to give you a clear picture of the condition of the major systems in the house. As we look for major issues that may affect your buying decision, we'll come across a number of smaller issues. We'll discuss those and include them in our report, but our goal is not to create a detailed maintenance or repair list.

"We'll start outside and then move indoors where we'll work from bottom to top, finishing with the attic. We'll complete our report at the end of the inspection, and you should have everything you need to make your decision. Do you have any plans for changes to the house?" Pause.

"Do you have any specific concerns about the home or are you looking for a general overview?" Pause.

"Please join me as we go through the home. I won't ask you to get up on the roof or go into the attic (or crawlspace), but otherwise we can work together, discussing our findings as we go.

"This is our Authorization Form that sets out the rules of the game. Please read it carefully while I get started with the roof. Please check that we have your name, address and phone numbers right, and if everything is in order, sign it here (indicate where to sign). You may want to look at the report layout. We'll complete this and give it to you at the end of the inspection."

Go inspect the roof. When you're finished, continue the discussion.

"Was everything in order?" Pause.

"Great. I'll put that away." Put contract in your bag.

"Let's get started with the exterior. Please feel free to ask questions as we go. We may not get the answers until we get the whole picture, but that's okay."

5.3 THE INSPECTION ITSELF

You have done at least one preliminary tour around the exterior of the home, concluded your introductory discussion and completed your roof inspection. Now is the time to establish your technical credibility. Here's one way to do it.

An Exterior Tour

Tour the exterior of the home walking around the house in the opposite direction than your initial tour. If you walked around the house clockwise the first time, walk around counterclockwise this time. You sometimes see different things from different angles. You want to give the client your findings from the roof and exterior inspection. Walking around the exterior with the client allows you to show them what you have looked at and because you have already seen it before, you have an advantage.

Simple Explanation

Your first technical comments should be an explanation of components. You can explain the wall construction, siding makeup, window type or air-conditioning condenser unit, for example. Use lay terms and perhaps include a maintenance tip, such as keeping trees and shrubs trimmed back from siding or air-conditioning units.

You don't want to intimidate or overwhelm the client with your first sentence. They may still be nervous. You want them to get a sense that you understand houses and, in a down to earth fashion, can help them understand their home.

Improvement Recomm-endations

If there are improvements to make to the roof or exterior, or both, start by describing the system and explain the improvement. You might say, *"The asphalt shingle roof is a typical installation. These roofs usually last about 15 to 20 years. You'll want to reshingle this year to prevent leaks and water damage."*

Ballpark Costs

If you provide ballpark costs, add what the approximate cost would be. We might say, *"The cost for this work is typically $2,000 to $3,000."*

You've gotten the message through that the client needs to replace the roof within the next year.

What You've Accomplished

This approach explains to people that roofs do wear out and that this is not a defect in the construction of the house. You've told the clients exactly what they have to do and if you give them costs (beyond the Standards), you've quantified the issue. You've told them when the work should be done (beyond the Standards).

Implications

We've also told the client what will happen if they don't fix the roof. The roof will leak and they will have water damage to the home. This helps the client understand the importance of your recommendations and, in our experience, clients are happier and more likely to take your advice if they understand the reasons for it. Simply giving clients direction may leave them puzzled as to why you are suggesting it. They are less likely to take action if they don't understand why.

Keep Perspective

You haven't horrified the client by telling them that there are torn valley flashings, missing shingle tabs, rusted chimney flashings, lost granular material and severe cupping of the shingles. Starting a discussion this way can panic a client who is struggling to understand what all this means. For the layperson, this can create an image of the top of the house rotting away and a $50,000 repair. By the time you get to the end of your discussion, they may be so distraught they don't hear you try to put things into perspective.

Focus On Actions

Throughout the inspection, we focus on telling people what needs to be done and why, rather than describing in gory detail all of the clues and symptoms of non-performance. Our intention is not to gloss over problems, but to allow the client to focus on what needs to be done and why, keeping things in perspective.

Tremendous Power

Many home inspectors don't understand how much power they have during the inspection process. Clients are paying you as a professional for your opinion. Many hang on your every word and consider it authoritative. Careless phrases like *"the roof is shot"* can terrify clients. You have to assume that they do not understand house construction and components and, therefore, will not understand the extent of the problem or the implications of various systems not being able to do their job. It's your responsibility to help them understand what needs to be done to make the house work properly and why it's important. Telling people to replace rusted, leaking rain gutters seems absolutely trivial to the layperson. It's not until they understand that leaking rain gutters cause wet basements that they see the wisdom of replacement.

What To Do And Why

Let's emphasize this point. Your discussion with clients should focus on what they should do to the home and why. Very few inspectors practice this concept exclusively. Those who do are generally successful.

Let's look at some other communication issues.

Use Names

Keep the lines of communication open between you and your clients. Use their names in discussions. This is an indication of your respect for them and shows that you have taken the time to learn their name. It helps reinforce the connection.

Show Them

As you describe things to clients, it's helpful to show them the components that you are talking about so that they will better understand your recommendations and the reasons behind them. Showing a client a crack in a wall or a rotted soffit eliminates the need to describe the problem in words, and helps prevent overreaction. It also helps to record your recommendation permanently in the client's mind. When they read your report later, they will remember seeing the problem and their understanding will be enriched.

Some Clients Won't Come

Some clients do not go through the house with you, even though you have encouraged them to do so. You can't force people to follow you. In these cases, you'll have to drop by and talk to the client at appropriate times throughout the inspection. When you've finished your roof and exterior work and move inside, find your client and summarize that part of the inspection. You may then move on to do the mechanical, electrical and structural systems and then report back to the client again. It's not as effective, but it's beyond your control.

No Jargon

Many home inspectors, especially early in their careers, use a lot of technical terms and jargon. They believe that this helps to establish their credibility. Most clients are simply puzzled by this and may be frustrated by the low quality communication. Whether the clients blame themselves for not understanding you or resent you for speaking over their head, the result is the same.

Mix Good News With Bad

It's absolutely acceptable to point out good features of a home. Many people don't record these in their report, but if something is better than average, that's valuable information. A brand new clay tile roof, for example, is going to last considerably longer than an asphalt shingle roof. A new top-of-the-line high-efficiency furnace is certainly better than a 25-year-old conventional furnace.

Helps Provide An Accurate Picture

Sometimes there are a number of problems in a home. Clients can become dismayed and overwhelmed, especially if it's early in the inspection and everything you look at needs expensive improvement. Clients need to be given the correct perspective. If every system in the house is bad, they need to know that. However, if you can sense a client overreacting to typical situations, it may be appropriate to mix good news with the bad so that clients develop a balanced picture of the home. The goal of the inspection is to have clients understand the house in exactly the same terms that you do at the end of the inspection. If it's well below average, they should understand that. If it's an average home, they should understand that too. If the house is above average, let them know.

Clients Jump From House To House

Many home inspectors are perfectly capable of unintentionally talking a client out of buying a house. If you simply list the deficiencies in a home and do not provide clients any perspective, they may well choose not to move forward with that purchase. When they find another house and have you inspect it, you may come up with a similar list of problems. This is particularly true if the house is in the same neighborhood as the last one you inspected for them.

There Are No Good Homes!

If it takes three or four houses for the client to realize that you've never met a house that's any good, they are going to be extremely unhappy. You need to lend perspective to your discussion. Roofs wear out. Furnaces wear out. These things are inevitable and part of the reality of home ownership. Part of the valuable service you provide is to help clients understand this. A house with a worn out roof and a furnace with a failed heat exchanger is not a bad house. This is abundantly clear to home inspectors, but unless they communicate well, is often lost on clients.

Watch For Reactions

If you are in control of the inspection and are comfortable with your work, part of your attention can be focused on your client's reaction to your comments. Are they puzzled, angry, frustrated, overwhelmed or tired? When we sense a lack of understanding, we'll often say, *"Let me try to explain that a different way...."*

Repeating your message in different words can help it get through. It doesn't cost you anything to assume the responsibility for what you suspect is poor communication and to offer it in a different way. This is a courteous gesture.

Nervous Jokes

Some clients handle the stress of buying a house and having a home inspection by making jokes. They will sometimes make fun of the house or the furniture. Don't mistake this for a good comfort level. It's very often just the client's way of dealing with awkward pauses in conversation and trying to appear casual. Under no circumstances should you join in the discussion. If the client is obviously trying to be funny, you should smile politely, acknowledging their comment. Don't make your own jokes or comments. You'll undoubtedly offend the buyer, the agents, the seller or all of them.

Learn What Client Does For A Living

During the course of the inspection, there's often an opportunity to ask the client what they do for a living. One opportunity to ask this is while you are removing the cover on the electrical panel. This question helps to establish rapport and gives you some insight into the areas of interest and expertise that a client has. Most people like to talk about themselves.

Answers May Affect Your Inspection

We've found more than once as we were taking the cover off the electrical panel that the client was an electrician. Obviously, this changes your presentation of the electrical part of the inspection.

Don't Ask Too Early

Our preference is not to ask this question during the introductory discussion because it is not absolutely critical to your work and may appear overly familiar. We usually ask the question within the first third of the inspection and only after we have established a comfortable relationship with the client. There is no substitute for common sense.

Stay In Control

We keep telling you to stay in control, but it's hard to overemphasize. Don't get drawn in to long side conversations and don't get pulled out of your normal routine unless it's absolutely unavoidable. You need to lead the process for all kinds of reasons, including –

• your credibility
• staying on schedule
• staying within your scope
• not omitting any steps
• leaving things as you found them

Don't Get Overwhelmed

Some houses are big, complicated and run down. Looking at the whole thing can overwhelm you. Don't let that happen. Everything you do in a home inspection is simple and easy if you do it in small chunks. Break complicated houses down into individual components. If the house has ten chimneys, you're still only looking at one chimney at a time. There are a finite number of issues to look at with chimneys. Sure, you have to repeat the process, but you know the process and can follow it. Doing it on all ten chimneys will take a little longer, but there is nothing difficult about it.

Taking Notes

Some inspectors use checklists and some inspectors use blank notepads as they go through the home. Some inspectors use neither. Some inspectors use their actual report form as a guide while going through the house. Different approaches work for different people. You'll need to experiment to see what works for you.

Excessive Notes

A common mistake made by inspectors early in their career is excessive note-taking. One of the ways you can learn to control note-taking is to practice inspecting houses without allowing yourself to take any notes. At the end of the inspection, sit down and try to write the report and see how much you can fill in without the benefit of notes. Our guess is that you will be astounded. Many experienced inspectors use notes only to record long numbers and the most unusual circumstances, including things that are not on their standard report forms.

Reports Prompt You

Many report formats work as a memory prod. As you go through your report to fill it out, you are asked to answer questions. If you can't answer a question about whether the furnace was gas- or oil-fired, you'll need to go back and have another look. It's one of the advantages of completing your inspection report in the house. If you're back at the office, it's tough to check whether that furnace was gas- or oil-fired.

The Macro/ Micro Approach

Throughout this program, we talk about two different ways of looking at homes. We call it the **macro/micro** approach or the **active/passive** approach. Different people's brains work differently, although few work exclusively in one domain or another. As a result, we recommend that you use both approaches to inspection. The micro or active approach to inspection is the regimented, disciplined routine of going through things step by step, often following a checklist. The checklist doesn't have to be written down to be real. The macro or passive approach involves looking at the building and simply asking, *"What do I see? What is the building telling me?"* It doesn't matter which approach you take first, but we do encourage you to use both the macro and micro approach.

A Double Tour Approach

We talked in the last section about doing two tours around the exterior of the home. We sometimes do three for client-relationship reasons we'll discuss shortly. In the Interior Module we also talk about two tours through the interior of the home. This provides an opportunity to employ the active or micro approach on one pass and the macro or passive approach on the other tour.

Follow Your Plan

As you move through the home, you will have a routine. Some people move from the bottom to the top, others work from the top down. Some work in a circular pattern through each floor level, others work end to end. What matters is that you have given this some thought, have decided how you are going to approach it, and do it **the same way every time**. The more consistent your routine is, the less likely you are to leave something out or make a mistake.

Consistent Depth At Each Inspection

Clients may have very detailed questions about specific systems. They may have had a problem with carbon monoxide fumes at a furnace in a previous house. They may be concerned about furnace spillage or backdraft. Do not change your inspection routine based on these concerns. If you don't normally use a carbon monoxide sensor or combustible gas analyzer, don't do it on this inspection either. You can tell the client that there is more testing that can be done, but the process of the home inspection includes only the testing you perform.

Real estate agents watch inspectors and if your depth of inspection is inconsistent, you may find yourself being asked in front of a client, *"Why didn't you use that fancy tester on the furnace like you did last week?"* or *"Why didn't you go on the roof like you usually do?"* These can be very awkward questions.

You'll Get Tired

A two-and-a-half-hour performance is a long one. As you get close to the end of the inspection, you'll probably begin to get tired. You'll have to work a little harder to keep your focus and maintain concentration. Understand that this is happening and address it.

What If You Fall Behind?

Because you have an inspection schedule, you should know, for example, that –

- forty minutes into the inspection, you should be moving into the house.
- seventy minutes into the inspection, you should be finished with the mechanical, electrical and structure systems, for example.
- one hundred minutes into the inspection, you should only have the attic and crawlspace left to inspect.
- after 115 minutes, you should only have to record your results and have your closing discussion.

If you fall behind and have no chance of catching up, you need to make a decision. Is it all right to extend the inspection? Do you have another appointment that you'll be late for? If so, explain to your client that you need to reschedule your next appointment so that you can spend the time your client deserves. Although it is a disruption to the inspection, your clients will probably appreciate your honesty, and understand that you are extending a courtesy to the next client that they would appreciate themselves.

Discussing Changes To The Home

In the introductory discussion, we ask the client if they have any changes planned for the home. We did this outside the home because we didn't want to have the discussion in front of the seller. Inside the home, avoid having discussions about changes to the home in front of the seller. Many sellers are offended by such discussions. It is distressing to people to think that the home they've spent years getting right is going to be torn apart. The objection is at an emotional rather than logical level, but it's real nonetheless. If your client wants to discuss changes while you're in the house, it's better when the seller's not there. This isn't always within your control, but be aware of it.

Questions Outside Your Scope

Sometimes you'll be asked questions that are beyond the scope of a home inspection. As we said earlier, you should definitely not work outside of your scope. What you can do, however, is have a list available of consultants or specialists in other fields who can provide answers your clients are looking for.

Leave Things As You Find Them

During the course of inspection, you are going to be turning lights on and off, operating faucets, flushing toilets, testing furnaces and air conditioners, opening access hatches, moving fireplace screens and opening dampers to look at chimneys, etc. It's easy to say that you should leave things as you found them. It's actually quite difficult to do. Some common mistakes that inspectors make include –

- leaving the heat turned up
- leaving the air conditioning turned down
- leaving appliances on
- leaving doors unlocked
- leaving the power off (for a stove, for example, because fuse blocks were not pushed all the way in)

- leaving clocks flashing because power was inadvertently turned off
- leaving access covers dirty, loose or not in place
- leaving clothes on a bed that were removed from a closet to get to an access hatch
- leaving fireplace screens in the middle of the living room floor
- leaving fireplace dampers open that were found closed, or vice versa

Helping To Keep Things In Place

There are a couple of things you can do to minimize this problem. We recommend putting your vehicle keys on the thermostat when you turn a heating system up or an air conditioning system down. It's very difficult to leave the house without retrieving your keys, which will remind you to turn the thermostat back. If you have to move things to get a look at something, we recommend that you put them either in your path (block the doorway out of the room with them) or put them on top of your clipboard or flashlight, for example, so that you can't carry on without putting the system back in place.

Electrical Power Issues

While home inspectors do not normally turn power off, it may be done inadvertently, or with the permission of the seller. If you turn power off and find that clocks and VCRs are flashing as a result, you can reset the clocks to the correct time as a courtesy to the seller. If the sellers keep their clocks ten minutes fast, resetting them to the correct time will cause problems. Let the seller know, or leave a note apologizing for turning the power off momentarily for testing, and explaining you reset the clocks to the current time and this may affect some timers or alarm settings, for example.

Don't Bluff

You will occasionally come across things that you do not understand, but are apparently within your scope. Don't guess as to their function and condition. Let people know that you will need to research this to get them an answer. You may be able to contact a colleague to get some help. If not, you should do your research and report back to your clients as quickly as possible. In some cases, you may be able to complete the inspection and telephone manufacturers or other sources of information to get answers before you leave the home.

Stay Out Of Arguments

We've touched on this before. You have no place in disagreements between clients and agents, agents and sellers, or buyers and sellers. It's true even if the disagreement is about you. If the seller is unhappy with the agent for allowing you into the house, this isn't your problem and you have no place in the discussion. You do not want to try to be an arbitrator or a mediator. If invited to enter the discussion, it's usually best to decline. The house belongs to the seller. If they don't want you there, they should be able to ask you to leave and expect you to comply immediately.

Don't Compete With Noise

Traffic noise, noise from trains or other sources may prevent you from communicating clearly. Don't try to talk over such noise. Wait until the noise stops or until you have gone to another part of the house, for example, before starting to talk again.

Your last tour of the interior of the home is an opportunity to put things back as you found them. It's also an opportunity to notice and clean up any bits of insulation that have fallen out of the attic or fingerprints that you've left on walls or doors.

Recording
Your Findings

You've completed your inspection and are ready to compile your notes. Some inspectors spend very little time doing this; inspectors who provide on-site written reports spend more time, understandably. We explain to our client what we are going to do and excuse ourselves: *"I'm going to take 15 or 20 minutes and compile the report. I'll catch up to you then and we'll summarize the inspection."* After you've excused yourself, make sure you have all your tools and your ladder assembled and by the door. It's embarrassing to have to come back to the house to pick up things that you left there.

Summary

Let's summarize the inspection itself.

• Start house with an exterior tour in opposite direction to your first tour.
• Start by giving a technical explanation in layman's terms.
• Include a maintenance tip.
• For improvement recommendations, follow this format:

> *"The asphalt shingle roof is a typical installation."* Describe material and function if not apparent.

> *"These roofs usually last about 20 years."* If it's a system that is simply wearing out in an expected manner, let the client know.

> *"You'll want to reshingle this year to prevent leaks and water damage."* Give client direction and implication. Time frame and costs are optional.

> *"The brick chimney serves the furnace and fireplace. The top three feet should be rebuilt **immediately** from the roof level up to prevent bricks blocking the chimney or falling on someone outside the home. This is a safety issue."* Again, provide direction and implications.

• Use clients' names.
• Discuss things while you show them to the client.
• Use simple words.
• Mix good news with bad.
• Watch clients for overreaction.
• Maintain perspective appropriate to home.
• Don't join in jokes.
• Find out what client does for a living.
• Stay in control.
• Break house down into component parts to keep it simple.
• Use macro/micro approach.
• Consider two tour approach.

- Stay in your routine.
- Increase your concentration level as you begin to get tired.
- If you fall behind, call ahead to reschedule a next appointment.
- Discuss changes to home away from seller.
- Direct clients to other specialists for questions outside your scope.
- Leave things as you found them.
- Reset clocks and leave a note if you cut off power.
- Don't bluff or guess. Say you don't know.
- Stay out of arguments.
- Don't compete with noise.
- At end say, *"I'm going to take 15 or 20 minutes and compile the report. I'll catch up to you then and we'll summarize the inspection."*
- Assemble tools and ladder at front door before writing your report.

Communication & Professional Practice

MODULE

QUICK QUIZ 3

☑ INSTRUCTIONS

- You should finish Study Session 3 before doing this Quiz.
- Write your answers in the spaces provided.
- Check your answers against ours at the end of this section.
- If you have trouble with the Quiz, re-read the Study Session and try the Quiz again.
- If you did well, it's time for Study Session 4.

1. List the four parts of a home inspection.

2. List the individual components of a typical routine or flow for a home inspection, in their appropriate order.

_____

_____

_____

_____

_____

3. List the amount of time typically spent on each of the various parts of the inspection listed in Question 2.

_____

_____

_____

_____

_____

_____

_____

_____

_____

_____

4. List four key elements of the seller introduction.

_____

_____

_____

_____

5. Write a sample script for an introductory discussion during a home inspection. This might be 10 to 15 sentences, for example.

_____

_____

_____

_____

_____

_____

_____

_____

_____

_____

_____

_____

_____

_____

6. Explain in one sentence how improvement recommendations should be presented during the inspection itself.

_____

7. Describe the **macro/micro** approach to home inspection in two sentences.

_____

_____

_____

_____

8. List 10 things that inspectors commonly fail to put back the way they were found.

_____

_____

_____

_____

_____

_____

_____

_____

_____

_____

9. Describe in one sentence what you should do when you see something you don't understand.

_____

_____

If you had no trouble with the Quiz, it's time for Study Session 4.

Key Words
- ***Pre-inspection routine***
- ***Introductory discussion***
- ***The inspection itself***
- ***Closing discussion***
- ***Time goals***
- ***Vehicle check***
- ***Personal check***
- ***Arriving early***
- ***Knowing the players***
- ***Seller introduction***
- ***Using names***
- ***Taking control***
- ***Macro/micro approach***
- ***Contract***
- ***Perspective***
- ***Consistent depth***

Communication & Professional Practice

MODULE

STUDY SESSION 4

1. You should have finished Study Sessions 1, 2 and 3 before starting this Session.

2. This Session covers the closing discussion, which is the last part of the inspection process, strategies for awkward situations, common mistakes new inspectors make and an overview of the real estate transaction.

3. By the end of this Session, you should be able to:
- describe in one sentence the purpose of the closing discussion
- explain in one sentence why home inspectors do not pass or fail homes as a result of the inspection
- write a script for a closing discussion of five to 10 sentences
- describe in one sentence each how you handle 14 awkward situations
- list six common mistakes made by new inspectors
- describe in one sentence each 20 common real estate terms
- list six simplified steps in the real estate sales process
- explain in one sentence the term *caveat emptor*

4. This Session may take you roughly one and a half hours.

5. Quick Quiz 4 is at the end of this Session.

Key Words

- *Summary*
- *Perspective*
- *One piece of the puzzle*
- *Limitations*
- *Control*
- *Payment request*
- *Client feedback*
- *Client questionnaire*
- *Real estate agent and broker*
- *Listing and selling agent*
- *Buyer broker or buyer agent*
- *Agreement of purchase and sale*
- *Conditional offer*
- *Irrevocable date or expiry date*
- *Closing or closing date*
- *Firm deal or firm agreement*
- *Seller disclosure*
- *Substitute disclosure*
- *Escrow*
- *Waiver*
- *Closing adjustments*
- *Mortgage*
- *Equity*
- *Mortgage insurance*
- *Title insurance*
- *Commission*
- *Multiple Listing Service*
- *Sign back*

5.4 THE CLOSING DISCUSSION

Purpose

The main purpose of the closing discussion is to summarize the major points of the inspection and make sure your client understands those issues.

Location

Compile your report and prepare your invoice, if necessary. If you haven't had an opportunity to check if the contract was signed, now is the time to do that. Once you finish your paperwork and have organized yourself, it's time for the closing discussion. Find your clients and ask, *"Is this a good place to summarize the inspection, Mr. Brown?"*

The agent will sometimes direct you to a dining room table, the kitchen or may suggest that the closing discussion should take place outside the home. This is one part of the inspection where you cannot take control. You need to respect the requests of the client, seller and agent. The closing conversation can take place anywhere that is convenient to your audience.

Buyers May Control

The buyers may want to have the report summary as a private conversation. This is their privilege.

Use Names And Speak To Everyone

As you discuss your findings, you should again be using your clients' names. If both agents and the sellers are in the room, that should be fine with you, but don't try to manipulate your clients away from the agents. If they choose to do so, that's fine with you. Again, you don't want to take the lead in this area.

A Brief Summary

If you have done a good job on your inspection and your clients have accompanied you, they will have already been told everything they need to know. However, you'll also know that they will have only absorbed about 50 percent of what you've said. Within a week or two, they will only have retained about 10 percent of the 50 percent that they did hear. It's important to understand this because your summary is the thing they are most likely to remember. That's because it's the last thing that happens during the inspection and if it is well presented, it is a big picture overview. One of the best ways to practice an inspection summary is to force yourself to sum up the house in one sentence. We know – that's impossible. It is impossible, but try it anyway. You might say things like:

- *"The roof and furnace will have to be replaced in the next year and we've got some minor electrical safety improvements, but overall the systems that we looked at and tested appear to be doing their job."*
- *"We saw no evidence of problems with the structure but we'll need to update all of the mechanical and electrical systems and replace the roof in the near future."*
- *"All of the major house systems appear to be performing their tasks, except for the shower stall and the gutters and downspouts, as we discussed."*

More Detailed Review?

People who provide on site reports often show the clients how the reports are laid out and walk them through a sample page or two. Some inspectors show clients everything written in the report. If you're going to do this, allow more time for your closing discussion. We prefer to simply make sure that the client is familiar with the report and understands how to read it. We've discussed it once and provided an overall summary. The client will be able to find the specific recommendations in the report when they need them. This is usually some months after the inspection when the people have settled into the house and are ready to make changes.

Perspective Statements

As you prepare to summarize, you'll want to have a clear picture in your mind of the big issues and the little issues. You'll want to differentiate between safety issues and nuisance, convenience or comfort issues. You'll also want to determine which issues are immediate and which can be deferred. Reassure the clients that they have it in writing. Explain to clients that you appreciate how overwhelming the process can seem. Assure them that all of the important points are in the written report.

Verbal Report Same As Written

There can be a temptation to hedge or sugarcoat the bad news. This way everyone will be happy at the inspection. Some inspectors downplay problems during their closing discussions and protect themselves by putting the hard reality in the report. This results in a very unhappy client. This approach is short term gain for long term pain. Put the cards on the table during the closing discussion. You are not there to try to sell the house to the client, nor are you there to try to talk them out of it.

Only Part Of The Picture

Understand that the physical condition of the house is only one piece of the puzzle that home buyers have to put together for themselves. We are **never** in a position to know whether people should buy the house. If the house needs $50,000 worth of immediate repairs, but the purchase price is $75,000 less than market value, it's a great deal. If the house is clearly in very poor condition, it still may be a good deal because of a tremendous financing opportunity. The house in poor condition may be the right house for a client because it's the only house for sale in a neighborhood close to a special school or medical facility that a family member relies upon. There are hundreds of issues that you can't possibly know about. Provide the facts and your professional opinion and leave it at that. Anything other than a neutral, unbiased summary and report is a recipe for trouble.

Don't Pass Or Fail Homes

Inspectors report the conditions. They do not pass or fail homes. Buyers may decide not to buy a home based on the inspection report. This is because the home did not meet the buyers' expectations in some way. This does not mean it's a bad home, or that it is overpriced. We should offer no opinion on such issues.

Discuss Actions And Implications

We talked earlier about not focusing on problems, defects, concerns, etc. During your verbal summary, you'll want to focus on what improvements need to be made to the home and why those are important.

Who's Responsible For Improvements?	We should not discuss who should fix the broken components. It's not the role of a home inspector to determine whether the buyer, seller, builder or someone else should be responsible for fixing a problem. You can't know all of the history and circumstances, and so it is inappropriate to offer an opinion. If asked, explain that it's not within your scope.
Reiterate Limitations	At the end of your summary, you'll want to point out that you have discussed the major issues and have documented some of the smaller issues you've come across. Tell the client that they will find other issues when they move in and to be ready for them.
Specific Limitations	If there was snow on the roof or no access to a crawlspace, make sure that's included in your summary discussion.
Stay In Control	We've mentioned staying in control several times through the inspection process. It's just as true at the end of the inspection. You want to be in control. You should not be rushed or flustered at the end of the inspection. Your inspection is a performance and this is the final act. Here are a few possible impressions that you could leave your client with. It should be easy for you to choose the appropriate ones – • polite or rude • pleasant or distant • thorough or rushed • patient or impatient • understanding or arrogant • helpful or disinterested • relaxed or nervous • organized or scattered
Report Delivery	If you provide the report on site, you can give the client the final report. If you're not providing the report, tell the client when they may expect to receive it.
Asking For Payment	If it is your policy to be paid on site, you may have payment offered by the client. You may have to ask for it. One way to do that is to say, *"Will you be paying by check?"*
Let Clients Speak	When you've finished your summary, make sure the client is finished. You might say, *"Did we answer all your questions?"* or *"Is there anything we should go over again?"* This once again displays your genuine interest in their understanding.
Call With Questions	We encourage our clients to call us at any time about any question related to their home. Few ever do, but it does provide peace of mind to know that they can contact us if they need us.
Client Questionnaire	If you use a client questionnaire, you can give it to the client at this point and ask them to send you their feedback. You might tell them that you are interested in continuous improvement of your service and welcome any constructive comments.

Know When
To Leave

When you are sure your client is satisfied and you have dealt with report delivery and payment, you're ready to leave. Don't linger in the house, unless invited. You should typically be the first one to leave. Agents and buyers often have business to discuss after the inspection. Move as purposefully at the end of the inspection as you did at the beginning. If the agents and sellers are there, thank them for their patience and courtesy. Thank the clients again for choosing your firm to do the inspection and wish them well. Gather all your belongings and say goodbye.

Summary

Here is a brief summary of how you might handle the closing discussion. We'll include some tips and some scripted comments.

- Compile notes or report.
- Prepare invoice.
- Check the contract has been signed.
- Find the clients.
- *"Is this a good place to summarize the inspection, Mr. Brown?"*
- *"The roof and furnace will have to be replaced in the next year and we've got some minor electrical safety cleanup, but overall the systems that we looked at and tested appear to be doing their jobs."*

– or –

"The house structure showed no evidence of movement, but we will need to update all of the mechanical and electrical systems and replace the roof in the very near future."

– or –

"All of the systems we looked at appeared to be performing their tasks, except for the shower stall, gutters and downspouts, as we discussed."

- *"These items are detailed in the report as are a number of the other things that we talked about. This is how the report is laid out."* Show people how the report is organized and where the summary statements and individual conditions are recorded.
- *"We've talked about all of the points in the report already and they are included here for your reference. We won't go through all of the details again. When you do get a chance to have a look at it, feel free to call us if you have any questions."*
- *"We've covered a lot of ground in the last two and a half hours, trying to identify the big issues and we've come across some of the smaller ones. When you move into the home you'll find some other issues and there will be a few that arise after you get settled in. This is part of home ownership. There are always improvements to be made and unexpected issues crop up regularly in every home."*
- *"Remember, we didn't get into that crawlspace or the small attic over the rear extension. Once you take possession of the home, you will want to provide access into those places."*

- Don't discuss who is responsible for improvements.
- Discuss actions and implications, rather than problem descriptions.
- *"Have we answered all your questions?"*

– or –

"Is there anything we should go over again?"

- *"Great! If you ever have any question about anything in the home, please give us a call. We'd be happy to help and there's no fee for this service."*
- *"Will you be paying by check? Very good. I'll fill out the receipt while you do that."* Have a spare pen the client can use or keep.
- *"I've included a client questionnaire and a postage paid return envelope in the front of the report. It would help us if you'd take a few minutes and mail that to us when you get a chance. We're always looking for ways to improve."* Receive the payment.
- *"There we go and here's your report. Thanks again for choosing us to do your home inspection. I hope things work out very well for you."*
- To agents: *"It was good to meet you, Ms. Jones and Mr. Adams. Thanks very much for your patience."*
- To the seller: *"Thank you very much for your cooperation. Goodbye for now."*
- Gather your things and leave.

We've outlined a typical home inspection and hope this gives you a good sense of the inspection process. Do things always go smoothly? Of course not. While the process we outlined is typical, there are many situations that crop up. Let's look at some of these.

5.5 STRATEGIES FOR AWKWARD SITUATIONS

There are many things that can happen during a home inspection. We'll address some of the more common ones here and give you our thoughts as to how they can be handled.

1. Electricity, Gas and Water Turned Off

No Utilities

Sometimes you'll arrive at the house to find that all of the utilities are off. This hampers your inspection in several ways. Your first reaction may be, *"Why didn't they tell me when they booked the inspection?"* A better question might be, *"Why didn't I ask?"* Your next thought might be, *"I'll just turn them on."* **Don't.** Utilities were probably turned off for a reason. This may have been simply because the house was vacant. It may have been because of an operational or safety problem. Even if there was no problem when the utilities were turned off, there may be now. Animals may have nested in the furnace or chimney.

Winterized Plumbing

If the plumbing system was winterized, there will be antifreeze in all the traps. If you turn the water on and test the plumbing fixtures, you will flush the antifreeze out of the traps and down the drain. The house is no longer winterized, even if you shut off the water and drain the pipes again.

Discuss With Your Client   Discuss the limitations of the inspection with your client and make a decision together as to whether you should go ahead or reschedule the inspection when the utilities have been turned back on by someone else. Your booking procedure should include asking this question.

2. The Client Doesn't Show Up

No Client   If you understood that the client was going to be there, and the client does not appear, there's obviously a communication problem. We recommend that you do not go ahead with the inspection, because we have found that often the client has canceled the inspection and either forgotten to notify us or expected the agent to notify us.

You won't likely have a signed contract so you have no written agreement to do the inspection. Your client has not agreed to the scope of the inspection or the fee in writing.

What To Do?   Our practice is to call the client or agent. If we can't reach anyone, we typically wait at the site for 45 minutes from the appointment time in case the client has simply been delayed.

Seller May Know   If the seller is home, ask the seller if you have the right time and address for the inspection. You may find that your clients are waiting on the next block. Both clients and agents sometimes give the wrong address. We've also written down the wrong address on occasion.

3. The Agent Doesn't Show Up

No Agent   If the real estate agent doesn't show up, again we try to call them. If the seller was expecting us, the client may choose to go ahead with the inspection. This is the client's decision, rather than yours.

4. Client and Agent Cannot Attend

No Client Or Agent   In some cases, you're asked to inspect a house alone. We try to get contracts signed before the fact in this case, via fax, for example. If the seller is home, we are happy to perform the inspection. If there is no one home and we are given a key or lock-box number, we will inspect the home. Some inspectors will not work under these circumstances.

We are insured (some people are bonded) so that we are protected if people accuse us of damaging or stealing something from the home. You will have to consider this issue and decide whether or not you will inspect houses under these circumstances. You should try to speak with your client by phone at least, after the inspection.

5. Clients Have Pages of Questions

Pages Of Questions   We touched on this earlier. We do not accept responsibility for answering pages of questions. If you take the time to read them all, you're already behind on your inspection. We recommend that you go through your normal routine, and put the onus on the client to address any unanswered questions at the end of the inspection.

6. Uncle Charlie, the Building Expert

The Building Expert

Many clients have a friend or relative who accompanies them as their technical advisor. This person can undermine your credibility if you are not careful. Understand that the technical advisor is usually a family member or friend. This puts you at a disadvantage because there is an existing relationship between the client and that advisor. You should also understand that the advisor is in an awkward spot, because if he does not point out problems in the house, he is likely to hear about it. Family pressures can be far more intense than business pressures.

What To Do?

The technical advisor is often insecure, feeling that she may well be in a confrontational situation with the home inspector. Our approach is to establish our credibility early in an authoritative fashion, while enlisting the technical advisor as an ally. This is not as difficult as it sounds. The technical advisor usually has a field of expertise. This puts her at a disadvantage because you are a general practitioner. If the advisor is a carpenter, talk about plumbing. If the advisor is a plumber, talk about electricity.

Establish Your Credibility

Discuss a component or system in the house that the layperson would not typically be aware of. Don't chose a component that is in need of attention. You simply want to let people know that you understand houses. When you have chosen a component to discuss (within the first five minutes of the technical part of the inspection), describe the system using more technical language than you typically would. Then invite the technical advisor to agree with you. You can say, *"These neutral supported service drops and these type of goosenecked mastheads have become popular and are performing quite well from our perspective. Is that your experience, Mr. Smith?"*

There are several reasons to take this approach:

- You aren't putting the advisor directly on the spot because she can simply respond in the affirmative.
- You have also recognized her expertise and drawn him into the conversation.
- You do not appear arrogant or confrontational.
- You are sensitive to her expertise and considerate of her insecurity.

This approach does not always work, but in most cases will prevent the technical advisor from challenging you or being disruptive. In the best cases, the technical advisor will become a supporter.

7. Agent or Seller Disrupts the Inspection with Constant Challenges or Distracting Stories

Agent Or
Seller Disrupts
If the pace and effectiveness of your inspection are destroyed, you need to stop the inspection and do something. We ask the agent or seller to hold their comments until our work is completed, without diminishing the validity of their comments. Express your willingness to discuss these issues but establish control by saying that you need to follow through with your routine and complete your work before discussing these things. From that point on, discuss very little in the presence of the agent or the seller so they have very little opportunity to challenge you.

If the seller or agent keep dragging the client away to explain things to them or tell them how wonderful something is, again you should ask them to hold off until you have completed your work. Explain to them gently that you need your client's attention to do your job properly. This is a very delicate situation and, if handled incorrectly, can cause the tension level to rise. Something like this may work: "It would be great if we could get through my work with Mr. Brown, and then let you two focus on the issues you don't need me for."

8. The Client Asks You Not to Speak in the Presence of the Agent or Seller

Some clients are very concerned about confidentiality. They may have asked you before the inspection or at the beginning of the inspection to speak only to them about the home. This is, of course, their right. We respect the clients' request not to discuss anything when the seller or agent are there.

The Agent
Asks
The situation gets trickier if the agent asks pointed questions about the results of the inspection. We'll typically respond to the first and second question with responses like, *"Things are going along pretty well"* or *"I'm still putting the story together."* If pointed questions persist, the clients should step in and say that they have asked you to speak to only them. In some cases, the client doesn't speak up. At that point, you have to do something, or the agent will think you are being rude.

In our opinion, the right thing to say is, *"I'm sorry. We've been asked not to discuss anything about the inspection with anyone."* Don't point at the client and say, *"He said I shouldn't talk to you."*

Keep it in the third person and indicate that you're not supposed to speak to anyone, rather than a specific person or group of people. The agent will figure out that it was the client who asked, but you are not pointing a finger and putting someone immediately on the spot. It's an awkward situation any way you look at it, but it's one that you have been unfairly put into. You should not have to suffer the wrath of an agent or seller unjustly. The clients may be mildly embarrassed but in our experience, this has not been a big problem.

9. The Client Has More Questions about Your Liability and Errors and Omissions Insurance than about the House

When clients ask about liability and insurance, we become very uneasy. We explain to the client that if they are looking for an insurance policy or a warranty on the home, we're not going to be able to help them. Perhaps the best approach is to say the home inspection isn't going to meet their expectations and you'd be happy to waive the fee and end the process. Clients will often back off at this point, but you should be warned that this is likely to be an inspection with repercussions. Depending on the situation, you may decline to do the inspection, although this is a pretty dramatic step. Good home inspectors are often able to turn a hostile, suspicious client around during the two-and-a-half hour inspection process.

10. The Client Wants to Audiotape or Videotape You

You can't prevent this, at least not gracefully. We agree to this process, but do not disturb our inspection routine. We typically speak less and stand still when we do summarize so that people can record our comments. The effect is usually a less satisfactory inspection for the client. Sometimes this is a tough message to get through.

11. Client Has Heard Enough

Sometimes the client will stop the inspection because of a number of conditions that they weren't expecting. You cannot insist that you complete the inspection. Your report will have to reflect the circumstances, and you may or may not reduce your fee. The reality is that the client usually stops the inspection with the expectation that the fee will be lowered.

12. Listing Information Is Wrong

Sometimes your findings disagree with those reported on the published listing information or feature sheet for the home. If you have reported the electrical service is 100 amps, and the listing sheet shows it as a 200-amp service, you may be challenged. Once you are sure you are correct, you can indicate that this is very difficult to determine for a layperson and that there may be some misleading evidence that you can point to as the possible reason for the confusion. You obviously should not back down, but there's nothing to be gained by saying things like, *"Oh, those listing sheets are always wrong,"* or *"Real estate agents don't know anything about houses. Why would you believe that?"*

13. If You Break Something

If you do enough inspections, you will eventually break something in someone's house. This is fairly simple. You advise the owner and offer to repair or replace it. We carry comprehensive general liability insurance that protects us and the homeowner if something expensive is broken.

14. Life-threatening Issue

Sometimes you'll come across a condition in a house that is an immediate and serious safety issue. A chimney that's completely blocked, exposed live wiring, and a foundation that is in danger of collapse are all issues that you may find. The question is whether you go about your business and report your findings to your client only.

Duty To Occupant

In our opinion, you have a duty to inform the occupant of the house, whether it's the seller, a tenant or someone else, of the life safety risk. If there is no seller or occupant there, it may be adequate to inform the real estate agents and ask them to pass the message on. You may want to speak with your legal advisors as to whether this is appropriate.

Judgment Call

The tough part is to know when a life-threatening condition exists that warrants this kind of action. In almost every house that you inspect, you will find some electrical deficiencies. Are all of these life hazards or fire hazards? Ultimately, yes. Do they frequently cause serious problems? No.

You'll need to make a determination as to how unusual the situation is and how immediate the threat is. If there's smoke coming out of the electrical panel, that's pretty easy. If there's a strong odor of gas in the house, that's pretty easy. However, there are many situations that are not black and white. Again, you'll need to rely on your professional judgment and common sense.

Summary

These are just a sampling of situations that you may come up against. Our purpose here is to give you an idea of the general approach to handling these, rather than to provide you with an all-inclusive list of how to handle every situation.

5.6 COMMON MISTAKES MADE BY NEW INSPECTORS

Common mistakes that home inspectors make, especially early in their career, include all of the following:

- Home inspectors feel the need to find problems to **justify** their fee or their presence in the home.
- Home inspectors can be **alarmist** in an effort to make sure the client's attention is drawn to a given problem.
- The home inspector does not provide the **implications** of a condition that is described. The client has a difficult time knowing how critical the issue is. Clients will often overreact if left to determine the implications for themselves.
- The inspector can't resist the temptation to **recommend** buying or not buying the property.
- Home inspectors often use technical **jargon** to help enhance their credibility. This may confuse and frustrate the client.

• Home inspectors will tend to **show off** their knowledge by giving long discussions about technical topics that don't have any immediate importance to the client. The problem is worsened if they show off their knowledge at the expense of the seller or real estate agent. This often has the opposite effect of the one intended.

▶ 6.0 THE REAL ESTATE TRANSACTION

A home inspection is part of a much larger process – the transfer of ownership of a home from one person to another. Buying and selling real estate is complicated. Specialists, often called **real estate agents, real estate salespeople, real estate brokers, realtors** or **real estate professionals**, work with sellers and buyers to facilitate the process.

Tip Of
The Iceberg

Home inspectors need to stay within their scope of work. However, it is useful to understand the process that you are part of. Although this is not a course in residential real estate transactions and real estate sales are handled differently in different parts of North America, we will give you a quick snapshot and encourage you to learn more about how real estate is bought and sold in your area. There are all kinds of places to learn. You can start with your local real estate board or take courses at community colleges, for example. We encourage you to do this research and caution you that some aspects of the overview we're about to give you may not apply in your working area.

Real Estate Terms You Should Know

• Real Estate Agent

Real estate agents are salespeople working on straight commission. They typically represent a real estate broker as part of a company, although they are, to a great extent, independent. The term **agent** is somewhat loose, and in some areas not completely accurate. It is commonly used, however, in most areas of North America.

• Real Estate Broker

A real estate broker has additional credentials than a salesperson and has the right to own and operate a real estate brokerage or real estate company. In some areas it is the broker who is the **agent** within the legal definition of agency.

• Listing Agent

The listing agent is the salesperson representing the **seller** of the home. The agent has worked with the seller to help establish an appropriate asking price for the home and is responsible for marketing the home through advertising, open houses, lawn signs, etc. The listing agent has a duty to the seller to try to get the highest possible price for the home. A listing is a contractual agreement between the seller and the agent that lasts for a fixed amount of time. It might be 60 or 90 days, for example.

• Selling Agent

The selling agent, or cooperating agent as they are sometimes called, is the person who works with the prospective home **buyer**. The selling agent has discussed with the buyers their needs and preferences with respect to a home and established a price range. The selling agent is responsible for finding and showing homes to the prospective buyer and helping with the negotiation process. The selling agent is usually the one who drafts the offer.

Obligation To Seller

Although the selling agent works with the prospective buyer, until recently in most parts of North America, real estate has been arranged so that the ultimate responsibility of the selling agent is to the seller of the home, even though they might not have met the seller. The selling agent's responsibility is to get the highest price possible for the seller, even though they have been working exclusively with a prospective buyer, in many cases for several months. Selling agents are expected to be fair and honest with buyers, but their higher responsibility is to the seller.

• Buyer Broker or **Buyer Agent**

The concept of **buyer brokerage** became popular in the 1990s. These are commission real estate salespeople who make an agreement with the prospective buyer to work on the buyers' behalf and negotiate in their best interest throughout the process. This non-traditional approach obviously provides the buyer with some additional value.

Why Does This Matter To Home Inspectors?

It can be argued that if the obligation of both the listing and selling agent is to the seller, and the goal is to get the highest possible price for a seller, there may be little incentive for either agent to recommend that a buyer engage the services of a professional home inspector. A **buyer broker** on the other hand has a much stronger incentive, and perhaps an obligation, to at least advise the buyer that the services of professional home inspectors are available to protect the buyer's interests. This may result in the sale not being completed, or being completed for a lower price as a result of subsequent negotiations after the inspection report is published. This, of course, may not be in the seller's best interest.

• Agency Disclosure

In many areas, traditional listing and selling agent relationships still exist, but there is now a duty of real estate agents to explain the arrangements and their obligations to all prospective clients. If agency disclosure works properly, buyers are aware whom the agent is working for.

• Agreement of Purchase and Sale or **Offer**

The **offer** is the legal document that forms a contract between the buyer and seller if signed by both. It is usually a standard form prepared by a real estate board or real estate company. There may be several revisions or additions to standard contracts, and each is unique.

• Conditional Offer

A conditional offer is an agreement between a buyer and a seller dependent on the outcome of one or more things. For example, an offer might be conditional upon the buyer arranging mortgage financing. The offer may be conditional upon the buyer selling their existing house. The offer may also be conditional on the property being approved for some changes or special use that the buyer is interested in. The offer may be conditional upon the results of a home inspection being satisfactory to the purchaser. There are other conditions, but these are the most common.

Time Frame   The time frame for these conditions usually runs from a few days to a few months. Home inspection conditions are almost always less than 10 days. They can be as short as 24 hours.

• Irrevocable Date or Expiry Date

When an offer is made, typically by a buyer to a seller, the seller is given a limited period of time to respond. It can be as short as 12 hours, although it's typically a day or two. The irrevocable date or expiry date is set by the prospective buyer who's making the offer to purchase.

• Closing or Closing Date

The closing date is the date on which the transaction is completed and the house changes hands. This is typically some months after the agreement has been struck.

• Firm Deal or Firm Agreement

This refers to a signed agreement between the buyer and seller with no conditional clauses outstanding. There is an agreement to close the transaction on a given date.

• Seller Disclosure

Seller disclosure is a voluntary or mandatory statement by the seller representing the condition of the property. The seller typically fills out a form, sometimes with the help of the listing agent. Disclosure forms often include legal issues as well as property condition issues. There is diversity in the makeup of disclosure forms throughout North America. These are only used in some areas.

• Substitute Disclosure

In some areas where disclosure by the seller is required by law, there may be a provision for substitute disclosure. This means that the seller does not have to undertake disclosure if someone else does it for them. That other person could be real estate salesperson, contractor, home inspector, etc. In some areas, the real estate agent's disclosure obligations may be avoided by the undertaking of a professional home inspection.

• Escrow

Money held in escrow or in trust is money held by mutual agreement by an independent third party. This is typically a lawyer involved in the real estate transaction who holds a buyer's deposit, which will be turned over to the seller at the appropriate time (usually closing).

• Waiver

A waiver is a written agreement that removes a condition. A buyer may waive the home inspection condition if satisfied with the results.

• Closing Adjustments or Adjustments on Closing

Closing adjustments is money paid by the buyer or seller on closing date. They can include a number of things, including compensation to the seller for the fuel in the oil tank, the property taxes paid by the seller for dates beyond the closing date or rent deposits from a tenant which are payable to the buyer.

• Mortgage

A mortgage is a loan made to the buyer of real property (a home). The agency lending the money (**mortgagee**) typically uses the home as security (**collateral**) in case the buyer (**mortgagor**) doesn't make the appropriate loan payments.

Default A buyer who doesn't meet his or her payment obligations on his or her mortgage is said to be **in default** on the mortgage. The lender (mortgagee) usually has the right to take ownership of the property if the mortgagor (the buyer and borrower) is in default. The process by which the lender takes over the property is often called **foreclosure**.

Power Of Sale A mortgagee can have **power of sale** for a property if the mortgagor fails to meet their obligations. The mortgagee has the right to sell the property to satisfy the loan. Any extra proceeds are the property of the mortgagor.

• Equity

This is an amount of money that represents the part of the home that is owned outright by the buyer (borrower or mortgagor). If you bought a house for $100,000 and got a $70,000 mortgage, your equity in the home would be $30,000. If the value of the home went up to $125,000 before you paid down the mortgage amount, your equity would climb to ($125,000 – $70,000 mortgage =) $55,000. If the value of the home dropped to $70,000, your equity would be zero.

• Mortgage Insurance

This insurance is bought and paid for by the home buyer (borrower or mortgagor). It works to the benefit of the lender (mortgagee). The lender may insist that the mortgage be insured because the lender feels there is a risk that the buyer may not be able to make the mortgage payments. The mortgage insurer agrees (for a fee) to reimburse the lender if the borrower defaults.

• Title Insurance

Title insurance can be purchased by the buyer, again, sometimes at the insistence of a lender, to ensure that the property is owned outright by the buyer. It's not unusual to find that there are old mortgages which have been paid off but not properly discharged. Lawyers can search the title and make sure it is clear, but in many cases it provides equal protection and is less costly to purchase title insurance.

• Commission

Commission is the amount of money that the real estate agents receive from the proceeds of the sale. A common total commission is six percent. The commission on a $200,000 home would be $12,000. This may be split between the listing and selling agents equally. The listing agent would get three percent and the selling agent would get three percent. It is very common to find that the agent gets half of the three percent commission that goes to their side and the company that employs the agent gets the other half. Each individual agent then gets one and a half percent and each real estate company gets one and a half percent of the purchase price.

Higher Commissions And Desk Fees

Agents often receive more than 50 percent of the three percent part of the commission. They can receive most of this commission, as a matter of fact. In some real estate organizations, the agents pay a fee to the real estate company for services provided by the company and the agent keeps virtually all of the commission. These fees are often referred to as **desk fees**.

• MLS or Multiple Listing Service

This is a service by which information on properties for sale is distributed to all of the real estate companies who are part of that service.

• Caveat Emptor

Real estate in many parts of North America has traditionally worked under the concept of **caveat emptor**. This Latin term means, "Let the buyer beware." The concept is that the buyer must examine the property that he or she is buying and assume responsibility for satisfying him or herself about the condition of the property.

Real Estate Sales Process

Let's take a quick look at how a typical real estate transaction might proceed:

- A prospective buyer has looked at a house that is listed for sale and decided to make an offer. The prospective buyer works with the selling agent to prepare an offer. The offer is drawn up and signed by the prospective buyer.
- The seller's agent presents the offer to the listing agent and perhaps to the seller. The seller may decide to accept the offer, reject the offer or revise it and send it back to the buyer. If the seller revises the offer, this is often called a **signback** or **counter offer**. If the seller signs the offer back, he or she also puts a time frame in, during which the prospective buyer must respond.
- The buyer can accept the counter offer, reject it, or sign it back again. It's not unusual for negotiations to go back and forth a number of times before a deal is struck.
- After some negotiation, the buyer and seller may agree on the purchase price, a date when the house is to change hands and what things are to be included in the sale. The offer may be conditional upon a home inspection, among other things.
- The seller agrees to allow the buyer to bring a home inspector through the property. The buyer engages a home inspector who prepares a report on the home.
- The buyer may choose to accept the agreement (firm up the deal or waive the condition). The buyer may also abort the transaction by exercising their right in the inspection condition.

In most cases, these are the only two options for the buyer within the terms of the contract. As a practical matter, the buyer may want to reopen negotiations based on the inspection results. If the initial conditional offer was for $100,000, for example, that offer may be abandoned (fall through, become null and void or expire). An amendment to the agreement may be drawn up for a lower amount based on the results of the inspection. The negotiation process starts over. The transaction may or may not be completed.

In some areas, the seller is given the option of correcting any deficiencies so that the transaction can be completed.

As you can see, the home inspection is a small part of a bigger process. The real estate salespeople only receive their commission when and if the deal closes. Let's look at this from the real estate agent's perspective.

The Agent's Perspective

The selling agent has worked with this young couple for three and a half months. The agent has shown them more than one hundred houses. The negotiations on this home took three full days, including a final negotiation that lasted until 3:00 a.m. this morning. The agent has a great deal invested in this transaction at this point. After weeks, and sometimes months, of work the transaction is finally signed, sealed and almost delivered – until the home inspector kills the deal!

All of the agent's work falls apart instantly and neither the selling agent nor the listing agent can look forward to receiving the commission they felt they had earned. Further, the seller who thought he or she had sold his or her house now has to go back to square one and try to sell the house all over. It may be harder to sell the home now, especially if word gets out that the house did not "pass" an inspection. Although we've already discussed that home inspectors do not pass or fail homes, what we intend and what the market perceives are not always the same.

The Stakes
Are High

A six percent commission on a $200,000 home is $12,000. This is a considerable amount of money. The average agent may sell four or five homes per year. It's easy to understand how real estate salespeople can develop strong opinions about home inspectors, especially if they perceive the inspectors to be –

• wrong about technical issues
• heavy handed in their approach
• insensitive to the needs of all parties in the transaction
• lacking perspective
• scaring clients away from perfectly good houses

The Unique
Position Of
The Home
Inspector

Home inspectors practice their profession in a very complicated environment. Our work involves not simply a client who is satisfied or dissatisfied with our work. The home inspector's work typically impacts on four parties, at a minimum. These include –

• the client who is the prospective home buyer
• the seller of the home
• the selling agent who's been working with the buyer
• the listing agent who's been working with the seller

These people do not have common goals and interests. Your work may be viewed very differently by each of these different people. Home inspectors and their work are scrutinized more closely than many other professionals because of the nature of the transaction.

The Agent's
Perspective

Real estate agents may feel differently about home inspectors at different times. These feelings can include one or more of the following. Home inspectors are—

• deal killers
• time wasters
• always trying to justify their existence
• a way of reducing my liability
• a valuable aid to my client
• a technical reference source
• a marketing tool for me
• a tool to help convince a reluctant buyer to move forward
• a necessary evil
• often the reason I have to sell a house twice (a second time after the inspection)

The Cruel Reality

When the real estate transaction moves forward after the home inspection, everyone is usually happy. As long as the home inspector has not misrepresented the home or made substantive errors in his or her report and the buyers understand the scope of the inspection report, everyone will continue to be happy.

Buyer Happy — Others Unhappy

If the transaction does not go through, the buyer who was your client may be very happy with your service. The real estate agents and the seller may not be happy. Your report will often be scrutinized and your words will be challenged. We said earlier that you are not at liberty to discuss your findings with anyone other than your client. This includes the seller and real estate agents involved in the transaction. The unfortunate reality is that sometimes clients simply get **cold feet** or change their mind about a home for reasons that are beyond the home inspection results. **This is beyond your control and you will often be blamed for killing a deal that had nothing to do with how you conducted yourself.**

What Can You Do?

One of the best defenses for a home inspector is to have the agents attend the inspection and listen to what you say. Ideally, the agents receive a copy of the report, although this is at the buyers' discretion.

Give The Seller A Copy

Some real estate transactions are worded so that if the transaction does not go through as a result of the home inspection report, the seller receives a copy of the report as a courtesy. On the surface, this allows the seller to understand the problems with the property and make appropriate corrections if they so choose. At a different level, the intention of this clause is to prevent buyers from misrepresenting the home inspection results as a means to abort the transaction for reasons other than the inspection.

It's better for the inspector if everyone can see the report. The quality of communication is much better. People who are unhappy with you at least have the facts.

The Agent's Role in Home Inspection

From the home inspector's perspective, the agent's role is to facilitate the inspection, make the arrangements and make sure the client shows up on time. Many agents ensure that the sellers are not home since the home inspection process can be difficult for the seller. Many agents also like to keep the buyer and seller from speaking directly to each other.

Agent's Perspective

From an agent's perspective, the role of the agent at a home inspection is to make sure the home inspector does not abort the transaction unnecessarily. Many agents attend the inspection with a view to protecting the transaction.

Some Participate

Some agents will actively participate in the inspection from start to finish. Others will stay out of the picture while you do your work. This can be a function of a number of things, including the agent's style, schedule, confidence in you, previous experiences and so on.

The Relationship Between the Home Inspector and the Real Estate Agent

In many cases there is virtually no relationship and very little interaction between the agent and the home inspector. In other cases, there may be a level of familiarity between the agent and the home inspector because they have met on previous inspections. Home inspectors may know agents because, through their marketing efforts, they interact with the agents. They may participate in company golf tournaments, sit on committees in real estate boards, etc. In some cases, there may be a financial relationship between the agent and the home inspector. This may create ethics problems for the home inspector and care is recommended when entering any arrangement such as this. You can refer to our discussion on ethics.

Excessive Familiarity

Even if you know the real estate agent well, it may make clients uneasy if you are overly familiar with the agent during the inspection. It can create the perception of a conflict of interest when none exists.

Referrals

Some home inspectors resent the role that real estate agents play in the home inspection business. Some inspectors also object to home inspectors who market to agents and have any kind of relationship with them. They feel that the inspectors should be completely independent and should have no contact with the real estate agent. We'll stay out of that discussion, but recommend that you evaluate it and make your own decision.

Refer Three Names

Many real estate agents will refer three home inspectors to their clients rather than recommend a single inspector. This is a liability reduction measure on the part of the agents.

Agents Oversell

One of the problems that real estate agents can inadvertently cause for home inspectors is to oversell the inspection to the client. We have heard agents say things like, *"The home inspector will tell you **everything** about the house"* or *"They'll take care of anything that goes wrong."* The real estate agent does the home inspector no favors by creating unrealistic expectations in the mind of the prospective purchaser.

Communication & Professional Practice

MODULE

QUICK QUIZ 4

☑ INSTRUCTIONS

- You should finish Study Session 4 before doing this Quiz.
- Write your answers in the spaces provided.
- Check your answers against ours at the end of this section.
- If you have trouble with the Quiz, reread the Study Session and try the Quiz again.
- If you did well, it's time for the Field Exercise.

1. Describe in one sentence the purpose of a closing discussion at the end of a home inspection.

   _____

2. Explain in one sentence why home inspectors do not pass or fail homes as a result of their inspection.

   _____

S4

3. Write a script for a closing discussion. Assume—
    • you have no recommended improvements
    • you use a client questionnaire
    • the agents and seller are present during the closing discussion

    Restrict your script to five to ten sentences.

    _____

    _____

    _____

    _____

    _____

    _____

    _____

    _____

    _____

    _____

4. Describe in one sentence each how you would handle each of the following situations:

    1. The utilities are off.

    _____

    2. The client doesn't show up.

    _____

    3. The agent doesn't show up.

    _____

    4. The client and agent cannot attend.

    _____

    5. Clients have pages of questions.

    _____

    6. A relative who is a building expert attends the inspection.

    _____

7. The agent or seller disrupts the inspection with constant challenges or distracting stories.

_____

8. The client asks you not to speak in the presence of the agent or seller.

_____

9. The client has more questions about your insurance than about the house.

_____

10. The client wants to audiotape or videotape you.

_____

11. The client has heard enough and wants to end the inspection.

_____

12. Information on the house listing is wrong.

_____

13. You break something.

_____

14. There is a life threatening issue.

_____

5. Describe in one sentence each the following terms.

• **Real estate agent**

_____

• **Real estate broker**

_____

• **Listing agent**

_____

• **Selling agent**

_____

• **Buyer broker** or **buyer agent**

_____

• **Agency disclosure**

_____

• **Agreement of purchase and sale** or **offer**

_____

• **Conditional offer**

_____

• **Irrevocable date** or **expiry date**

_____

• **Closing** or **closing date**

_____

• **Firm deal** or **firm agreement**

_____

• **Seller disclosure**

_____

• **Substitute disclosure**

_____

S4

• **Escrow**

_____

• **Waiver**

_____

• **Closing adjustments** or **adjustments on closing**

_____

• **Mortgage**

_____

• **Equity**

_____

• **Mortgage insurance**

_____

• **Title insurance**

_____

• **Commission**

_____

• **Multiple Listing Service**

_____

• **Caveat Emptor**

_____

6. List the six steps in the simplified real estate sales process outlined in the text.

_____

_____

_____

_____

_____

_____

If you had no trouble with the Quiz, you're ready to try Field Exercise 1

Key Words

- **Summary**
- **Perspective**
- **One piece of the puzzle**
- **Limitations**
- **Control**
- **Payment request**
- **Client feedback**
- **Client questionnaire**
- **Real estate agent and broker**
- **Listing and selling agent**
- **Buyer broker or buyer agent**
- **Agreement of purchase and sale**
- **Conditional offer**
- **Irrevocable date or expiry date**
- **Closing or closing date**
- **Firm deal or firm agreement**
- **Seller disclosure**
- **Substitute disclosure**
- **Escrow**
- **Waiver**
- **Closing adjustments**
- **Mortgage**
- **Equity**
- **Mortgage insurance**
- **Title insurance**
- **Commission**
- **Multiple Listing Service**
- **Sign back**

Communication & Professional Practice

MODULE

FIELD EXERCISE 1

☑ INSTRUCTIONS

This Field Exercise has two parts. In Part A, we ask you to go through a mock home inspection. In Part B, we ask you to do some research with real estate agents.

You should allow yourself three to five hours for this Field Exercise.

Exercise A

This Field Exercise is designed to give you a feel for the actual home inspection and although it's not technical, we will ask you to walk through the inspection of a home as you complete the Exercise.

Keep Your Notes   As you work through this Exercise, keep your notes. We'll use them in the Field Exercise in Section 2.

1. Establish a routine for going through a home as you inspect it. Decide, for example, if you are going to start on the inside or outside, top or bottom. Feel free to use our approach or establish your own. If you are going to be working for a company, they may have their own procedure established that they will ask you to follow.

    Decide if you are going to do a single or multiple tour of various parts of the home. Decide whether or not you are going to get onto roofs and whether or not you are going to crawl through entire attics and crawlspaces, if possible.

2. Establish a goal for how much time you plan to spend at the inspection. Allocate your time to each part of the routine you designed in Question 1. It doesn't matter whether these numbers are accurate at this point. The thought of having an overall time goal and breaking it up into segments is the important concept for now.

3. If you own a vehicle, evaluate whether it is appropriate for home inspection work. Use the parameters in the text as a guide.

4. Envision all of the tools, equipment, paper and accessories you'll need in your home inspection work.

   • Will they be kept in your vehicle?
   • How will you keep them in order and in good shape?
   • Will you keep them out of view?

5. Give some thought to the type of clothing that you'll wear during your inspection work.

   • Will it be a uniform? Will it include a tie and a jacket?
   • What about footwear? Do you have a pair of lace-up, rubber-soled shoes? More than one pair might be desirable.

6. You don't need to own the tools at this point, but envision a set of basic tools, and decide how many of the optional tools on our list you may want to use.

   • Are there any other tools that you'll want to use?

7. Are you going to use a seller's letter? If so, draft a letter. Feel free to use ours ours as a base and modify it.

8. Write and practice a brief seller introduction until you can recite it without referring to notes.

   Practice delivering the introduction into a mirror first and then to a family member or friend.

   • Do you look and sound like the kind of person that you would hire as a professional consultant?
   • Does your script need to be refined?

9. Write and practice an introductory discussion for your inspection. Hint: your client's name is Gerard Gransaull.

   • Will you be using a contract?
   • Does your introductory discussion include this?
   • Will you be providing your report on site or delivering it after the inspection?

10. List as many of the possible responses to your specific questions in your script as you can think of.

   • How will you address these responses?

11. Walk through the inspection, following your routine and picturing yourself performing the inspection tasks (these can be vague). Envision yourself speaking to your clients as you perform your work.

   • How many exterior tours are you going to do?
   • Do you use a macro and micro approach? Throughout the whole house or only certain areas?

- Assuming that you get on the roof, where will you place your ladder?
- Did you find a technical issue on the exterior that is a logical spot to start your discussion with?

- Assume that the electrical system for the house has to be upgraded to 100 amps and all of the distribution wiring has been replaced. How exactly will you describe this to your clients? Did you focus on the recommended actions and implications?

- Did you stay on schedule as you went through?
- Did you take notes? How did you record them? How many notes did you take?
- Did you get into the attic and crawlspace?
- Did you drop insulation into the house?
- Did you leave dirty fingerprints on walls or ceilings?
- Did you adjust the thermostat to test the heating or air conditioning system? Did you put it back as you found it?

12. At the end of your inspection routine, stop to record your findings and compile your report. While you would be doing this, you could ask your client to complete a client questionnaire if you intend to use one.

13. Write and practice a closing discussion until you can recite it without using notes. Then practice your presentation in the mirror and then for a family member or friend.

- Do you present a relaxed, professional image?
- Do you seem knowledgeable and in control?
- Did you remember to ask clients for their feedback?
- Did you ask for payment?
- Did you acknowledge the agents and seller during your closing discussion?
- Did you use people's names?

14. Write down as many of the possible responses to your script questions as you can think of and determine how you will address these responses.

- Are you still on schedule?

How Did You Do? Did you feel foolish doing your mock inspection? It's much better to feel foolish and make mistakes in private, rather than in front of your clients. Although it may be uncomfortable for you, you should practice the repetitive elements of this Exercise as frequently as possible until you start your practice of home inspection. Then your field work will become your practice. Home inspection is like any other endeavor, whether professional or athletic. Your performance improves with practice and repetition. Our guess is that your first draft of seller's introductions, introductory discussions and closing discussions will be revised over time.

Exercise B

This Exercise involves speaking to real estate experts to learn more about the real estate transactions in your area. We recommend speaking to at least two people from different areas of the business. These can include a real estate salesperson, a real estate broker or a real estate board representative. You may also wish to speak to attorneys who specialize in residential real estate.

Here's a list of some of the points to cover in your discussion.

15. Go over the list of definitions we've included in the text.

    Which are different in your area?

    Which basic real estate terms are missing?

16. Are there mandatory disclosure laws in your area?

17. Are seller disclosure forms common in your area (these are called vendor disclosure forms in some areas)?

18. Is buyer brokerage common?

19. Are home inspections usually performed?

    On roughly what percentage of sales?

20. What is the general sentiment toward home inspection among the real estate community?

21. Do agents typically recommend one home inspector? Three home inspectors? Something else?

22. Review the real estate sales process outlined in the text. A condensed version is included here.

    a. Prospective buyer makes an offer.
    b. Selling agent presents offer to listing agent.
    c. Seller accepts, rejects or signs back offer. Assume that it is signed back.
    d. Buyer accepts, rejects or signs back the offer again.
    e. After negotiation, buyer and seller agree on purchase price, closing date and things included in sale. Offer conditional on home inspection and financing.
    f. Buyer hires a home inspector to prepare a report on home.
    g. Buyer decides to accept the agreement or reject it based on the results of the inspection.
    h. If buyer aborts transaction, buyer can initiate a new offer of purchase and sale and start the negotiation process over, or ask for further amendments to the agreement.

Which parts of the process are different in your area?

Are there any that will impact your activities as a home inspector?

(There will be many variations on the basic theme we've outlined. Real estate can be purchased and sold without real estate agents, for example.)

After your discussion with real estate experts, you should have a clear picture of how real estate is bought and sold in your area. This background information is helpful to home inspectors.

When you've finished this Field Exercise, you're ready for the Final Test.

► ANSWERS TO QUICK QUIZZES

Answers to Quick Quiz 1

1. Inspections provide the client with information regarding the condition of the systems and components of the home inspected at the time of the home inspection.

2. 1. Things unsafe, inoperative or near the end of their lives
    2. The implications of the deficiencies
    3. The recommendations
    4. What things were not inspected and why

3. 1. Inspections are visual and not technically exhaustive
    2. Inspections applicable to four family units or less and associated garages or carports

4. Inspectors are not required to report on:
    1. Life expectancy
    2. Causes of conditions
    3. Methods, materials or costs of correction
    4. Suitability of property for specialized use
    5. Compliance with regulations
    6. Market value
    7. Advisability of purchase
    8. Components or systems not observed
    9. Presence of pests, including insects
    10. Cosmetic items, underground items or items not permanently installed

5. Inspectors are not required to:
    1. Offer or perform any service contrary to law
    2. Offer warranties or guarantees
    3. Offer engineering, architectural, plumbing or any other job function
    4. Calculate the strength, adequacy or efficiency of a system
    5. Enter areas or do anything that may damage the property or be dangerous
    6. Operate systems that are shut down
    7. Operate systems that don't respond to their normal controls
    8. Disturb insulation
    9. Move personal items, including furniture, equipment, plant life, snow, soil, ice or debris
    10. Determine the presence of hazardous substances
    11. Evaluate the effectiveness of systems that control hazardous substances
    12. Predict future conditions
    13. Provide operating costs
    14. Evaluate acoustical characteristics of components

6. Technically exhaustive includes dismantling, extensive use of measurements, instruments, testing or calculations.

7. A person hired to examine any system or component of a building, in accordance with these Standards of Practice.

8. 1. Express an opinion only when you have the experience and are being honest.
   2. Act in good faith toward your clients.
   3. Don't disclose the results to anyone other than your client without their approval.
   4. Don't accept compensation from more than one person for the same work.
   5. Don't accept or offer commissions from other people working with your client.
   6. Disclose any conflict of interest and don't use the inspection to get work in another field.
   7. Uphold the integrity of the profession and report any violations of the code by other members to the association.

   Answers to Quick Quiz 2

1. The profession is not regulated in most parts of North America.

2. 20,000 to 25,000 inspectors.

3. Average fee $240 to $250.

4. 1. Pre-purchase inspections
   2. Pre-listing or pre-sale inspections
   3. Pre-renovation inspections
   4. Problem solving inspections
   5. Maintenance inspections
   6. Course of construction or progress inspections
   7. Legal dispute inspections
   8. Inspection of relatively new homes as warranties expire

5. A home inspection determines physical condition and an appraisal determines market value.

6. 1. The home buyer
   2. The home seller
   3. The listing agent
   4. The selling agent
   5. The home
   6. The home inspector

7. Two and half hours.

8. 1. Better communication
    2. Showing is better than telling
    3. Reduced liability
    4. Opportunity to adjust expectations

9. 1. Technical wizard
    2. Enjoys people
    3. Great communicator
    4. Actor or performer
    5. Diplomat
    6. Investigator or detective
    7. Organized but flexible

10. A home inspector's vehicle should be presentable and not particularly notable.

11. Your dress should be comfortable enough to allow you to do your work and should reflect your clients' expectations of an inspector. This may vary depending on the area that you work in.

12. 1. Binoculars
    2. Flashlight
    3. Flashlight batteries and bulbs
    4. Ladder
    5. Screwdriver
    6. Carpenter's awl
    7. Telescopic mirror
    8. Measuring tape
    9. Electrical circuit testers
    10. Knife
    11. Gloves
    12. Coveralls
    13. Mask
    14. Pliers
    15. Briefcase or toolkit

13. 1. Clients want to make an informed buying decision
    2. Clients want positive reinforcement
    3. Clients are looking for leverage to get out of the deal
    4. Clients are looking for leverage to renegotiate the deal
    5. The husband and wife feel differently about the home
    6. Real estate agents insist on an inspection to minimize their liability
    7. The lender may insist on the inspection to protect their investment
    8. The mortgage insurer may insist on the inspection to protect their interests
    9. The client's employer is paying for the inspection

14. 1. Is this home a money pit?
2. I wish it were over.
3. Do we really need a home inspector? If so, is this the right inspector?
4. How will we know if he's any good?
5. Who picked this inspector?
6. Do the home inspector and agent have a relationship?
7. Am I paying too much for the inspection?
8. Will the inspector make me feel stupid?
9. How should I act?
10. Should I ask questions or let the inspector do his work?
11. Will the inspector think we're fools for choosing this home?
12. What will the sellers think?
13. Will the seller be rude?
14. This is just one more step in a process I don't understand.
15. Why does everything about buying a house include so much paperwork and cost so much?

15. 1. The opulence of the home
2. Loud arguments
3. Erotic art
4. Vicious dogs
5. Rats, mice, insects, snakes, etc.
6. Extremely high or low temperatures
7. A full bladder
8. A flashlight with failing batteries
9. Missing critical papers
10. The next appointment
11. A lack of sleep, hangover or illness
12. A recent dispute with a family member or co-worker

Answers to Quick Quiz 3

1. 1. Pre-inspection routine
    2. The introductory discussion
    3. The inspection itself
    4. The closing discussion

2. 1. Introductory discussion
    2. Exterior inspection
    3. Roof
    4. Heating plant
    5. Electrical system
    6. Water service entry and water heater
    7. Structure
    8. Interior rooms
    9. Attic
    10. Crawlspace
    11. Closing discussion

3. 1. Introductory discussion – 10 minutes
    2. Roof and exterior – 30 minutes
    3. Mechanical, electrical, basement and structure – 30 minutes
    4. Interior inspection – 30 minutes
    5. Attic or crawlspace – 15 minutes
    6. Recording inspection results – 20 minutes
    7. Closing discussion – 15 minutes
    8. Total – 150 minutes

4. 1. How long the inspection will be
    2. Where in the house you'll be going
    3. Assurance that the inspection is not destructive or invasive
    4. Asking whether there are any pets or people sleeping who should not be disturbed

5. Good morning, I'm John Smith from Smith Home Inspections.

    It's good to meet you, Mr. Brown, and thank you for choosing us to perform your home inspection. Have you bought a home before? Have you ever had a home inspection? So, you've been through this before.

    Our goal over the next two and a half hours is to give you a clear picture of the condition of the major systems in the house. As we look for significant issues that may affect your buying decision, we'll come across a number of smaller items. We'll discuss those and include them in our report as a courtesy, but our goal is not to create a detailed maintenance or repair list.

    We'll start outside and then move indoors where we'll work from the bottom to the top, finishing with the attic.

    We'll complete our report at the end of the inspection and by the time we're done, you'll have everything you need to make your decision.

Do you have any plans for changes to the house?

Do you have any specific concerns about the home or are you looking for a general overview?

Please join me as we go through the home. I won't ask you to get up on the roof or go into the attic or crawlspace, but otherwise we can work together and discuss our findings along the way. Please feel free to ask questions as we go. We may not get answers until we get the whole picture, but that's okay.

This is our authorization form that sets out the rules of the game. Please read it carefully while I get started on the roof. Please check that we have your name address and phone number correctly and, if everything is in order, sign the form here. You might want to look at the report layout. We'll complete this and give the entire book to you at the end of the inspection.

6. Describe the system and explain the improvement rather than the problem

7. The macro and micro approach includes a big picture macro look at things from a distance that is somewhat passive. The micro part is a detailed look from up close that may reference a checklist.

8.
   1. Leaving the heat turned up
   2. Leaving the air conditioning turned down
   3. Leaving appliances on
   4. Leaving doors unlocked
   5. Leaving the power off
   6. Leaving clocks flashing
   7. Leaving access covers dirty, loose or not in place
   8. Leaving clothes on a bed
   9. Leaving fireplace screens in the middle of the living room
   10. Leaving fireplace dampers open

9. Indicate that you do not know what it is but will find out.

Answers to Quick Quiz 4

1. The closing discussion summarizes the major points of the inspection and makes sure the client understands these issues.

2. The home inspection is only part of the picture for the client so we cannot pass or fail the home.

3. Is this a good place to summarize the inspection, Mr. Brown?

    The roof and furnace will have to be replaced in the next year and we've got some minor electrical and safety cleanup, but overall the systems that we looked at and tested appear to be doing their jobs.

    These items are detailed in the report, as are a number of the other things we talked about. This is how the report is laid out.

    We've talked about all the points in the report already and they are included here for your reference. We won't go through all the details again. When you do get a chance to have a look at it, feel free to call us if you have any questions.

    We've covered a lot of ground in the last two and a half hours, trying to identify the big issues and we've come across some of the smaller ones. When you move into the home, you'll find some other issues and there will be a few that arise after you get settled in. This is part of home ownership. There are always improvements to be made and unexpected issues crop up regularly in every home.

    Remember, we didn't get into that crawlspace or the small attic over the rear extension. Once you take possession of the home, you'll want to get into those places.

    Have we answered all your questions? Great. If you ever have any question about anything in the home, please give us a call. We'd be happy to help and there's no fee for this service.

    Will you be paying by check? Very good. I'll fill out the receipt while you do that.

    I've included a client questionnaire and a postage paid return envelope at the front of the report. It would help us if you'd complete it and mail it to us. We're always looking for ways to improve.

    Here's your report. Thanks again for choosing us to do your home inspection. I hope things work out very well for you.

    It was good to meet you, Ms. Jones and Mr. Adams. Thank you very much for your patience. (That's to the agents).

    Thank you very much for your cooperation. Goodbye for now. (That's to the seller and the goodbye is to everyone.)

4.
1. Let the client know about the limitations this creates and decide whether or not to go ahead.
2. Try to contact the client or agent. If unsuccessful, wait at the site for roughly 45 minutes.
3. Try to contact the agent and discuss with the client whether you should go ahead with the inspection. This is up to the client.
4. Try to get your contract signed before the inspection. Contact your client after the inspection.
5. Go through your normal routine and ask the client if they have any questions at the end. Do not take the pages of questions.
6. Display your technical expertise and try to get the expert on side as an ally.
7. Ask permission to perform your part of the work so that they can have their discussions afterward.
8. If you are asked questions by the agent or seller, indicate that you've been asked not to discuss the inspection report with anyone other than the client.
9. Explain to the client that you are not offering an insurance policy or warranty.
10. Allow the client to tape you but keep your presentation brief.
11. Client can stop the inspection whenever they want. You may or may not lower the fee as a result.
12. If it is brought to your attention, indicate how difficult it is for the layperson to determine this sort of thing.
13. Advise the occupant and offer to repair or replace it.
14. Notify the occupant of the home.

5.
- Real estate agent – commissioned salespeople involved with homes
- Real estate broker – the right to operate a real estate brokerage, the actual agent
- Listing agent – the person who represents the seller
- Selling agent – the person who works with the buyer and may represent the buyer or seller's interest
- Buyer broker or buyer agent – a person who works with buyers and represents their interests
- Agency disclosure – an obligation to make buyers and sellers aware of whose interests the agent is working in
- Agreement of purchase and sale or offer – the contract between the buyer and seller, agreeing to transfer the property
- Conditional offer – an agreement dependent on the outcome of one or more things
- Irrevocable date or expiry date – the time that a party has to respond to an offer from another party
- Closing or closing date – this is the date the transaction is completed
- Firm deal or firm agreement – an agreement that contains no conditional clauses
- Seller disclosure – a statement by the seller representing the condition of the property and addressing some legal issues typically

- Substitute disclosure – the seller's right to have someone else represent the condition of the property
- Escrow – money held in trust by an independent third party
- Waiver – a written agreement that removes a condition
- Closing adjustments – monies paid by the buyer on closing date to give the seller credit for fuel in a tank, property taxes paid in advance, etc.
- Mortgage – a loan made by a mortgagee (lender) to a mortgagor (home buyer or owner)
- Equity – the part of the home's value that is controlled by the owner. The excess of the home's value over the mortgage amount.
- Mortgage insurance – insurance that protects the lender in case the homeowner defaults on the mortgage payments
- Title insurance – insurance that protects the buyer in case title to the property is not clear
- Commission – money paid to an agent upon completion of a transaction
- Multiple Listing Service – a service in which information about properties for sale are distributed to all real estate companies who are part of the service
- Caveat emptor – let the buyer beware

6. 1. The buyer prepares an offer.
2. The offer is presented and accepted, rejected or signed back.
3. The buyer accepts the counter offer, rejects it or signs back again.
4. A purchase price is agreed upon, along with the closing date and any inclusions in the sale
5. The offer is conditional on a home inspection
6. A home inspector prepares his report.
7. The buyer waives the condition or aborts the transaction.

2 COMMUNICATION AND REPORT WRITING

Communication &
Professional Practice
MODULE

► TABLE OF CONTENTS

► 1.0 OBJECTIVES

The goal of this Section is to provide you with a good understanding of the verbal communication and report writing issues involved in a home inspection. We will also touch on the liability issues faced by home inspectors. A 50 step, sample home inspection process is included in this Section. This can be used as a template for your inspection format.

Subjective Information

Much of the information in this Section is not authoritative. It is our opinion based on our experience. You may find certain elements of our discussion do not apply to you, or you may find other approaches that work better. This information should not be viewed as the last or only word on home inspector communications.

By the end of this Section, you should have a good understanding of how home inspectors communicate with their clients. You will recognize some of the barriers to effective communication and some of the techniques for improving communications. Much of the material discussed in this Section is not unique to home inspection.

Communication & Professional Practice
M O D U L E

STUDY SESSION 1

1. This Session covers verbal communication.

2. At the end of this Session, you should be able to –
- define communication
- list 10 issues involving verbal communication
- list the five basic elements of verbal communication
- list four additional elements of verbal communication
- explain in one sentence each of the following words:
  - sender
  - receiver
  - message
  - medium
  - encoding
  - decoding
  - feedback
  - personal filter area
  - noise
- name two things, other than words, that express your message to your audience
- list five categories of body language
- list five types of body language that home inspectors should avoid
- list eight common obstacles to effective communication
- list eight techniques for improving communication

3. This Session may take you roughly one hour.

4. Quick Quiz 1 is at the end of this Session.

Key Words

- *Communication*
- *Sender*
- *Receiver*
- *Message*
- *Encoding*
- *Decoding*
- *Feedback*
- *Medium*
- *Noise*
- *Personal filter areas*
- *Perception*
- *Paraverbals*
- *Body language*
- *Illustrators*
- *Emblems*
- *Regulators*
- *Adaptors*
- *Affect displays (emotional displays)*
- *Mimic technique*
- *Credibility*
- *Jargon*
- *Semantic differences*
- *Proximity*
- *Information overload*
- *Time constraints*
- *Empathy*
- *Trust*
- *Distractions*
- *Swearing*
- *Slang*
- *Sarcasm*
- *Derision*
- *Self-deprecation*

► 2.0 VERBAL COMMUNICATION

2.1 INTRODUCTION – COMMUNICATION DEFINED

Important Skill

This section covers the communication skills required by the home inspector. It is important to properly communicate the results of your inspections. Without good communication between clients and inspectors, the value of the home inspection is seriously impaired.

This section focuses on the skills needed for clear verbal communication. In the next section we'll discuss report writing.

Much of the material in this section is provided through the courtesy of Mr. Darren Smith of NDS Consultants, who has prepared the following information. We have edited and added to the information slightly to gear it specifically to the home inspection profession and have tried not to destroy Mr. Smith's message along the way.

Highlights

In this section our goal is to give you an understanding of –

• the definition of communication
• major elements in the process of verbal communication
• nonverbal messages in communication
• obstacles to effective verbal communication and how to remove them
• effective verbal communication
• the use of feedback and listening skills

Definition Of Communication

Communication can be defined as the **transfer of information and comprehension through the use of common symbols**. Our focus here is on verbal communication.

Here is a list of some of the issues involved in verbal communication:

Communication Issues

1. Sender (of the communication)
2. Receiver (of the communication)
3. Message
4. Encoding
5. Decoding
6. Feedback
7. Improving communication
8. Communication elements
9. Communication obstacles
10. Effective listening

There may be some words on the list that are unfamiliar to you. Don't worry about them. We will be covering all of these terms, and others, throughout this section.

An Exercise in Decoding Language

Communications should be simple so they are easy to understand. We've talked already about avoiding jargon. Play this game to see what we mean.

Each of the following statements is a well-known saying or slogan which has been reworded using complex language. Your task is to decode the statement.

1. *A feathered vertebrate enclosed in the grasping appendage has a valuation that is superior to a couple encapsulated in a branched shrub.*

Your translation:

_____

_____

2. *The smallest medium of currency that is stored aside is the smallest medium that is brought in by way of returns.*

Your translation:

_____

_____

3. *It is highly inadvisable to espy an equine largess in the oral cavity.*

Your translation:

_____

_____

The answers are:

A feathered vertebrate enclosed in the grasping appendage has a valuation that is superior to a couple encapsulated in a branched shrub.

Translates to—

A bird in the hand is worth two in the bush.

The smallest medium of currency that is stored aside is the smallest medium of currency that is brought in by way of returns.

Translates to—

A penny saved is a penny earned.

It is highly inadvisable to espy an equine largess in the oral cavity.

Translates to—

Don't look a gift horse in the mouth.

Decoding Is Hard

Did we frustrate you? In the exercise, you had to decode the message. Depending on your familiarity with the language used and the sayings, you may have found the activity easy or difficult. Clients who have to decode inspectors' messages feel the same way that you feel about us right now. Did you have time to think about the message, or was all of your focus on understanding it?

With that in mind, let's look at defining communication and what elements make up the process of communication.

Defining Communication

At its most basic level, the communication process is presented in the figure.

A simple model of the communication process

Medium Is
The Message

In this diagram, we see five basic parts to the process of communication. The person on the left is the **sender** of the **message**. This person has an **intention**. The person on the right is the **receiver** of the message. This person has a **perception**. Both receive and deliver messages through their own **filter** system. There is the receiver's **response** (or feedback) to the message. In this example, the medium of the message is verbal.

5 Elements

Simply put, the five basic elements are –

• The sender...	*Who?*
• The message...	*Says what?*
• The medium...	*In which way?*
• The receiver...	*To whom?*
• The response (feedback)...	*With what effect?*

Communication is successful if the receiver gets the message that the sender intended. There must be **common** ground for this to occur. Indeed, the word **communication** has its root in the Latin word **communis** which means common. We define communication as—

Communication
Defined

• The transfer of information and comprehension through the use of common symbols.

In the diagram, the common symbols are spoken words. In our decoding language exercise, the symbols were printed words. Communication involves more than just words. It also includes many nonverbal factors.

2.2 ELEMENTS OF THE COMMUNICATION PROCESS

We have just looked at the five basic elements in the communication process. However, communication is slightly more complex and involves more than the five basic elements.

A more refined communication model

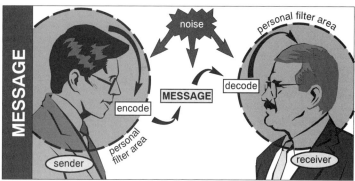

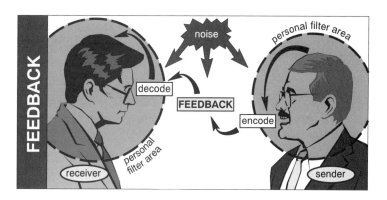

This figure depicts a more refined model of communication. To the five basic parts we have now added **encoding, decoding, noise** and **personal filter area**. We'll assume the medium is the spoken word. This depiction of the communication process is based on one of the most widely used models, first created over 40 years ago. Let's look at each of these eight parts.

Communication Model

1. The sender
2. Encoding
3. The message
4. Decoding
5. The receiver
6. Feedback
7. Noise
8. Personal filter areas

1. The Sender

Sender – Inspector

The sender is the person who starts the communication. She or he is the person who has information to be transferred. This is usually the home inspector, but is sometimes the client, seller or real estate agent.

2. Encoding

Sender's Words

This is the process of taking the sender's ideas and information and translating them into a set of symbols. As we noted previously, the set of symbols typically takes the form of language. For our purposes, **encoding** is the action of transforming information into words. This is not always simple.

3. The Message

Words And Delivery Style

Once the sender has encoded the message, it is sent in some form. The form it takes (fax, telephone, e-mail, face-to-face dialogue) is the **medium**. The **message** is what the sender hopes to communicate. Many things affect the message including verbal and nonverbal influences. Some are unintended, leading to an improper message being received. Since the medium also has a great impact on the message, it is considered inseparable from the message.

4. Decoding

Client's Interpretation

Decoding is the process of translation and interpretation of the message by the receiver. Depending on the receiver's prior experiences, value system, thought processes and numerous other factors, the decoding may come close to the sender's original intent or it may be quite different. When the decoded message is close to the sender's intent, the communication is said to be **effective**.

5. The Receiver

Receiver Is The Client

The **receiver** is the person who receives and decodes the message. Different receivers decode messages in different ways and may attach different meanings to them. For example, a home buyer may receive the home inspector's message differently than a seller. We often find husbands and wives have very different impressions of what was said, even though both are buyers who hear exactly the same words.

6. Personal Filter Areas

Poor Communication

This is one of the most important areas in the communication process. We have seen how communication is a two-way process and how the word communication has its roots in the word **common**. We have also looked at decoding and encoding. One of the keys to effective communication is the **commonness** of the encoding and decoding processes. If the senders and receivers use very different encoding and decoding processes, then poor communication will result. In short, good communication depends upon the sender and receiver speaking the same language. If you or your clients don't have a good command of English (or whatever language is chosen for the communication) the risk of poor communication is great.

Relate New Experiences To Old

To make sense out of our world, we **cubby-hole** or sort our experiences. When confronted with a new situation, we choose past experiences to help relate to the situation at hand. This process of sorting carries over to the communication process. Problems arise when the sender and receiver do not **cubby-hole** in the same way. The sorting processes don't have to be identical, but if there is a large common experience between the persons involved, communication will likely be more effective.

Frame Of Reference

Another part of the personal filter area includes the frame of reference. In an earlier example, we saw how a home buyer and seller may see things differently. This is because they have different frames of reference. The real estate agent has a different frame of reference than either the buyer or seller.

Different Frames

Another example of this effect can be seen in the differing frames of reference between a teenager and a parent. Their views as to the time of a curfew, for example, will naturally differ. The teenager **hears** only how early the curfew sounds while the parent believes this time to be very late.

7. Feedback

Receiver Repeats Message

This is the response that the receiver gives the sender after decoding the message. Typically, it takes the form of the receiver paraphrasing, re-stating or otherwise showing that she or he understood the sender's intended message. The sender, in turn, may provide feedback or clarification to the receiver's response. When there is no feedback, there is a greater possibility that communication will break down since the sender cannot be assured that the receiver got the message that was intended.

Home inspectors often try to get clients to repeat the important issues at the end of the inspection to ensure they have gotten the message across. This has to be done without putting the client on the spot.

8. Noise

Distractions

Noise includes all of those things that distort or break down the communication process. It is not limited to any one part of the process. For example, a distracting mannerism, sound, odor or article of clothing may distort the receiver's perception of the message. The surroundings may also hinder communication. If the people involved cannot speak in normal tones of voice, communication will be affected, literally, by the noise. If the environment is hot, cold or wet, the communication may suffer. If the receiver is tired, hungry or otherwise uncomfortable, the results may be poor.

Poor Communications

It is impossible to list all the factors which can be categorized as noise, because so much depends on the specific circumstance. Remember, however, that noise causes breakdowns in communication. It is an important factor. Your clients may be distracted trying to figure out how they'll pay for the home, whether they've overpaid, which room the baby will get, and so on.

An Exercise in Perception

Perception

When we looked at the relationship between the sender and the receiver, we saw that the sender had an **intention** and the receiver had a **perception**. To demonstrate how we perceive communication, try the following exercise. If possible, do not read the story. Rather, have someone read it to you, then answer the questions following it. If there is no one to read the story to you, read it once yourself before answering the questions.

The Incident

The store lights had just been turned off by a businessman when a person appeared and demanded money. The owner opened the cash drawer. The contents of the cash drawer were scooped up, and the person sped away. The police were notified immediately.

If you have read the story once, or have had it read to you, answer these questions:

1.   A man appeared after the owner turned off the lights.

True ☐   False ☐   Don't Know ☐

2.   The robber was a man.

True ☐   False ☐   Don't Know ☐

3.   This situation happened at night.

True ☐   False ☐   Don't Know ☐

4.   The businessman was the owner.

True ☐   False ☐   Don't Know ☐

5.   The person who opened the cash drawer was the owner.

True ☐   False ☐   Don't Know ☐

6.   While there was money in the cash drawer, the story does not state how much money.

True ☐   False ☐   Don't Know ☐

7.   The person who appeared did not demand money.

True ☐   False ☐   Don't Know ☐

8.   Someone opened a cash drawer.

True ☐   False ☐   Don't Know ☐

9.   The robber demanded money.

True ☐   False ☐   Don't Know ☐

10.   The store owner scooped up the cash drawer contents and ran away.

True ☐   False ☐   Don't Know ☐

11.   A businessman turned off the lights when a person appeared.

True ☐   False ☐   Don't Know ☐

12.   No one demanded the contents of the cash drawer.

True ☐   False ☐   Don't Know ☐

13.   The following events occurred in the story: a cash drawer was opened; a person ran out of the store; the contents of the cash drawer were scooped up.

True ☐   False ☐   Don't Know ☐

14.   The person who appeared opened the cash drawer.

True ☐   False ☐   Don't Know ☐

15.   In the story there are only three persons involved including: the owner of the store; a police office; and the man who demanded money.

True ☐   False ☐   Don't Know ☐

Turn the page to see the answers.

The Answers:

1.   **Don't Know.** *Someone* appeared after the lights were turned off. We don't know if the person was a man or woman.

2.   **Don't Know.** The person who appeared may have been a man or a woman and/or may not have been a robber.

3.   **Don't Know.** Although the lights were turned off, this may have occurred during daylight hours.

4.   **Don't Know.** Nothing in the story states that the businessman and the owner are the same person.

5.   **True.** The person who opened the cash drawer was the owner.

6.   **False.** The cash drawer had contents but the story does not state that the contents were money.

7.   **False.** The person who appeared **did** demand money.

8.   **True.** The owner opened the cash drawer.

9.   **Don't Know.** If the person was a robber, then this is true. However, the story does not state that the person who appeared was a robber. It may have been a creditor that the owner owed money to.

10.   **Don't Know.** The story states that the contents were scooped up, but not by whom.

11.   **True.** The lights had just been turned off when the person appeared.

12.   **True.** The person who appeared demanded money, not the cash drawer contents.

13.   **Don't Know.** The person who appeared *sped* away but we don't know if she or he ran, used a car, bicycle, etc. The other two events did occur.

14.   **Don't Know.** The owner opened the cash drawer. However, the person who appeared may have been the *owner*. There is nothing in the story that suggests otherwise.

15.   **Don't Know.** The owner, business, police officer, and the person who appeared may be all separate individuals giving us four people. Nevertheless, the owner could also be the businessman or the person who appeared giving us three people. As well, we know that the local police service was notified but we don't know if any police officers were involved.

How well did you do? Many people do not do well on these type of exercises. Why do you think this happens?

Here are some of our conclusions.

Fill Gaps
- People sort communication according to their prior experiences. Some may selectively **hear** the communication and other may **fill in the gaps** when information appears to be missing, albeit unintentionally. Typically, people make assumptions about the story. For example—

  – turning off the lights implies it is nighttime

  – someone demanding money is a robber

  – the owner and the businessman are the same person

Make Up Information
- It is natural for us to make up information in order to satisfy our need to understand, even if the information is false or inaccurate.

Vague Or Incomplete
- Communication often involves an exchange of ambiguous or incomplete information. This results in distortions of meaning and message.

Prior Experiences Matter
- Our experiences influence our perceptions of messages.

Watch For Noise
- An effective communicator knows and can identify the sources and the circumstances that might distort the sending and receiving of a message. The things are often **noise**.

In order to minimize sending and receiving distorted messages, we suggest you:

Ask For Feedback
- Ask for feedback when sending a message. This helps ensure the message was received as intended.

Control Your Filters
- Be aware of your own experiences, perceptions and assumptions that influence the way you send and receive messages. Try to identify some of your own filters which affect you. Your knowledge of home construction and problems is an obvious one.

Use Model
- Use the model of communication from Page 11. The eight parts apply and can help you anticipate and prevent or correct misunderstandings.

This exercise applies equally well to written communication. We often leave out information when speaking or writing because we think it is obvious. Home inspectors are often guilty of not including all the necessary facts. When you tell a homeowner that the furnace has a cracked heat exchanger not all of them will know—

- this is the most important and expensive part of a furnace.

- this usually means replacing the furnace.

- the gas company usually shuts off the gas and red-tags a furnace with this problem.

- this is a life safety issue – carbon monoxide poisoning is a possibility.

We read many reports and listen to many communications that force the listeners or readers to draw their own conclusions and fill in the gaps.

2.3 NONVERBAL MESSAGES IN COMMUNICATION

Look at the diagram below and write down what you believe it means.

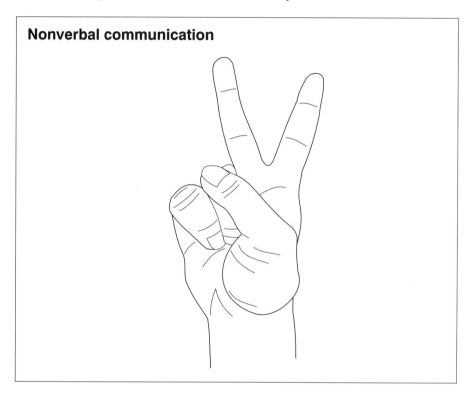

Nonverbal communication

Did you know that this hand signal has many different meanings?

Check the meanings listed below and see if your meaning matches one of them.

• It is a gesture of greeting without any other meaning attached to it.
• It is the hand signal for the number 2.
• It is the **peace** symbol.
• It is the signal for victory ("V").
• It is an aggressive and deliberate gesture of disrespect (in some cultures).

More Than Words

It is easy to see how we can misinterpret communications. Words can mean different things to different people, but words only make up part of the communication. Albert Mehrabian, a behavioral science researcher found that words comprised only 7% of the communication whereas 38% came from **paraverbals** and 55% from **body language.**

Paraverbals

How We Say It By paraverbals, we mean **how something was said.** It includes the volume used, rate of speech, tone of voice, pitch of voice and vocal inflection. Angry people often speak loudly and more rapidly. Their words may not betray their anger but their voice does. Your paraverbals send much of the message.

Body Language

Gestures, Posture And Position Body language includes the gestures used, how a person is holding him/herself, and facial expressions. Since body language can play a very significant role in an interpersonal communication process, it's very important that we understand body language, or as we sometimes refer to it, the **nonverbal** ways that we send and receive messages. We can classify body language or nonverbal communicators into five categories. Three of these categories are conscious actions by the user and the other two are subconscious, nonverbal communicators. We will consider the three conscious actions first.

1. Illustrators

Gesture To Emphasize An **illustrator** is a gesture used to paint a picture of what is being said. In our example of the hand with two fingers raised, we could interpret the meaning to be the number "2," the "2" could reference length, weight or size of something, or the second point being made in conversation. Whenever a gesture is used to **illustrate** a point, it is known as an illustrator.

2. Emblems

Stand For Something The two raised fingers may also be an **emblem**. Emblems are the informal sign language that we use to immediately transmit a message. In some cultures, this gesture is a deliberate insult to the receiver. During the Second World War, the **V** for victory was a powerful emblem for citizens of Britain, signifying their resolve in the face of great difficulty.

Thumbs Up In another example of emblems in our North American society, the **thumbs-up** sign can mean "everything went well" or , if you are hitchhiking, "I need a ride to town." Many years ago, in Roman gladiator games, this same emblem was used to let the loser of the contest live.

3. Regulators

Control The Communication A **regulator** is a gesture used to control the interpersonal communication. Shaking of the head can show disapproval or disagreement. A raised palm turned downwards can mean to slow down, and a single finger spun quickly in front of you usually means to speed up or wind it up (finish). Like illustrators and emblems, regulators can also mean different things to different people. In parts of India, the shaking of the head from side to side is actually a gesture of approval and agreement, the exact opposite of what it means in North America. Someone from a Mediterranean culture (Italy, Spain, Greece, etc.) may use the slow down gesture (raised palm turned downwards) to mean "come here."

Illustrators, emblems and regulators are conscious nonverbal body language messages. Now let's look at the subconscious, unintentional body language communicators.

1. Adaptors

Nervous Habit An adapter is a body motion used by people to adapt or adjust to a communication process that is occurring. It may be a stress-induced reaction such as a person who bites his nails, or one who taps her foot or fingers, or uses another repetitive body motion during the conversation. Adaptors are not consciously controlled and have often been with the person for most of his or her life.

2. Affect Displays (Emotional Displays)

Heart On Your Sleeve The word **affect** is related to the word **emotion** and means much the same thing when we are talking about body language. An affect display is the unintentional display of an individual's emotions. To use an old saying, it can be likened to **wearing your heart on your sleeve**. Affect displays may be reflected in a person's body position or posture. People who hook their thumbs in the belt loops and rock back on their heels may be perceived to be swaggering or domineering. The crossing of arms and legs, and the tilting back of the head while sitting has been said to communicate defensiveness and non-receptiveness.

Mirror Other Person Interestingly, some researchers have found that when two people have established good compatibility in an interpersonal communication process they will subconsciously imitate each other's movements. When one moves forward, so does the other. They act like **mirrors** to each other. However, when compatibility no longer exists, this imitation stops.

Reading Body Language – So What?

Don't Rely On Body Language Be careful about trying to read another person's body language. Even behavioral scientists may do this poorly. Many of these nonverbal body language communicators are culturally bound so they may not mean what you think. Different gestures and body postures mean different things to different cultures. In our North American culture people have been taught to look at another person in the eye to show that they are speaking the truth. In many aboriginal cultures, looking a figure of authority in the eye is a sign of disrespect.

Do not attach too much meaning to another person's body language.

Control Your Body Language

Control Yours It is important to realize that your body language is part of your communication whether or not you intend it. Control your body language to reduce the risk of poor communication. Let's look at some examples:

- Failure to establish and maintain eye contact. Staring at your shoes or another object may make you appear defensive or unfocused.
- Nervous habits such as biting fingernails, pulling at an article of clothing or shifting your weight continuously may suggest anxiety and uncertainty. These are not messages you want to send.
- Speaking quickly or mumbling may be viewed as nervousness or lack of confidence.
- Sitting while your listeners are standing may seem arrogant.
- Leaning against a wall while talking may make you seem disinterested or excessively casual.

You can probably think of many others.

The Mimic Technique Some good communicators, including good home inspectors, use a mimic technique in one-on-one communication as a device to improve the quality of communication. This includes adopting the other person's speech pattern and body language. If the receiver speaks slowly and softly, so does the sender. If the receiver speaks quickly and with lots of energy, so does the sender. This is a dangerous technique because if done poorly, may be perceived as mocking the receiver. We don't suggest you use this technique but you should know it exists.

2.4 OBSTACLES TO EFFECTIVE COMMUNICATION

Many Stages There are many stages to the communication process. Communication can break down in any one of these stages. Many things can cause communication breakdown, some of which we have discussed already.

Obstacles The following is our list of eight obstacles to effective communication. The list is not exhaustive.

1. Different personal filter areas
2. Credibility of the sender
3. Jargon
4. Semantic differences
5. Proximity of the persons communicating
6. Information overload
7. Time constraints
8. Poor location

1. Different Personal Filter Areas

Frames Of Reference

As we have discussed, the more **commonality** that the sender and receiver share, especially with encoding and decoding, the greater the chance that the communication will be effective. Different frames of reference may cause poor communication. A real estate agent's frame of reference may differ significantly from a home buyer. Either or both parties may misinterpret information they exchange based on their personal filters. At a more subtle level, a husband may be enthusiastic about a home (dream home!), and a wife uncertain (money pit!). It's amazing what different messages these two will get from exactly the same communication from the inspector, because of their different frames of reference.

2. Credibility of the Sender

Receiver Has Confidence In Sender

The receiver places a value on what he or she has been told. This value judgment is influenced by prior experiences the receiver has and any dealings that the receiver may have with the home inspector or **other** home inspectors. If the receiver places a high level of confidence and credence in the home inspector, the receiver will react differently than if she or he places little or no trust in the sender. Therefore, it is critical that you retain your credibility throughout the inspection and throughout the entire community you serve. People will be more apt to **listen** to you and respect the information you're conveying.

3. Jargon

Avoid Jargon

Every occupation has its own terms. The meaning of these terms is known by persons employed in the job but not often to others. For example, 10-33 is simply two numbers to the average person, but to a police officer these two numbers may mean "emergency." A PBR is a "Personal Banking Representative" in the world of banking. Home inspectors have jargon understood only by other home inspectors. Jargon is fine for communicating with other home inspectors because it gives the occupation its own distinctness and improves the efficiency of communication. But outside of your occupational group, jargon can confuse communication and become an obstacle to it. Avoid jargon during home inspections. Don't tell clients to replace their crickets.

4. Semantic Differences

Same Words – Different Meanings

Different people may use the same words to describe different things. Simply put, we may speak the same language but attach different meanings to the words. It becomes essential to choose words that both the sender and receiver commonly understand.

The word **header** has a very different meaning in word-processing than in house framing. Even within house framing **headers** associated with trimmers on a stairwell opening are different from **headers** or lintels over windows. These are all different from the **header** that means a bad fall. Who came up with this language?!

5. Proximity of the Persons Communicating

When we communicate with another person, we try to do so from a distance that is comfortable to us. The distance varies depending on the situation and the person we are communicating with. Research has shown that there are four zones that we communicate within. In North America, these zones generally adhere to the following measures –

Close Enough
But Not Too
Close

• Public zone:	12 or more feet
• Social zone:	4 to 12 feet
• Personal zone:	1.5 feet to 4 feet
• Intimate zone:	1.5 feet to physical contact

Factors

Cultural factors, however, also influence comfort zones. Some cultures feel very comfortable communicating from distances that North American culture may view as far too close. When someone gets too close to us, we may feel that she or he is **getting into our personal space**. On the other hand, if we communicate with a person when we are too far away, in his or her view, we can be viewed as being cold, distant and unapproachable.

Typically, the intimate zone is reserved for close relatives and close friends. The personal zone is for friends, the social zone for colleagues and acquaintances, and the public zone is more for business relations. To ensure effective communication, we should converse from the zone within which the receiver feels most comfortable. There is no hard and fast rule as to what zone you should use. But if there seems to be difficulty in a conversation, try adjusting your distance from them. You may have inadvertently invaded someone's space. We have found over several thousand inspections that roughly four feet between people is often a comfortable spacing.

6. Information Overload

Too Much

Our definition of communication includes, *"The transfer of information and comprehension...."* Sometimes there is too much information in the transfer that limits understanding by the receiver. If you unload too much information at once, the receiver may feel overwhelmed and bombarded. (Home inspectors are often guilty of this.) At that point he or she is no longer able to **hear** any more information. Provide information in easily understood small doses. If the receiver understands, continue the process. Discussing issues as they arise over the course of an inspection is more effective than a 25-minute **lecture** at the end.

7. Time Constraints

Sender
Problem

We sometimes have too much to do in too little time. When this happens, we look for shortcuts. One of those may be our approach to interpersonal communication. We may gloss over areas and not provide adequate understandable information to the receiver. We may not allow the receiver to give us feedback that would tell us whether the message is being received properly. The best approach may be to stop the process and remove the time pressure, if possible. Call to reschedule your next appointment, for example.

*Receiver
Problem*

Conversely, if our receiver is pressed for time, he or she may not be giving us his or her full attention. Receivers who appear to be distracted by time should be encouraged to give feedback on your message so that you can be sure they understand. This may simply frustrate the truly distracted client. It is sometimes best to cut off the discussion and offer to call the client to discuss the results when they have more time.

8. Poor Location

Quiet

Conversations must be held in areas where all people involved can be easily heard. Speaking at a noisy renovation site can lead to communication problems. Find a place where all persons involved in the communication can speak at a normal volume and be readily heard.

Same Height

North Americans are vertically sensitive during the inspection process. Most people like to speak "eye-to-eye," or at the same height. Don't stand on a step above the client and "talk down" to them. If they are sitting, try to sit at the same elevation. Don't sit if your clients are standing. Looking up to your clients during your presentation does not help.

*Comfortable
Environment*

Consider your client's comfort. An elderly person or someone on crutches may appreciate your suggestion of finding a place to sit and discuss the inspection. Don't make your client squint into a setting sun to speak to you. Cold or hot weather may not bother you but what about your client? Perhaps sitting in a car would be more appropriate. (It's a good thing you keep the interior of your vehicle presentable.)

2.5 TECHNIQUES FOR IMPROVING COMMUNICATION

Let's look at some techniques for improved communication.

These Help

1. Use the feedback part of the communication process
2. Provide the message at a rate that the receiver can absorb
3. Ensure the timing of the message is appropriate
4. Use simple language
5. Be empathetic to the receiver
6. Use repetition
7. Encourage trust to enhance credibility
8. Create an effective listening environment

1. Use Feedback

*Receiver
Repeats
Message*

Feedback is the stage of the process where the sender finds out if the receiver got the message that the sender intended. The sender may then offer **feedback** to the receiver. If the receiver does not give you feedback that shows he or she understood, consider asking a few tactful questions that would assess the receiver's understanding. At that point, the receiver may restate or paraphrase your message which can indicate the level of comprehension. If you don't get feedback on your message, you can't be sure they got it.

2. Provide the Message at a Reasonable Rate

Little At A Time

Information overload is one of the biggest obstacles to effective communication. Give your message in **bite-sized** pieces and get feedback on each piece to ensure understanding before moving on with the message. Avoid mixing non-essential information with the key information, as this can lead to confusion. Each receiver can **hear** information at a different rate. Know your audience and adjust the information flow to fit the audience.

The Bottom Line

This is why the closing discussion includes only the major issues. It's also why we focus on telling people what they should do (recommended improvements) and why (implications) rather than lead up to these with long descriptions of defects.

3. Timing Is Appropriate

Need Time

Make sure the timing is appropriate for both you and the receiver. If you are in a hurry, you may rush, delivering incomplete or distorted communication. On the other hand, the receiver may have more urgent things on his or her plate at the time and simply cannot **hear** your message. Assess the receiver's current situation and make sure that you have the time to give the message properly.

4. Simple Language

Keep It Simple

Hippopotomonstrosesquipedalians should be avoided. See what we mean? This word is sometimes shortened to sesquipedalian and it means **pertaining to a very long word**. Avoid unnecessarily complex language. Use simple terms to explain matters. When a technical or complex term is used, explain the meaning of the term. We talked about jargon and suggested that while it may be useful among colleagues, it should be avoided with others.

5. Empathy

How Does Receiver Feel?

So far we have focused on what you can do as the sender of messages. Further, to be a good communicator you should be receiver-focused. Put yourself in the receiver's shoes. How is he or she feeling about what is being said? What are they thinking about? The more you know about the receiver's decoding processes, the better a communicator you can be. By being empathetic, you can choose the way you communicate with the receiver and increase the likelihood of his or her understanding.

6. Use Repetition

Say It Again

People normally attempt to avoid redundancy, but home inspectors often repeat key pieces of information different ways to help the receiver understand. Receivers may not understand information in one form but when they hear it another way it becomes clear. Use repetition to assist with the learning process during your inspection. A home inspection is an educational experience. You are the teacher and the client is the learner.

7. Encourage Trust

Be Trustworthy   Your business is built on credibility. People need to trust your judgments and you need to encourage that trust. Actions that tear down trust mean that people will not listen to you and the relationship (and career) will flounder. When people know that your recommendations are credible and bring about the desired results, your success as a communicator is greatly enhanced.

8. Effective Listening

You Need To Listen   A lot has been said about you as the sender of messages. But you are also the receiver of messages. Even when you start a conversation, at some point you become a receiver. Therefore, it is important to learn how to become a good listener. It has been said that we were given two ears and only one mouth for a reason. To create an effective listening environment, we must first **decide to listen**. Research shows that we can hear and decipher several times more words than can

Really Listen   be spoken. Our minds can wander and may begin to construct what we are planning to say next. We must be disciplined enough to focus on the speaker and listen to what he or she is saying. To help us with the listening environment, minimize distractions. These can take many forms, including:

Distractions   • **Environmental distractions**. External noise, poor ventilation, too hot or too cold and uncomfortable surroundings can all detract from effective communication.

• **Sender distractions**. Some people have habits or do things that are distracting and sometimes even annoying. One of the more common distractions is verbal. We call these **word whiskers**. Typically, these are utterances like "Got it" or "okay" repeatedly said during a conversation. Remind yourself that you are thinking about the distraction and re-focus on the message being sent.

• **Internal distractions**. These are the distractions within you. You may have many things to think about and your mind may start to wander. You may disagree with the speaker and start formulating your reply rather than listening. When you feel this happening, refocus on the speaker and listen to the entire message.

Being a good listener is a learned skill. Other things you can do include the following:

• Hold your temper when you vehemently disagree.
• Ask questions that show the speaker you are interested and allow him or her to talk and you to listen.
• Argue and be critical only when necessary and then only sparingly.
• Always be patient.
• Just stop talking and learn to listen.

Summary

That completes our discussion on improving communication. Let's review the important things you can do to communicate better.

1. Use the feedback part of the communication process.
2. Provide the message at a rate that the receiver can absorb.
3. Ensure the timing of the message is appropriate.
4. Use simple language.
5. Be empathetic to the receiver.
6. Use repetition.
7. Encourage trust to enhance credibility.
8. Create an effective listening environment.

We'd like to summarize some of the key points for home inspectors.

• Your role is to educate and inform clients.
• Speak clearly.
• Be concise.
• Focus on recommended actions and their implications.
• Recognize that people will only comprehend 50 percent of what you say and retain only 10 percent of that within two weeks.

• Avoid the following:

  – swearing
  – slang
  – technical jargon
  – sarcasm
  – derision
  – self-deprecation (making fun of yourself)

The Use Of Humor

A two and a half hour home inspection is a long performance. It can be made more pleasant for everyone if you are entertaining as well as informative. However, you are being paid to be informative rather than entertaining. Exercise considerable discretion when using humor. We would never recommend using humor during the early parts of an inspection, and only well into the inspection if you are absolutely confident in your abilities to read people correctly and gauge the acceptability of your comments to all.

We've just given you a list of things to avoid. All of these things lend themselves to the arena of humor. If you are going to use humor, it should be free of swearing, slang, derision, sarcasm and self-deprecation. Where there is even a shred of doubt, refrain from using humor.

Communication & Professional Practice

M O D U L E

QUICK QUIZ 1

☑ INSTRUCTIONS

- You should finish Study Session 1 before doing this Quiz.
- Write your answers in the spaces provided.
- Check your answers against ours at the end of this section.
- If you have trouble with the Quiz, reread the Study Session and try the Quiz again.
- If you did well, it's time for Study Session 2.

1. Define communications in one sentence.

   _____

2. List 10 issues involved in verbal communications.

   _____
   _____
   _____
   _____
   _____
   _____
   _____
   _____
   _____
   _____

3. List the five basic elements of verbal communications.

   _____

   _____

   _____

   _____

   _____

4. List four additional elements of verbal communications.

   _____

   _____

   _____

   _____

5. Explain in one sentence each of the following words:

   a. **Sender**

   _____

   b. **Receiver**

   _____

   c. **Message**

   _____

   d. **Medium**

   _____

   e. **Encoding**

   _____

f. **Decoding**

_____

g. **Feedback**

_____

h. **Personal filter area**

_____

i. **Noise**

_____

6. Name two things, other than words, that express your message to your audience intentionally or unintentionally.

_____

_____

7. List five categories of body language.

_____

_____

_____

_____

_____

8. List at least five types of body language that home inspectors should avoid.

_____

_____

_____

_____

_____

_____

9. List eight common obstacles to effective communication.

_____

_____

_____

_____

_____

_____

_____

_____

10. List eight techniques for improving communications.

_____

_____

_____

_____

_____

_____

_____

_____

If you had no difficulty with the Quiz, you're ready for Study Session 2.

Key Words

- *Communication*
- *Sender*
- *Receiver*
- *Message*
- *Encoding*
- *Decoding*
- *Feedback*
- *Medium*
- *Noise*
- *Personal filter areas*
- *Perception*
- *Paraverbals*
- *Body language*
- *Illustrators*
- *Emblems*
- *Regulators*
- *Adaptors*

- *Affect displays (emotional displays)*
- *Mimic technique*
- *Credibility*
- *Jargon*
- *Semantic differences*
- *Proximity*
- *Information overload*
- *Time constraints*
- *Empathy*
- *Trust*
- *Distractions*
- *Swearing*
- *Slang*
- *Sarcasm*
- *Derision*
- *Self-deprecation*

Communication & Professional Practice

MODULE

STUDY SESSION 2

1. You should have completed Study Session 1 and Quick Quiz 1 before starting this Session.

2. This Session covers report writing.

3. At the end of this Session you should be able to –
- list four reasons reports are needed
- list two different time options for delivering reports
- list three general report formats
- list ten common components of the body of the report
- give a one sentence example of each of the components
- indicate which components are required according to the Standards

4. This Session may take you roughly one and a half hours.

5. Quick Quiz 2 is at the end of this Session.

Key Words

- *Standards*
- *Customer service*
- *Liability control*
- *Marketing*
- *Third-party liability*
- *On-site reports*
- *Report delivery*
- *Checklist*
- *Narrative*
- *Combination*
- *Contract*
- *Scope*
- *Report summary*
- *Report body*
- *Limitations*
- *Client questionnaire*
- *Maintenance tips*
- *Filing system*
- *Cost estimates*
- *Homeowner letter (seller letter)*
- *Scope/contract*
- *Description*
- *Conditions or evaluations*
- *Causes of conditions*
- *Implications of conditions*
- *Recommended actions*
- *Limitations*
- *Life expectancy*
- *Priorities*
- *Ballpark costs*
- *Further investigation*

► 3.0 REPORT WRITING

3.1 WHY REPORTS ARE WRITTEN

Why Write Reports?

Some home inspectors view reports as a necessary evil, while others see them as an opportunity to promote their business and protect themselves and their clients. Let's look at some of the reasons you should write reports.

Standards Say So

1. The ASHI® and **Standards require a written report**. Since the large international associations' Standards of practice call for written reports, you may have a tough time defending yourself if someone makes a claim against you and you have not provided a written report.

Help The Client

2. The obvious customer service reason to provide a written report is to **help your client**. We have already said the clients will only understand about 50 percent of what you say in the field and only remember about 10 percent of that for any length of time. A written report documents your findings for your client so they can refer to it in future.

Which Client Are You Trying To Help?

Reports can be written many different ways. It's helpful to think of your clients' needs before settling on a report writing format.

Home Buyer

• When your client is looking to buy the home, he or she is trying to decide whether to purchase this property. The immediate purpose of the written report is to give them the necessary information to make an informed decision.

Homeowner

• The next phase your client enters is as a new homeowner. There are typically a number of improvements that should be made to the home. The client may rely on your report to help decide what work should be done and to help explain to tradespeople exactly what they want done. Some reports go into considerable detail to help the client understand the nature of the problem and the general approach for corrective action. This helps clients deal with tradespeople from a position of strength and knowledge. Some inspection reports include ballpark costs for the improvements they have recommended. Priorities may also be set for various recommendations in the report. Some things may be immediate while others can be deferred.

Home Maintenance

• Some reports help clients maintain their home over the long term, providing guidance on regular activities to preserve the property.

Future Expenditures

• Some reports recognize the components that are functioning now may wear out in future and require replacement. Reports may alert clients to systems that may be approaching the end of their life.

All home inspection reports are, to a greater or lesser extent, educational documents for the benefit of the client.

Liability
Control

3. Reports are written to **protect inspectors from claims** that may be made subsequently by clients. If a claim is made against an inspector, the words spoken during the inspection have very little importance. The written report takes on tremendous significance. The report can help with or ruin a home inspector's defense against a claim.

Marketing
Tool

4. Some inspectors use their report as a **public relations document** designed to help increase their credibility, enhance their image and generate more business. Most home inspectors recognize that clients show their reports to friends, families and real estate agents. This is especially true if they are impressed with the report. It helps them say to their peers, *"Look at how smart I am. I did the prudent thing in getting an inspection and was clever enough to find a wonderful inspector who gave us this terrific report."*

Report
Distribution

The report is the exclusive property of your client. Your client may choose to distribute the report to anyone they choose, including the real estate agents, seller of the property, and so on. You do not have the opportunity to distribute the report or discuss it with anyone.

Third Party
Liability

In some cases, people may rely on your report that you did not intend. If your report was passed to another party who relies on it and subsequently has a complaint, this creates an interesting situation. Do you have a duty to this third party? While this is a question for a lawyer, many home inspectors do make a statement in their contract that the report is for the exclusive use of their client and no use by a third party is intended. Inspectors do not want to be responsible to anyone except the client.

3.2 WHO WRITES THE REPORT

This is usually a trivial question, since the home inspector is usually the one who writes the report. There may be a word processor or transcriber who converts field notes to a finished report, but it is the inspector on site who provides the technical information.

Multiple
Inspectors

While it is not common, some people have more than one person on site performing the inspection. The report may be jointly authored with different inspectors providing different parts of the finished report. The report may be authored by a single person if they're working with an assistant who does not sign the report and takes no responsibility for its preparation. Reports should be signed by the inspector who prepares the report.

3.3 HOW IS THE REPORT CREATED?

Inspectors may document their notes by writing, using a keyboard or other electronic means to record their information. Some inspectors dictate their field notes.

The Final Copy

The final copy is most often on paper, although it can also be on disk, tape or delivered via e-mail, for example.

3.4 WHEN ARE REPORTS DELIVERED?

Generally speaking, there are two options for report delivery.

1. On-site reporting
2. Report delivery at a later date

Some people prepare and deliver their finished report on site. Others go back to their home or office to generate the report and send it out from there via mail, courier, fax, e-mail, etc. There are advantages and disadvantages to both approaches.

Advantages of On-Site Reporting

Transaction Not Slowed
- On-site reports do not slow down the real estate transaction and real estate agents may like them for this reason.

Clients Can Move Quickly
- Clients often appreciate the immediate feedback so that they can make their decision with all the facts in front of them immediately after the inspection. Clients sometimes have to make their decisions very quickly. Conditional offers can be quite short, or the inspection may be arranged near the end of the conditional offer.

Check What You Missed
- Home inspectors who prepare their reports on site have an opportunity to go back as they fill out the report and check things they have omitted. This is much easier than realizing that you have forgotten to check a fireplace when you are back in the office. Arranging a subsequent visit is usually difficult and disruptive, not to mention embarrassing.

Paid On Site
- Home inspectors often request that they be paid on site in an effort to minimize receivables. If the report is completed and delivered on site, it's easier to ask for payment. Where the report has not yet been delivered and the client will have to wait for the written report, clients may be reluctant to pay the entire fee on site.

No Time Spent Writing Reports
- One of the big advantages to providing reports on site is that the work is completed when you leave the site. No additional time or money is required for report preparation. Your overhead may include less hardware, software, supplies and staff if you generate reports on site.

Forget House
- Inspectors who prepare the reports on site have the luxury of forgetting the house as soon as they leave it so they can go on and focus their complete attention on the next house. Inspectors who prepare their reports later may have to store information about houses in their head. In some cases, they may have to store information about more than one house. This is challenging.

Shorter Days

• Inspectors who provide on-site reports often have reduced travel time because they do not have to go back to offices to deliver rough reports to be transcribed. They also do not have to proofread reports. This again may reduce travel time as well as working time.

Advantages of Reports Delivered after the Inspection

Better Presentation

• The presentation of on-site inspection reports can be weak. Relying on handwriting for reports may be a disadvantage. Portable computer systems help resolve this problem to some extent.

Research

• Reports delivered after the inspection allow for the luxury of going back to the office and thinking about what you want to say. This also makes it possible to do research and provide better information in the final report, in some cases.

Proofreading

• The advantage of proofreading, of course, is that it allows you to catch some mistakes. With on-site report delivery there is no proofreading function and, therefore, no safety net. For multi-inspector firms, a senior inspector can review the work of other inspectors before it gets into the hands of clients. This may help with quality control and consistency.

Include Extras

• Reports prepared after the fact can be bound and include customized additions, such as articles, illustrations and copies of pertinent maintenance tips.

Consistency Needed

One of the dangers of written reports, whether they are provided on site or after the inspection, is the possibility for discrepancies between what was said and what was included in the report. You should be very careful that your verbal comments are consistent with your written report. People are quick to pick up inconsistencies and resent having the bad news buried in a written report that was not explained to them on site. This unprofessional approach is likely to cause problems for the inspector.

3.5 REPORT STYLE OR FORMAT

There are many report writing options. They can generally be categorized as –

• checklist
• narrative
• combination

Reports can be filled out by hand or computer-generated. Reports can be a very few pages or can be a few hundred pages. While many home inspectors spend hundreds of hours developing their own inspection report formats, others purchase prepared inspection formats. There are many prepared reporting systems on the market.

3.6 WHAT SHOULD THE REPORT CONTAIN?

There are many varying opinions about home inspection reports. We will try to present this discussion in a generic format and try to separate the essential items from the optional ones. In short, the essential items are those required by the Standards of Practice of an association, such as ASHI®.

Common
Report
Components

Reports may contain some or all of the following –
• contract
• detailed scope of work, including Standards of Practice
• a report summary or executive summary (before or after the body of the report)
• the body of the report
• limitations to the inspection
• client questionnaire
• maintenance tips and cost estimates

With respect to meeting the Standards, only the body of the report is required. Most inspectors provide something in addition. Let's talk about these briefly before we discuss the body of the report.

Contract

The decision to include a contract is a business decision rather than one that affects the practice of the inspection itself. It has become common for inspectors to use pre-inspection agreements or contracts. Most rely to some extent on the advice of their attorneys and other business advisors in the use and wording of contracts. ASHI® has a series of model contracts available for review by members and candidates.

Getting Your
Contract
Signed

If you use a contract, you'll want to establish some policy about when the contract is signed. While it is ideally signed before people arrive at the inspection, many inspectors settle for having it signed at the beginning of the inspection. Some inspectors do not get the contracts signed until the end of the inspection. You may want to discuss this with your legal advisors.

Scope of Work

The contract may contain a well defined scope of work, or may refer to a scope of work such as a Standards of Practice of an association. We've talked a number of times about the challenge of clients with unrealistic expectations. Agreeing on a scope of work before the inspection starts is one of the best ways to adjust expectations and control your liability. Unless clients are told what is and what is not included in an inspection, they might reasonably expect inspectors to provide any and all pertinent information about the property. Clients might reasonably call back when anything goes wrong with the house.

Scopes Are
Common

Most professions have a scope of work that is agreed upon before the service is provided. You can't play a game without rules and home inspection is like a game. Without any rules, a home inspection can be anything and is likely to be something different to everyone.

Limitations

Some inspectors include limitations in their contract document. Others include them in the body of the report. As long as they are communicated to the client, we don't think it matters where they are presented. The ASHI® Standards of Practice have a number of general limitations. Inspectors also have specific limitations that arise during inspections. These might include such things as –

• snow on the ground preventing an examination of the grading
• cold weather preventing an inspection of the air conditioning system
• the roof inspection limited by the presence of snow and ice, solar panels, trees overhanging the roof, excessive height or steep slope of the roof (making it unsafe to climb)
• carpeting over steps, decks and porches
• no access under decks and porches
• storage that limited visibility
• vehicles in garages restricting access
• attics and crawlspaces that were not accessible or were viewed only from an access hatch
• finishes covering structural components (usually mentioned if these components are typically exposed)
• electrical power turned off
• fuse blocks that could not be pulled to check them without disconnecting the power
• cover on a service panel or main distribution panel that could not be opened
• data plates on equipment missing or not legible
• temperatures too high or too low to test equipment
• water turned off or winterized, preventing testing of the plumbing system
• gas shut off, preventing testing of the heating system
• pilots turned off, preventing testing of gas-fired equipment
• no fuel available in oil tanks for combustion equipment
• some areas that could not be accessed at the request of the occupant
• fireplaces or wood stoves that could not be examined because they were in use

In short, you should include in your report any part of the inspection that you would have normally have completed but could not because of these circumstances.

Client Questionnaire

Some home inspectors provide a questionnaire for their clients to complete. This provides a valuable source of feedback and, in some cases, can be used as a marketing tool. Questions commonly included in client questionnaires include these:

1. How did you hear about us?
2. Why did you choose to use us?
3. How did our performance rate overall?
4. Please rank from 1 (poor) to 5 (excellent) each of the following:
   - The inspector's ability
   - The inspector's communication skills
   - Our telephone skills
   - Our reporting system
   - Overall value of service verus fee
   - Likelihood of using us in the future
5. Was there anything about the service that you found especially positive?
6. Was there anything about the service that you found especially negative?
7. Do you have any suggestions for improving our service?

Letter to the Homeowner (Seller's Letter)

Some inspectors provide a letter to the occupant of the home explaining the inspection process. This is a courtesy as well as a marketing piece. We discussed this in the Professional Practice Section. It might read like this:

Seller's Letter　　*Thank you for allowing ABC Inspections to inspect your home today. As the owner of the house, you are entitled to know the details of the process.*

The practice of home inspection has become very popular. Our firm has performed thousands of inspections. We are sensitive to the privacy of homeowners and we respect your property. We strive to leave things exactly as we found them and, yes, we take off our shoes at the front door.

A typical inspection takes two to three hours. The exterior of the house is our normal starting point. We go up on the roof and then proceed around the outside of the home. From there, we move to the basement and/or crawlspace to examine the major systems of the house. Included are the structure, the heating and air conditioning systems, the electrical service, plumbing, and so on.

After completing our work in the basement, we go through the rest of the house. We test all of the plumbing fixtures, operate windows and doors, look under sinks, in closets and go up into the attic. We do no destructive or invasive testing. We consider alarms and security systems to be a private matter and do not test these.

Our goal is to fairly and accurately report the condition of the home. Our intention is not to "nitpick," nor do we feel compelled to find problems to justify our existence. At ABC Inspections, we strive to keep our findings in perspective for our clients. If a recommendation is typical for homes of that age or homes in the area, the client will be told that.

While some owners prefer to be home when we do our inspections, others find it easier to leave the house. Either situation is fine with us. Please understand that we cannot discuss our findings or release the report to anyone without our client's permission.

Again, thank you for allowing us to visit your home. Should you have any questions about our services, please do not hesitate to call.

Report Summary or Executive Summary

Many reports include a brief summary. It can be as short as one sentence or it can be a page. The summary provides an overview of the inspection results, and recognition of the fact that clients often want the house summed up in a very few words so that they can simplify things and make their buying decision based on this. We encourage you to write the report summary carefully if you use one. You want to make it clear that it does not provide all of the details that your full report does. You do not want to be accused of leaving out critical information in the report summary.

Costs And Priorities

If you provide ballpark costs and priorities for work to be done, these can be included in the summary. Again, this goes beyond the Standards.

Overall Rating

Some inspectors provide a ranking of the house against its peers. The rating is not a particularly substantive part of the report, but so many buyers ask for some kind of ranking or rating, that many inspectors include this as a courtesy, rather than a necessity. Factors considered (all measured against similar homes) typically include –

• original quality of construction
• current condition of major systems

Maintenance Tips, Filing Systems and Cost Estimates

Some inspection reports contain general maintenance recommendations for home-owners. These may be general or specific and can be cursory or quite detailed.

Filing Systems And Cost Estimates

Some reports go even further, providing a filing system for people to keep track of household bills, including utility costs. Some reports include generic ballpark costs for various home repairs and improvement projects as an aid to their clients. These sorts of things go well beyond the Standards, of course, and are marketing tools.

The Body of the Report

As we've already suggested, the body of the report can take several forms. It can also include a number of components. Again, some components are essential and others are optional. We'll list ten common report components and discuss each briefly.

Common
Report
Components

1. Scope/Contract – Optional
2. Descriptions – Required
3. Conditions or Evaluations – Required
4. Causes of Conditions – Optional
5. Implications of Conditions – Required unless self-evident
6. Recommended Actions – Required
7. Limitations – Optional
8. Life Expectancy – Optional
9. Priorities – Optional
10. Ballpark Costs – Optional

Before deciding on a report writing format, you may want to decide which report components you are going to provide your clients.

1. Scope/Contract – Optional

Again, the scope and contract are the rules by which the game of home inspection is played. The rules are ideally understood and agreed to by all players before the game is started.

2. Description – Required

Descriptions are included for a number of reasons:

- We have to describe the major components of the house to comply with the Standards.
- These descriptions let people know that you looked closely enough at the house to determine what components were there.
- Providing a description fleshes out the report since, if there are very few recommended improvements, a report can look very skeletal.
- Clients may find a description of the components useful when talking to insurers, mortgagees, mortgage lenders and home improvement contractors.

Give Credit
For Good
Quality
Materials

The description part of the report provides an opportunity for the home inspector to advise the client that there are superior-quality systems or products. A clay tile roof, for example, may be described as a **high-quality roofing material.**

Describe The
Function

Some reports include a description of the **function** of major components and the role they play in the **performance** of the house. This helps the client understand the home and appreciate the impact of changes that may be planned to individual components. This discussion may also give the client an appreciation of the implications of nonperformance of a component.

3. Conditions or Evaluations – Required

Finding The Problems

The condition statements are what we get paid for. When most people think of a home inspection, they think of the home inspector pointing out problems in the home. Some people call it the **evaluation process**. Some call it **defect recognition**. No matter what you call it, it is the observation of nonperformance. There are several hundred performance issues that you may find, including –

- leaking gutters
- missing flashings
- oversized fuses
- missing traps
- stuck barometric dampers
- cracked furnace heat exchangers, and so on

These condition statements describe items that may be missing, broken, worn out, undersized, oversized, improperly installed or otherwise prevented from performing their intended function. In the simplest terms, we have to look at a component and decide whether or not it is able to perform its intended task. If it can't do its job, we report that **condition, problem** or **defect.**

4. Causes of Conditions – Optional

The Standards specifically say that inspectors do not have to report on the cause of problems. While it can be helpful for the client, it is sometimes impossible, and often risky, to guess. Determining the cause of a problem is implicit in an item that we'll talk about in a moment – **recommended action**. If we're going to tell someone what to do about a problem, we may have to know the cause. Let's look at an interior door that does not open and close properly. One recommended action would be to trim the door so that it opens and closes freely. However, the cause of the sticking door may be ongoing structural movement because of a footing, foundation, column or beam problem, for example. The correct recommended action may be to repair the structure, rather than trim the door.

The Cause May Be Other Conditions

In many cases, the cause of one problem is in fact another problem itself. For example, you may report a wet basement as a condition. The cause of this condition may be any one of several other conditions, including –

- a clogged gutter or downspout
- a window well which doesn't drain
- improper grading slope around the house
- an obstructed catch basin
- clogged or collapsed perimeter drainage tile around the foundation

5. Implications of Conditions – Optional

Cause and implication are tied together to some extent. We believe that implications are more important to report than causes. Telling the client to take an action may not have much meaning. We need to tell the client why that action should be taken to help motivate the client to act. The Standards ask us to do this unless the implication is obvious.

Many homeowners ignore the recommendations of their home inspector because they do not understand the implications. Let's look at some examples.

- When we tell people to reconnect a disconnected downspout, it is rarely done. When we tell people to reconnect their downspout because it will cause a wet basement and rotted wall structures, they are more likely to take action.
- When we tell a client to replace a 30-amp fuse with a 15-amp fuse, people aren't likely to act on it until we add the fact that it may cause a fire in the home if they do not.
- If we tell people to replace a furnace because there is a crack in the heat exchanger, clients may view that the same way as telling someone to replace a window because there is crack in the glass. It's not until we explain the life-threatening implications of a cracked heat exchanger that people understand the need to replace the furnace.

Every Condition Has An Implication

The examples above are easy to understand. Do all conditions that you report have implications? If they don't, you shouldn't be reporting them. Every time you tell a client to do something, you should be prepared to answer the "why" question. Not all of your recommended improvements are going to be life and death issues and it's important to have your clients understand that. They can make informed decisions about which things to correct immediately and which to defer if they understand the implications of all of your recommendations. Clients will be able to set priorities. Typical implications include things such as these:

- **Life safety** – hazards such as fire, trip or fall, electrical shock, building collapse
- **Damage control** – repairing a roof leak to protect the wood structure and finishes below or advising someone to remove vines from siding
- **Comfort** – recommending improvements to caulking and weatherstripping
- **Cost control** – recommending the addition of attic insulation
- **Convenience** – replacing an inoperative crank on a casement window to allow you to open and close the window
- **Security** – recommending the repair of an exterior door lock
- **Extended life** – advising someone to repair a cracked chimney cap will extend the useful life of the chimney and, similarly, cleaning clogged gutters will extend their life

6. Recommended Actions – Required

A critical part of the report in our opinion is advising clients what to do about the conditions you have identified. These recommended actions might include one of the following:

- **Repair** – if something is broken
- **Replace** – if something is broken beyond repair
- **Provide** – if something is missing
- **Improve** – if something is not arranged ideally, such as exterior grading
- **Monitor** – if something is functioning but is vulnerable to failure, such as a 20-year-old asphalt shingle roof
- **Further investigation** – where a specialist is needed to determine the cause of serious foundation movement, for example

Don't Be Specific

You'll notice that these recommended actions are general rather than specific. We should not be writing specifications as part of a home inspection. We shouldn't tell people how to replace an asphalt shingle roof with respect to setting out the brand and type of shingle, exposure, nailing or stapling pattern, underlayment, flashing material, flashing detail approach, etc.

Not Spec Writers

All home inspectors will have opinions on how repairs should be done, but we need to recognize that writing specifications for repairs is a different business than the home inspection profession. Offering this kind of service goes well beyond the scope of a home inspection. There are very few people who are qualified to write specifications for every condition on any system or component they may come across in a house.

Give Trades Latitude

In short, give tradespeople some latitude to make repairs as they see fit. You want the tradespeople to carry the responsibility and offer the warranty for the repair approach that they take. If you specify the repair approach, you will own part of the responsibility for that work. That may lead you into a project management role which, again, is beyond and different from a home inspection.

Don't Overuse ***Further*** *Investigation*

Some home inspectors fall into the trap of recommending tradespeople to look at every system in the house when they see or suspect any problem in a home. If the recommended action for every component in the home is *"contact a qualified roofer (plumber, electrician, carpenter, etc.) for further investigation,"* you will find that your audience is frustrated. They will quickly come to the conclusion that they should have engaged each of these tradespeople instead of you to perform the inspection.

You Are
Unbiased

One of the reasons people engage a home inspector is because the inspector is unbiased. If you ask a tradesperson what is wrong with a part of your home, it's easy to understand how he might make recommendations to improve things, thinking that you are looking to have work done, whether there is an existing problem. Since there are very few components in a house that are both of the highest possible quality and in the best possible condition, there is almost always room to improve any component in the home. Asking a remodeling contractor to evaluate the system may result in a considerably different improvement recommendation list than a home inspector would put together.

7. Limitations – Optional

We've talked about limitations earlier, and will simply remind you that the limitations help to frame the scope of the home inspection for the client. Your documented limitations help prevent you from assuming responsibility that you did not intend.

Reduce The
Risk

We try to make it clear to our clients that the home inspection process reduces the risk in buying a home, but does not eliminate the risk altogether. Similarly, we try to impress upon the client that, as a result of the inspection, the risk in buying a home is not simply transferred to the home inspector. It may seem to you that we are putting too much emphasis on this point. That is because we find that most home inspectors place too little emphasis on this point.

8. Life Expectancy – Optional

New Roof

This section goes beyond the Standards, but is included by many inspectors to help buyers plan and budget their expenditures. It also helps to provide perspective for clients. For example, if two houses side by side have roofs that don't leak, an inspector would not be required to go any further in the reporting of the roof covering. This does not tell clients that one house has a brand new roof covering and that a life expectancy of 15 to 20 years may be anticipated from the roof

Old Roof

shingles. The other house has shingles that are within a year of the end of their life. Is there a difference between the physical condition of these two houses? Of course. Home inspectors are specifically excused from commenting on life expectancy in the Standards. However, many comment on the life expectancy of house systems that fail on a cyclical basis as a courtesy to their clients, and as a competitive strategy in their marketplace.

What
Components
Are Addressed?

Life expectancy comments are commonly offered on such things as –

• roof coverings
• furnaces
• boilers
• water heaters
• air conditioners and heat pumps
• supply plumbing pipes

Only If Close　Many home inspectors will not raise life expectancy issues unless systems are
To The End　within the last three or five years of their life, for example. The Standards ask us to
report on component systems that are near the end of their life, in our opinion.
When systems are young, it can be difficult to determine how much life is remaining. As systems approach the end of their life, it becomes easier to predict how
much life remains. This is always a rough guess and should be framed as such.

Give A Range　Our approach is to give a broad range rather than a specific number when talking
life expectancy. For example, if we see a roof that is close to the end of its life, we
will try to envision the best possible scenario for how long it may last. We will
then say that the roof has a high probability of requiring replacement at some point
within the next three years. This does not mean that the roof has three years of life
remaining. It means that somewhere between now and three years from now, the
roof will probably have to be replaced.

9. Priorities – Optional

Helping clients establish priorities for repairs goes beyond the Standards, but many
inspectors offer this service. Priorities are typically tied to life expectancy and
implications. Clients should determine how quickly they have to make individual
improvements based on –

- whether the component has stopped performing its intended function or is
  likely to in the near future.
- whether the implications are life safety, comfort or convenience, for example.
  Replacing a 30-amp fuse with a 15-amp fuse is more important than upgrading
  attic insulation, for example.

Not Cost Based　Priorities are usually independent of costs. Life safety issues can be very expensive
or not expensive at all. In either case, they should be the priority for the client.
Discretionary improvements, on the other hand, are often governed by cost. People
may decide to make comfort or convenience improvements that are inexpensive
but defer large expenditure improvements. People may choose to add a bathroom
exhaust fan to improve indoor air quality and reduce humidity levels. They may
choose not to replace the windows in the house to end up with more convenient,
possibly more attractive, more energy-efficient windows. Adding a bathroom
exhaust fan costs in the hundreds of dollars. Replacing windows in the home is in
the thousands of dollars.

10. Ballpark Costs – Optional

Some inspectors avoid providing cost estimates altogether. Others do it if asked
and are reluctant to write down their numbers. Still others include it as a normal
part of their report. Whether or not you include costs may be determined in part by
the common practice in your market.

Increased Liability

Offering cost estimates, of course, exposes you to another layer of liability. If your ballpark costs are too low, clients may call back and complain that you misrepresented the condition of the home. If the quotes are unrealistically high, you can expect to hear from unhappy home sellers and/or real estate salespeople. Even if you don't hear back, you have not served clients well if you have given them a list of inflated costs for work needed on the home.

Provide A Range

Most inspectors who provide ballpark costs use a range rather than a single figure. Many also qualify their numbers, indicating that they are dependent on what approach is taken. Many inspectors encourage people to get at least three quotes. Our experience has been that it's not unusual for quotes to vary by 300 percent. Contractors may take different approaches to a problem.

Clients Looking For An Order Of Magnitude

During the purchase process, clients are simply looking for an order of magnitude. It may surprise you to learn that when you tell clients the roof covering needs replacement, that this may mean $1,000 to a husband and $25,000 to a wife. It comes as a surprise to both of them when you tell them that the cost of replacing the roof is $10,000 to $15,000.

Grouping Costs

Many home inspectors group repair costs to allow for some economies of scale and to avoid being pinned down on specific small issues. For example, if there are eleven minor electrical repairs, many inspectors will provide a single figure for electrical cleanup work in the home since it is likely to be done all at one time during a single visit by an electrician. It's wise to point out to the client that these repair costs have been grouped and that repairing them individually would result in a higher cost.

Pros And Cons

Like many things we discussed in this Module, offering ballpark costs for your recommended actions has some advantages and disadvantages. Improved customer service has to be balanced against increased research, time and liability.

Summary

We've talked about a number of report components. Let's go over them one more time and indicate which are required and which are optional with respect to Standards compliance.

1. Scope/Contract – Optional
2. Descriptions – Required
3. Conditions or Evaluations – Required
4. Causes of Conditions – Optional
5. Implications of Conditions – Required unless self evident
6. Recommended Actions – Required
7. Limitations – Optional
8. Life Expectancy – Optional
9. Priorities – Optional
10. Ballpark Costs – Optional

We have read many reports over the years. We are often surprised by the inconsistency of reports. On some issues causes will be included but not implications. On other issues only the implications are given. Sometimes neither are given. Whatever you decide to include in your report, strive to make it consistent.

Examples of Statements

The following are some actual statements from reports. The type of statement is indicated in the margin in italics.

Scope

1. *"The structural inspection includes a visual examination of all exposed structural members, and probing of exposed wood members where damage to finished surfaces will not be caused."*

Description

2. *"The concrete block foundations support wood-frame, brick-veneer exterior walls."*

Conditions

3. *"The two northern-most floor joists in the basement are rotted and unable to perform their intended function."*

Cause

4. *"The damage to the joists is a result of moisture penetration through the top of the foundation wall."*

Implications

5. *"Failure of the flooring system in this area should be anticipated. It is impossible to predict when the floor structure might fail, since it will be determined in part by the loads imposed. The failure may be sudden and catastrophic."*

Recommended Action

6. *"The floor structure in this area should be strengthened as necessary."*

Limitations

7. *"There may be similar damage to other structural members concealed by interior finishes."*

Life Expectancy

8. *"The asphalt shingle roof covering has an anticipated remaining useful life of three to six years."*

Priority

9. *"It is recommended that the fuse sizes be appropriately matched to the wire sizes in the electrical panel immediately. Overfusing is a safety hazard."*

Did you notice that this includes recommended action and implication statements as well?

Ballpark Costs

10. *"The approximate cost for the structural repairs described above is $500 to $1,000."*

Some Closing Thoughts

There are a few points to make with respect to report writing.

Consistent Depth

• Report your inspections at a consistent depth from system to system. Don't go into a lot more detail on the heating system just because you have a better understanding of heating systems than other house components.

Scope   • Stay within your scope. Resist the temptation to comment on other things. If asked about such items, either defer or recommend the appropriate specialist.

Facts Versus Opinions   • Distinguish facts from opinion. Only report as fact what you have seen and know to be true. Where you are offering a professional opinion based on deduction and less than complete information, make that clear. Be wary of using words like these –

- Satisfactory
- Good condition
- Operable
- Sound
- Serviceable

You may instead want to say, *"No problems were identified in the components inspected visually"* or simply, *"No deficiencies noted."*

Bad Situations   • Sometimes you'll see very poor roof flashing details or chimney caps, for example, that may lead to problems. You find no evidence of the resultant problems. Should you report these conditions? We usually describe these as *"vulnerable"* or *"susceptible"* and recommend monitoring. We explain the potential implications to our clients so they can watch for the problems that may result.

"This Roof Is Shot"   • While it may be accurate to describe the roof as being *"shot,"* it may be more helpful to say something like, *"The roof covering is near the end of its life. Replacement should be planned within the next year."* can lead to the client over-reacting. Many home inspectors don't realize how little home buyers know. When you use the word **roof**, many clients think of the roof structure, sheathing and covering in its entirety, although you only meant the roof covering.

House Isn't Necessarily Bad   • Many clients interpret the news that the roof is worn out as an indication that the entire house is inferior. It's helpful to advise clients that roof coverings wear out on a regular basis and this is no reflection on the quality of this home. Similar comments apply with respect to heating systems, water heaters and cooling equipment, for example.

No Code Comments

• Don't quote code references. Some inspectors do this to remove subjective issues and provide an authoritative source to justify their recommendations. However, there are significant risks in doing this.

> • Once you have quoted a code, you have assumed a position as an expert on all codes unless you state otherwise.

> • Measuring existing homes against current codes is unfair and may be misleading to a client.

> • It is unlikely that any one person could ever know all the applicable code issues for residential properties.

> • It's an even larger task to know what the applicable codes were at the time of construction for houses of all ages. Clearly this is not practical.

Study The Codes, By All Means

We are not suggesting that it is bad to learn as much as you can about applicable codes. However, you should have an understanding of the rationale behind the code issues. It's appropriate to point out problems that may be covered by codes, although you don't need to frame your comments as code compliance issues. If you describe the **condition** and tell the client the **implication**, your authority can be common sense. Clients are much more likely to act on recommendations that they understand, rather than those that are dictated without a rationale statement.

Summary

In summary, the goal of your written report is to share with clients your understanding of the physical condition of the home. If your report is well written, the client will develop the same mental picture of the home relative to its peers that you have developed. A well written report will also make it clear to the client the extent and limitations of your scope of work.

The Clients' Perception

When the report is prepared and presented properly, the client will recognize that they have received wonderful value for their investment in the home inspection and know that they have reduced their risk of home buying to a considerable extent. They will understand that there is some risk remaining, and that the home inspector should not bear responsibility for unforseen problems.

Communication &
Professional Practice

MODULE

QUICK QUIZ 2

☑ INSTRUCTIONS

• You should finish Study Session 2 before doing this Quiz.

• Write your answers in the spaces provided.

• Check your answers against ours at the end of this section.

• If you have trouble with the Quiz, reread the Study Session and try the Quiz again.

• If you did well, it's time for Study Session 3.

1. List four reasons written reports are needed.

_____

_____

_____

_____

2. List two time options for report delivery.

_____

_____

3. List three general types of report formats.

_____

_____

_____

4. List 10 common components of the body of the report.

_____

_____

_____

_____

_____

_____

_____

_____

_____

_____

5. Give a one sentence example of each of these components.

_____

_____

_____

_____

_____

_____

_____

_____

_____

_____

6. Which components are required by the Standards?

_____

_____

Bonus Question:

7. What elements over and above the 10 you have listed might be included in home inspection reports?

_____

_____

_____

_____

If you had no trouble with this Quiz, you are ready for Study Session 3.

Key Words

- *Standards*
- *Customer service*
- *Liability control*
- *Marketing*
- *Third-party liability*
- *On-site reports*
- *Report delivery*
- *Checklist*
- *Narrative*
- *Combination*
- *Contract*
- *Scope*
- *Report summary*
- *Report body*
- *Limitations*
- *Client questionnaire*

- *Maintenance tips*
- *Filing system*
- *Cost estimates*
- *Homeowner letter (seller letter)*
- *Scope/contract*
- *Description*
- *Conditions or evaluations*
- *Causes of conditions*
- *Implications of conditions*
- *Recommended actions*
- *Limitations*
- *Life expectancy*
- *Priorities*
- *Ballpark costs*
- *Further investigation*

Communication &
Professional Practice

MODULE

STUDY SESSION 3

1. You should have completed Study Sessions 1 and 2 before starting this Session.

2. This Study Session covers liability issues for home inspectors and a step-by-step inspection process.

3. By the end of this Session, you should be able to –
   • describe in one sentence the nature of the liability that home inspectors bear
   • list three possibilities with respect to the merits of a complaint against you
   • describe in one sentence how the **competent inspector concept** applies to evaluating liability
   • describe in one sentence how remodeling contractors impact on home inspector liability
   • describe in one sentence the **last-one-in syndrome**
   • describe two general strategies to limit your liability
   • give 10 examples of each strategy
   • list the 50 steps in a typical home inspection

4. This Session may take you roughly one and a half hours to complete.

5. Quick Quiz 3 is at the end of this Session.

Key Words
- *Liability*
- *Unrealistic expectations*
- *Clearly right or wrong*
- *Gray issues*
- *Competent inspector concept*
- *Contractors*
- *20/20 hindsight*
- *Last-one-in syndrome*
- *Someone's fault*
- *Prevention strategies*
- *Response strategies*
- *Walk-through inspections*
- *Model contracts*
- *Pre-inspection routine*
- *Introductory discussion*
- *The inspection itself*
- *Closing discussion*

▶ 4.0 LIABILITY

It's Real	The home inspection business does have some liability for the home inspector. You can wonder whether the liability we bear is fair or not, especially considering the fees that home inspectors are paid relative to the fees that some others in the real estate transaction are paid. None of that matters very much in the real world. The liability is real.
Where Does The Liability Lie?	You have performed an inspection to determine the physical condition of a property. We've spent some time talking about the limitations of that inspection. Within two and a half hours or so you cannot know everything about a property, no matter how technically skilled you are. The odds are very high that there will be things wrong with the property that you don't find. The odds are also very high that things will go wrong with the property after you inspect it, in some cases, even before the buyer takes possession of the home. When these problems are identified, it's becoming more and more common to hold the home inspector responsible for the problems.
Realistic Expectations	We've talked a lot about adjusting buyers' expectations of what a home inspection can and cannot do. Home inspectors are often guilty of not ensuring that the buyers' expectations are realistic. In other cases, it may be impossible to adjust buyers' expectations.
What You'll Hear	People will tell you that you let them down by failing to identify problems. They frequently tell you that had they known about this problem, they wouldn't have bought the property or would have renegotiated the purchase price. Clients often tell you how much hardship has been caused by your omission or mistake.
Are You Responsible?	Whether or not you have committed a mistake can be a relatively simple or very difficult question. Most situations fall into one of three categories – • You were clearly right • You were clearly wrong • It's difficult to know
You Were Right	Sometimes a complaint will come in that you respond to and find that you made no mistake at all. This may be because the problem that the client perceives does not exist or is of a different nature than reported. It may be that the problem is related to something outside of your scope, such as a home security system for example. It may also be that the problem does exist and is within your scope, but was accurately reported. The client may simply not have read or not remembered the report. This last scenario is more common than you might expect.
Easy Resolution	When you are clearly right, the situation is usually resolved easily. The client understands how this could not be your responsibility and you may provide him or her some helpful advice on moving toward a solution. You may end up generating goodwill as a result.

In rare cases, the client is not satisfied or does not agree that you were clearly right. The client may pursue matters with your professional association or through legal channels. There's not much you can do to avoid these unfortunate situations, but they usually have little more than nuisance value. They can consume a significant amount of time and money unfortunately. Even more unfortunately, they are hard on you emotionally. It's easy to say, *"Don't take it personally,"* but very difficult to do. Another unfortunate result of complaints like this is home inspectors become more defensive in their work and future clients get a diminished level of service because the inspector is worried about an attack.

You Were Clearly Wrong

Sometimes a brief investigation into the complaint shows you that you simply made a mistake. We find these ones relatively easy to deal with as well. If we clearly made a mistake, we will work with the client to set things right. This often includes some financial consideration, such as the refund of a fee. When clients are looking for far more than this, it may make sense to speak to your errors and omissions insurance company (if you are so insured) about a quick and amicable resolution.

No Insurance

If you were clearly wrong and are uninsured, you have a choice to make. You can make payments to the client that may be considerable in order to eliminate the bad will and create a satisfied customer. You may decide that that's a bad business decision and refuse to admit your mistake or make any financial arrangement with the client. You may be able to come up with a defense that allows you to avoid responsibility, even though you made a mistake. The risk is the clients may pursue all of their options and others may decide that you made a mistake as well. There can be serious financial implications.

It's A Gray Issue

Very often, the issue is not black and white. You may find a problem that clearly does exist in the home and is within your scope. It may, however, be unclear as to whether the problem existed at the time of the inspection or whether the problem could have been identified during the inspection. The following are all examples of difficult issues –

• Storage against a foundation wall
• A crack in a heat exchanger that was not visible with a mirror and flashlight
• An inoperative air conditioning system that was not operationally tested because of temperature considerations
• Problems in a crawlspace that only received limited inspection from the access hatch

Would A Competent Inspector Have Found It?

The approach that we take is to ask ourselves whether a competent inspector under the circumstances that existed during the inspection would have found the problem. If the answer is *"Yes,"* this suggests that we let our client down. If the answer is *"No,"* it leads to a difficult discussion wherein you acknowledge that the client has a problem, but explain that it would not likely have been discovered during any home inspection. Clients often have a difficult time understanding this, especially when the problem is apparent by the time they discover it.

The Contractor And 20/20 Hindsight

In many cases, the complaint is initiated by a contractor working in the home finding a condition and expressing surprise that the home inspector did not identify it. There are a number of reasons why this comment may not be fair or appropriate, but we can assure you that it is commonplace:

- The contractor may have partially disassembled some components to uncover the problem.
- The contractor is a specialist who works only in this field, and does not recognize that we are general practitioners.
- The contractor may have examined the problem for an hour or so before coming to his or her conclusion. During a home inspection, we cannot dedicate an hour to each component of the house or we would be in the home for weeks instead of hours.
- The problem may have manifested itself as a result of weather conditions (heavy rain or wind-driven rain from a certain direction), inadequate performance of the heating system during extremely cold weather, inadequate performance of an air conditioning system during extremely hot weather, tripping of branch electrical circuits during heavy use conditions, and so on.

Last-One-In Syndrome

These problems are doubly difficult to handle because there is a tendency among homeowners to believe the most **recent** information they have heard. By the time people have moved into the house and have a contractor at the property, some months have passed since the home inspection. The clients' recollection of the inspection process and results will understandably be diminished.

It Must Be Someone's Fault

In the modern world, everything that goes wrong appears to have to be someone's fault. The home inspector is a logical target to shoulder this responsibility. Clients often say, *"I did all the right things when I bought the house. Why should I be stuck with this problem?"*

So, What Can We Do?

Since the reality is that people will make complaints against you that are clearly legitimate, clearly not legitimate and arguable, you are going to have to find a way to address this. Two general strategies are used:

- Prevention
- Response

Prevention Strategies

Prevention

Preventive measures include such things as:

1. Perform a competent inspection.
2. Try to ensure that your clients' expectations are realistic.
3. Clearly describe the scope of work in your report.
4. Clearly define limitations specific to the home in your report.
5. Keep your comments within the scope of your report.
6. Inspect at a consistent depth (Many inspectors have run into trouble by going into more depth on one system than another. If you comment on an electrical **code** violation, the client can realistically expect you to comment on violations of any code.)

Hearsay   7. Don't report as fact things you are told. If agents or sellers report that:

– the roof is two years old
– the wiring is updated
– the plumbing is all copper
– the electrical system is 200 amps
– the furnace is new and high-efficiency
– the basement is high and dry
– the attic is insulated to R-40

you can include all of these in your report as long as you indicate the source of the information. You should be saying something like this, *"The seller advises that the roof covering is two years old."*

Avoid Quickie 8. Don't do mini inspections. In some cases you'll be asked to do less than a full
Walk Through   inspection for a reduced fee. People often say they're in a hurry, don't want a
Inspections   full inspection and just want you to do a quick walk through in less than an hour and give them your impressions. There is a huge liability attached to doing this. You are doing something less than a home inspection, and yet you are a home inspector collecting a fee for inspecting a home. Your liability may be very similar to what it is doing a conventional home inspection.

9. Use a clear and meaningful contract. The contract may indicate that there is a limit to your liability. The amount can be the fee or some other arbitrary number. Note: in some jurisdictions, home inspectors are not permitted to limit their liability to the fee. In other jurisdictions, this may or may not have any merit as a defense.

Model   If you are going to use a contract, the American Society of Home Inspectors has
Contracts   some model contracts available for review by members and candidates. It may be worthwhile to look at these. We also recommend that you get independent legal advice. **It should be clear to you that we are not lawyers or attorneys and are not intending to offer legal advice**.

Arbitration Your contract may include an agreement that if there is a dispute, arbitration rather than litigation will be the dispute resolution method. There are advantages and disadvantages to these issues that go beyond the scope of this program. You may want to check into this.

10. Tell clients what to expect. We give clients a note in our report that predicts the future. We tell them that they'll have problems and why we didn't anticipate them. We tell them what contractors are going to say and how they'll feel. We've enclosed this document because it's a powerful tool. While it's a prevention strategy, it is also used as a response strategy. Feel free to use it:

WHEN THINGS GO WRONG

There may be a time that you discover something wrong with the house, and you may be upset or disappointed with your home inspection.

Intermittent Or Concealed Problems

Some problems can only be discovered by living in a house. They cannot be discovered during the few hours of a home inspection. For example, some shower stalls leak when people are in the shower, but do not leak when you simply turn on the tap. Some roofs and basements only leak when specific conditions exist. Some problems will only be discovered when carpets were lifted, furniture is moved or finishes are removed.

No Clues

These problems may have existed at the time of the inspection but there were no clues to their existence. Our inspections are based on the past performance of the house. If there are no clues to a problem, a home inspector won't find it.

We Always Miss Some Minor Things

Some say we are inconsistent because our reports identify some minor problems but not others. The minor problems that are identified were discovered while looking for more significant problems. We note them simply as a courtesy. The intent of the inspection is not to find the $200 problems; it is to find the $2,000 problems. These are the things that affect people's decisions to purchase.

Contractors' Advice

The main source of dissatisfaction with home inspectors comes from comments made by contractors. Contractors' opinions often differ from ours. Don't be surprised when three roofers all say the roof needs replacement when we said that, with minor repairs, the roof will last a few more years.

Last-One-In Syndrome

*While our advice represents the most prudent thing to do, many contractors are reluctant to undertake these repairs. This is because of the **Last-One-In Syndrome.** The contractor fears that the last person to work on the roof will get blamed if the roof leaks, regardless of whose fault it is. Consequently, there is an understandable reluctance to do a minor repair with high liability when the entire house could be reroofed for more money and reduce the likelihood of a callback.*

Most Recent Advice Is Best

There is more to the Last-One-In Syndrome. It suggests that it is human nature for homeowners to believe the last bit of "expert" advice they receive, even if it is contrary to previous advice. As home inspectors, we unfortunately find ourselves in the position of "first one in" and consequently it is our advice that is often misbelieved.

Why Didn't I See It?

Contractors may say, "I can't believe you had this house inspected, and they didn't find this problem." There are several reasons for these apparent oversights:

1. It's impossible for contractors to know what the circumstances were when the inspection was performed.

The Wisdom of Hindsight

2. When the problem manifests itself, it is very easy to have 20/20 hindsight. Anybody can say that the basement is wet when there are two inches of water on the floor. Predicting the problem is a different story.

A Long Look   3. *If we spent half an hour under the kitchen sink or 45 minutes disassembling the furnace, we'd find more problems too. Unfortunately, the inspection would take several days and would cost considerably more.*

Conditions During Inspection   4. *It is difficult for homeowners to remember the circumstances in the house at the time of the inspection. Homeowners seldom remember that it was snowing, there was storage everywhere in the basement or that the furnace could not be turned on because the air conditioning was operating, etc.*

We're Generalists   5. *We are generalists; we are not specialists. The heating contractor may indeed have more heating expertise than we do. This is because we are expected to have heating expertise and plumbing expertise, roofing expertise, electrical expertise, etc.*

An Invasive Look   6. *Problems often become apparent when carpets or plaster are removed, when fixtures or cabinets are pulled out, and so on. A home inspection is a visual examination. We don't perform any invasive or destructive tests.*

Not Insurance   *In conclusion, a home inspection is designed to better your odds. It is not designed to eliminate all risk. For that reason, a home inspection should not be considered an insurance policy. The premium that an insurance company would have to charge for a policy with no deductible, no limit and an indefinite policy period would be considerably more than the fee we charge. It would also not include the value added by the inspection.*

We hope this is food for thought.

Response Strategies

We believe that liability can be managed to some extent by an appropriate response to complaints. Our suggestions include the following:

1. Respond as quickly as possible.
2. Don't avoid the issue.
3. Don't argue with the client over the phone.
4. Don't accept as fact **anything** you are told.
5. Go back to the home.
6. Try to find a resolution that leaves the client satisfied.
7. Follow up as quickly as possible.
8. If there is a problem with the home, acknowledge the problem.
9. Come to a resolution as quickly as possible.
10. Use the *WHEN THINGS GO WRONG* document in your report (if you use one).

If you get the impression that we think speed is important, you are right – not just on the initial response, but every step of the way.

You'll Take It Personally — Handling complaints is a very difficult process emotionally. We can almost promise that you will take the issues personally. Whether you respond with anger, fear, defensiveness or contrition, may be a matter of your personality and the circumstances. In our experience, handling complaints is best done like every other part of the home inspection – professionally. If you can avoid emotional discussions and decisions, and make logical statements and decisions, you may not win your client over or win each financial disagreement, but you will earn the respect of those you deal with.

Let Someone Else Handle? — In some ways, it's easier for someone else in your firm to handle the complaint because they won't have the emotional sensitivity that you do. This is good up to a point, but consider these factors:

• The inspector may remember the conditions during the inspection when he or she goes back to the home to investigate.
• It's much more difficult for a client to attack an inspector who is present during a discussion. The client is also less likely to attribute statements to the inspector if the inspector is in the room. You are less likely to hear, *"He told me the roof would never leak."*

The ideal approach may be to have the inspector go back with someone else who does most of the talking.

Who Owns The Report — There's one last issue on the liability question that we want to touch on. It's one that we've talked about briefly before. Your client owns the report. We've already said that you can't discuss the report with someone other than your client without the client's permission. Similarly, you probably don't have an obligation to anyone other than your client for that report. In some cases, reports are transferred to other people (called **third parties** in legal terms). If someone other than your client relies on the report and subsequently has a complaint, it's our understanding that you may not have any responsibility to that person. Many home inspectors have clauses in their contracts that indicate that their report is not intended for use by any third parties. They deny in advance any obligations to these other people. Again, check with your legal advisors.

Summary

Liability exists for home inspectors. We could spend a great deal of time discussing it, but we would be going beyond the scope of this program. Our goal here is to make you aware of the liability issue and provide you with some preliminary thoughts on addressing it.

► 5.0 THE STEP-BY-STEP HOME INSPECTION

While home inspection is not an exact science, we will outline here many of the steps involved in a typical home inspection. If you follow the 50 steps outlined here, you will have performed an inspection that is, at the very least, organized. We've juggled the order and specifics of some of the elements from those in the earlier discussions to show you there is more than one way to approach this. The key issues are all still addressed.

Assumptions   For the purposes of this example, we are going to assume:

- The home inspector is experienced and performs his or her inspections without an associate or an assistant.
- The home presents no unusual technical challenges.
- The inspector's firm has not inspected the home before, or worked with these buyers before.
- The home is owner-occupied.
- The home is being sold in a conventional real estate listing fashion.
- The listing agent and selling agent, who are separate people working for separate firms, will both attend the inspection.
- The seller is at home during the inspection.
- The buyers, who are a couple, will attend the inspection.
- The inspection time has been set for 9:00 a.m. The appointment was booked through your office.
- The agents and buyers will arrive on time.
- Your report will be prepared and delivered on site.

The stage is set. We'll break the inspection into segments and approach things in numbered steps with the understanding that the order is not always critical, but is reasonable. Some steps may seem trivial or self evident but please bear with us.

5.1 PRE-INSPECTION ROUTINE

1.   The office provides you with information about the inspection. The information includes –

- the inspection date
- the inspection time
- the inspection address and directions or map coordinates
- the house age and size, as estimated by the client or agent, depending on who booked the inspection
- the clients' names, address and phone number
- the listing agent's name, company name and phone number (mobile phone, too)
- the selling agent's name, company name and phone number (mobile phone, too)

2. If you use a contract, fill in the buyer's name and address if appropriate on the contract or the appropriate page on the report.

3. If you will be invoicing your client, have the invoice prepared.

4. Memorize the buyers' names.

5. Memorize the listing agent's name and selling agent's name.

6. Check your map to locate the inspection address and plan your route.

7. Determine the approximate travel time to the inspection address at that time of day. Let's assume that it's 20 minutes. Now, add 10 minutes for unexpected traffic delays and a drive through the neighborhood. The total time then is 30 minutes. Plan to leave the office at 8:15 to arrive at the inspection site at 8:45 a.m. If the traffic is as expected, you'll be there at 8:35 a.m.

8. Review your inspection routine. Your order should always be consistent. For example –

   • Seller introduction
   • Exterior – first tour
   • Introductory discussion
   • Roof
   • Exterior – second tour
   • Basement
   • Heating
   • Plumbing
   • Electrical
   • Interior – first tour
   • Interior – second tour and heating or air conditioning test
   • Attic/crawlspace
   • Report preparation
   • Closing discussion

9. As part of this process, review your script for your introductory and closing discussions. Are your current presentations working well, or should something be changed?

10. Review your time goals for the inspection. For example—
   • after 10 minutes, you should have completed the introductory discussion.
   • after 40 minutes, you should have finished the roof and the exterior.
   • after 70 minutes, you should have finished the mechanical, electrical and structural systems.
   • after 100 minutes, you should have finished the interior.
   • after 115 minutes, you should have finished the attic and crawlspace.
   • after 135 minutes, you should have finished recording your results.
   • after 150 minutes, you should have finished.

This is a two and a half hour inspection.

Vehicle Check **11.** Vehicle check:
- Is your vehicle clean and fueled?
- Is there room for your client or clients to join you if you have to discuss the report in the vehicle?
- Check that you have all of the things that you normally carry in your vehicle, including—
  – ladders
  – inspection tools
  – map
  – papers and reference materials
  – spare supplies including batteries, pens, report forms, seller letters, business cards, brochures, a clean shirt, an umbrella, coveralls, indoor shoes or slippers
  – cell phone or pager

Note: don't leave your rechargeable flashlight in the charger at home.

12. Self-check:
- Are you clean and presentable?
- Are you fueled? (Have you eaten recently?)
- Is your bladder empty?
- Do you have a comb, breath mints, deodorant? (You might have more than one inspection by the time the day is done.)

13. At about 8:15 a.m., leave the office or home to head to the inspection.

14. At about 8:35 a.m., you should drive past the home to confirm the address. There will usually be a lawn sign. You will develop your first impression of the home here.

15. From 8:35 to 8:45, drive the neighborhood to become familiar with it. Notice other houses that are for sale in the neighborhood. Chances are your clients have been through these homes.

16. Park on the street in front of or near the home. Don't take the only decent parking spot near the house.

17. Turn off your cell phone or pager.

18. Make sure you have memorized the names of buyers and agents.

19. Get your ladders, tools, report forms, checklist, contract, invoice, business cards and seller's letter out of your vehicle. Leave them near the front door.

20. With business card and seller's letter in hand, ring the front doorbell.

21. When the doorbell is answered, follow your seller's script. It might go something like this:

"Good morning, I'm John Smith from ABC Home Inspections." Pause briefly to allow the person answering the door to introduce themselves. If they don't introduce themselves, that's okay. Offer them a business card either way.

"I understand we have an appointment to look at the house this morning." Pause to let them acknowledge this fact. Note: we say **look at the house**, rather than **inspect the house** because the word inspect may be intimidating.

"We'll start with the roof and exterior and then come inside in about half an hour. The attic will be the last area that we will visit. We'll be roughly two and a half hours altogether. This letter explains the process in more detail." Hand them the seller letter.

"Is there anything I should know about the home before starting?" Pause to allow them to respond. If they ask what you mean, say something like,

"Is there a dog in the backyard or someone sleeping in the home?" Occasionally, you'll be given some valuable information about the condition of the property. Be careful not to take it at face value, whether positive or negative.

"Great, I'll get started on the outside if that's all right. Thanks very much."

22. Move your tools near the front door and select those you'll need for the exterior inspection. This might include a flashlight, electrical tester and your checklist. The buyers and agents will be able to see your ladder and tool bag near the front door and will know that you are on site if they arrive while you are at the back of the home.

23. Ideally, you will do two exterior tours around the home. Your first tour should be a very quick **macro** look at the house. Your second tour should be your first **micro** tour around the house. It should be done in a clockwise direction so your second micro tour can be in a counterclockwise direction. You should note where roof access is going to be most practical. Don't climb fences. You may damage them. Keep an eye and ear out for the agents and buyers. Interrupt your tour, if necessary, when you hear them arrive.

24. Smile as you approach the agents and/or buyers. Look them in the eye.

5.2 THE INTRODUCTORY DISCUSSION

25. Here's a sample introductory script,

"Good morning, I'm John Smith from ABC Home Inspections." Pause so they can introduce themselves. Because you've memorized names, you'll know whether these people are agents or buyers. Perhaps they are someone else. The buyers sometimes invite friends along, for example.

26. If the people who have introduced themselves are the agents or someone else, you can say,

"Will the Bradfords (the buyers) *be joining us this morning?"* You will get some sort of response. At this point, you can comment on the neighborhood, the weather, their car, etc. You can ask agents how long they have been with XYZ Realty or whether the market has been active, for example.

If the small talk is awkward or the people are not interested in talking, you can say,

"I've introduced myself to the people in the home. Perhaps I'll take a look at the exterior while we're waiting. Excuse me."

27. If the people are the buyers, you might say,

"It's good to meet you, Ms. Green, Mr. Brown." It's helpful to use their names so that you do not forget them during the inspection. Eye contact is important.

"Thanks for choosing us to perform your inspection. Have you bought a home before?" Allow them to respond.

"Great. Have you ever had a home inspection?" You'll only ask this question if they have bought a home before.

"Very good. Our goal over the next two and a half hours is to give you a clear picture of the condition of the major house systems. We'll focus on the big issues and we'll come across some minor ones along the way. We'll include those in the report as a courtesy, but it's not our goal to prepare a maintenance list.

We'll start on the outside and then work inside from the bottom to the top. You're welcome to come along with me and we can discuss things as we go. I won't ask you to join me on the roof or in the attic. We'll prepare the report and give it to you at the end of the inspection.

This is our inspection agreement which sets out the rules of the game. If you'll read it carefully and sign it, I'll get started on the roof. I'll catch up to you here in a few minutes. Thank you."

28. Go up onto the roof and perform the inspection of the roof, chimney, etc.

29. As you come down off the roof, you might say,

"Is everything in order?" Pause to allow them to respond.

"Great, I'll put that away." Put the contract in your tool bag or clipboard.

"Before we start, I should ask if you have any plans for changes to the home." Pause to allow them to respond.

"Okay, that's helpful. Are there any specific concerns you have with the home or is it a general overview you're looking for?" The general overview part of this question gives them an easy answer. You don't want to put them on the spot about coming up with specific concerns or make them feel stupid if they don't have any.

> *"Very good. Let's get started with the exterior. The people in the home already know we're here. Feel free to ask questions as we go. I may defer answering some of them until we get the whole story, but that's okay."*

5.3 THE INSPECTION ITSELF

30. Discuss the roof results, unless the roof is a disaster.

31. If the roof is bad, complete your exterior inspection, going around the property in the opposite direction that you did initially. This will allow you to mix good news and bad and hope the clients keep perspective. Clients are usually most nervous at the beginning of the inspection and are most likely to overreact to bad news at the outset.

32. During the exterior inspection, discuss things as you go. Display your knowledge and communication skills on a non-critical issue to break the ice, giving the clients a sense of the inspection flow. This is a good opportunity to establish rapport with the clients.

33. Remember to include the garage or carport as part of the exterior inspection if you can. If you can't get into the garage from outside, you'll have to remember to check the garage when you're inside the home.

34. When you're finished your outside work, summarize the roof and exterior of the home. *"We're all finished outside. Are there any questions before we head on in?"* Pause to allow for a response.

> *"All right, let's head inside."*

35. Knock on the door again so the owner can let you inside, unless the agent leads you into the house directly. If your practice is to remove your shoes or put on indoor shoes, do so as you go in. Bring your tool bag inside and leave your ladder on the front porch, just outside the door unless you're in a neighborhood where the ladder may disappear. We have had ladders stolen from front porches.

36. Let the seller know what you're doing, even though you've told them before.

> *"We're ready to get started downstairs (or wherever) if that's all right."*

37. Follow your typical routine. For example, check the heating and cooling system and summarize the results for your client.

38. Check the electrical system and summarize the results.

39. Check the plumbing system and summarize the results.

40. Check the structure and summarize the results.

41. Now perform your first tour through the interior. Follow your routine on a room by room basis. If you did not get into the garage from the outside, don't forget to include the garage here.

42. Perform your second interior tour which may include your test of the heating or air conditioning system. Summarize your results.

43. Using your ladder, check the attic and, if there is a crawlspace, check it immediately after. Put your ladder just inside or just outside the front door when you're finished. Summarize your results of the attic/crawlspace inspection.

5.4 REPORT PREPARATION

44. Now say,

"I'm going to take 15 minutes to put the report together. I'll catch up to you when I'm done and we can review things then." This makes it clear that the client can move through the house freely and puts the responsibility on you to find them. This avoids having the client come back to talk to you before you're ready to speak to them.

5.5 CLOSING DISCUSSION

45. When you're finished, check that the contract was properly signed and go find your clients. You might say,

"Okay, we're all ready. Is this a good spot to summarize the report?" This gives the buyer an opportunity to control the location of the closing discussion. If the buyer wants to have the discussion in private, this is his or her opportunity to say so. You have no interest in concealing your discussion from the agents or seller. If they listen in, that's fine, as there is less chance of miscommunication.

46. Review your findings in general terms and explain how the report works. Remember, your clients have already heard all of the specifics. Your overview should be a summary and should take into consideration the fact that your clients won't grasp everything you've said and will in fact retain very little in a few days.

47. *"Do you have any questions or is there anything we should go over again?"* Pause to allow them to respond.

48. *"Great. Will you be paying by check?"* Allow them to respond.

"Very good. I'll prepare the receipt while you do that."

49.   They give you the check and you give them their receipt.

"Thanks very much. There you are. There's a client questionnaire and postage-paid envelope in the front of the report. We would appreciate your mailing it to the office. Please feel free to call if you ever have any questions about the home. We are happy to help and there's no charge for telephone consultations. Thanks again for choosing us to do your home inspection."

50.   Also offer thanks to the agents for their patience and to the sellers for their cooperation. You should probably be the first one to leave. Don't linger unless someone has a specific question or comment for you. Make sure you have put everything back as you found it. Gather up your bag.

"Goodbye for now. Thanks again." And you're out the door. Put your ladder and tools in your vehicle, attach the check to your copy of the report and receipt, along with the signed contract, and you're finished!

Summary

As you read through this procedure, you may have realized that things could go differently depending on answers that you get to questions and things you may find in the home. We can't describe every situation, but it's helpful to have a set routine that you have to deviate from, rather than try to make things up as you go. As we indicated at the outset, you can do different things or do these things in a different order. Just make sure you have a good reason for doing things your way.

Communication &
Professional Practice

MODULE

QUICK QUIZ 3

☑ INSTRUCTIONS

- You should finish Study Session 3 before doing this Quiz.
- Write your answers in the spaces provided.
- Check your answers against ours at the end of this section.
- If you have trouble with the Quiz, reread the Study Session and try the Quiz again.
- If you did well, you're ready to have a look at the Inspection Checklists.

1. Describe in one sentence the nature of the liability that home inspectors bear.

   _____

2. List three possibilities with respect to the merits of a complaint against you.

   _____

   _____

   _____

3. Describe in one sentence how the **competent inspector concept** applies to evaluating liability.

   _____

4. Describe in one sentence how remodeling contractors impact inspector liability.

   _____

5. Describe in one sentence the **last-one-in syndrome**.

_____

6. Name two general strategies for limiting liability.

_____

_____

7. Give 10 examples of each strategy listed above.

_____

_____

_____

_____

_____

_____

_____

_____

_____

_____

_____

_____

_____

_____

_____

_____

_____

_____

_____

_____

_____

_____

8. List as many of the 50 steps in a Standard home inspection as you can. The numbering is not as important as including all of the key points.

_____

_____

_____

_____

_____

_____

_____

_____

_____

_____

_____

_____

_____

_____

_____

_____

_____

_____

_____

_____

_____

_____

_____

_____

_____

_____

_____

_____

_____

_____

_____

_____

_____

_____

_____

_____

_____

_____

_____

_____

_____

_____

_____

_____

_____

_____

_____

_____

_____

_____

_____

_____

_____

If you had no trouble with the Quiz, you're ready to have a look at the Inspection Checklist.

Key Words
- *Liability*
- *Unrealistic expectations*
- *Clearly right or wrong*
- *Gray issues*
- *Competent inspector concept*
- *Contractors*
- *20/20 hindsight*
- *Last-one-in syndrome*
- *Someone's fault*
- *Prevention strategies*
- *Response strategies*
- *Walk-through inspections*
- *Model contracts*
- *Pre-inspection routine*
- *Introductory discussion*
- *The inspection itself*
- *Closing discussion*

► 6.0 INSPECTION CHECKLISTS

In the other nine Modules of the Carson Dunlop Home Inspection Training Program, there are sample checklists for each of the major systems in the home. These checklists are presented with the specific Modules on a system-by-system basis. We believe this is the most valuable format for a client. We therefore recommend a system-by-system reporting format, rather than a room-by-room format.

Field Checklists Are Different

However, when it comes to field checklists, these should be organized the way you move through a house. We've provided sample inspection checklists here that combine various parts of the Module checklists in an order that flows the way an inspection is done. For example, when you are on the roof, you will also be inspecting the top part of the chimney, the attic ventilation system, plumbing stacks, and perhaps the electrical mast.

Organization Of Checklists

Your roof checklist should allow you to note problems on all of these systems. When you transfer your field checklist to your final report, you can sort comments back into a system by system order. You may create your own inspection checklists, but we offer these as a starting point. We've broken the inspection down into the following general areas. You will find that some of the checklists are redundant, which is perfectly logical because you are going to see components of some systems in more than one part of the home. Some of the problem lists have been shortened since you'll only see certain things from certain places. You won't see cut truss webs when on the roof, for example.

We've included sections at the beginning of the appropriate checklists that allow you to meet the ASHI® Standards with respect to describing required items in your report. It may be helpful to complete these as you do your inspection. You may want to add or delete items to these lists for your purposes.

Index of Field Checklists

1. Roof
2. Exteriors
3. Garages/Carports
4. Heating
5. Air Conditioning/Heat Pumps
6. Plumbing
7. Electrical
8. Structures
9. Kitchens/Laundry Rooms
10. Bathrooms/Washrooms
11. Rooms
12. Attics
13. Basements
14. Crawlspaces

Conditions Are Alphabetical

The individual conditions or problems listed under each sub-heading are presented in alphabetical order to help you find what you are looking for quickly.

► 1. ROOF – FIELD CHECKLIST

DESCRIPTION

Items that need to be described to meet ASHI® Standards:

ROOF COVERING MATERIALS

- ☐ Asphalt shingles
- ☐ Wood shingles or shakes
- ☐ Slate
- ☐ Clay tile
- ☐ Concrete tile
- ☐ Fiber cement
- ☐ Metal
- ☐ Roll roofing
- ☐ Built-up roofing
- ☐ Modified bitumen
- ☐ Synthetic rubber
- ☐ Plastic
- ☐ Metal

THE ROOF WAS INSPECTED –

- ☐ By walking on the roof
- ☐ From a ladder at the edge of the roof
- ☐ With binoculars
- ☐ _____

Location Legend   N = North   S = South   E = East   W = West
              1 =1st Floor   2 = 2nd Floor   3 = 3rd Floor

STEEP ROOFING			
LOCATION	ASPHALT	LOCATION	WOOD SHINGLES AND SHAKES
	• Blisters		• Buckling
	• Clawing		• Cupping, curling
	• Cracking		• Damaged, broken or missing pieces
	• Cupping, curling		• Exposed fasteners
	• Damage		• Exposure too big
	• Exposed fasteners		• Hip and ridge pieces falling apart
	• Exposure too great		• Ice dam potential
	• Granule loss		• Joints line up in every other row
	• Ice dam potential		• Knots, flame pattern (lower quality materials)
	• Multiple layers		• Loose pieces
	• No underlayment		• Moss, mildew, etc.
	• Overhangs too big, small		• Multiple layers
	• Patches		• No interlay on shakes (may be okay)
	• Shingles – torn, missing		• Overhangs too big, small
	• Slope too low		• Patches
	• Slots wide (old)		• Pieces too wide
	• Vulnerable areas		• Rot
			• Side-by-side
	SLATE		• Slope too low
			• Spacing too tight
	• Broken		• Splitting
	• Brown, white surface		• Vulnerable areas
	• Cracked		• Wear-through, burn-through
	• Damage		
	• Delaminating		CLAY/CONCRETE/FIBER CEMENT
	• Exposed fasteners (may be okay)		
	• Exposure too great		• Broken
	• Ice dam potential		• Color fading
	• Loose		• Cracked
	• Missing		• Damage
	• Overhangs too big, small		• Efflorescence
	• Patches		• Exposed fasteners
	• Ribbons (weak areas)		• Exposure too great
	• Slope too low		• Ice dam potential
	• Soft, crumbly		• Loose (ineffective fasteners)
	• Tarred		• Missing
	• Vulnerable areas		• Missing or loose hip, ridge, rake, eave pieces
			• Moss
	METAL		• Overhangs too big, small
			• Patched
	• Buckled		• Slope too low (no membrane below)
	• Dent, damage		• Spalling
	• Exposed fasteners (may be okay)		• Vulnerable areas
	• Exposure too great		
	• Failed fasteners		
	• Ice dam potential		
	• Loose		
	• Missing		
	• Open seams		
	• Overhangs too big, small		
	• Patched		
	• Rust		
	• Slope too low		
	• Tarred		

LOCATION	ROLL ROOFING	LOCATION	
	• Algae discoloration		
	• Blisters		
	• Buckling or wrinkling		
	• Cracks		
	• Damage		
	• Exposed nails not sealed		
	• Granule loss		
	• Open seams		
	• Rusted nails		
	• Seams facing uphill		
	• Vulnerable areas		

	FLASHINGS		
LOCATION	VALLEY FLASHINGS	LOCATION	SKYLIGHTS
	• Closed cut valleys not trimmed 2 inches back		• Cracked, broken glazing
	• Closed valleys with wrong material		• Curb – low, missing
	• Doesn't widen at bottom		• Damage, patched
	• Fasteners exposed		• Leak
	• Metal pieces too long		• Rot
	• Missing		• Skylight or solarium poorly secured to roof
			• Windows used as a skylight
	• No upstand		• Wrong, incomplete flashings
	• Points not cut		• Wrong application
	• Rust		
	• Shingles not sealed to metal		ROOF/SIDEWALL FLASHINGS
	• Too short		
	• Torn, patched		• Loose, damaged, patched, open seams
	• Wood joints break into valley		• No step or counter flashings
			• Not let into mortar joints
	CHIMNEY FLASHINGS		• Overlap inadequate
			• Pan missing, inappropriate
	• Cap flashing too short		• Rust
	• Cricket missing, loose, damaged		• Siding not cut back
	• Damaged, loose, open seams, patched		• Step flashings not set into shingles properly
	• Missing base or cap flashings		• Too short or narrow
	• Missing top, bottom, side flashings		
	• Not let into mortar joints		ROOF/WALL ABOVE FLASHINGS
	• Overlap inadequate on base or cap flashings		
	• Rust		• Damaged, loose, open seams, patched
	• Side base flashings not set into shingles properly		• Missing
	• Side base flashings too short		• Nailed through shingles
			• Not let into mortar joints
	PIPE/STACK FLASHINGS		• Open at top
			• Rust
	• Damaged		• Siding not cut back
	• Exposed, missing fasteners		• Too short
	• In a valley		
	• Missing		
	• Rust		
	• Top of flashing exposed or bottom buried		
	• Vertically misaligned		
	• Wrong material		

LOCATION	HIP AND RIDGE FLASHINGS	LOCATION	DRIP EDGE FLASHINGS
	• Coming apart		• Above eave protection
	• Exposed fasteners not sealed		• Above underlayment
	• Excessive exposure		• Behind gutter
	• Loose, misaligned, missing		• Loose
	• Overlaps not alternated (wood)		• Missing
	• Poor fastening		• Not continuous
	• Rust		• Rust
			• Too short

FLAT ROOFING			
LOCATION	BUILT-UP	LOCATION	ROLL ROOFING
	• Blisters, alligatoring		• Blisters
	• Damaged, punctures, tears		• Cracking
	• Debris on roof		• Damage, punctures, tears
	• Exposed felts		• Leaks
	• Gravel erosion		• Loss of granules
	• Leaks		• Old, worn out
	• Membrane movements, slippage		• Openings at seams or flashings
	• Multiple layers		• Patched, ponding
	• No gravel, paint etc. (UV protection)		
	• Old, worn out		MODIFIED BITUMEN
	• Patched		
	• Ponding		• Blisters
	• Ridging, fishmouths		• Cracking
	• Splitting		• Damaged, punctures, tears
			• Debris on roof
	EPDM		• Leaks
			• Loss of granules
	• Damage, punctures, tears		• Membrane movements, slippage
	• Debris on roof, oil on roof		• Multiple layers
	• Discoloration		• No UV protection (paint, granules, etc.)
	• Fasteners loose, backing out, corroded		• Old, worn out
	• Leaks		• Openings at seams or flashings
	• Leaning parapets, stacks, etc.		• Patched, ponding
	• Mastic on EPDM		
	• Multiple layers		PVC
	• Old, worn out		
	• Openings at seams or flashings		• Asphalt on PVC
	• Patched, ponding		• Brittle
	• Surface cracks, splitting		• Damage, punctures, tears, shattered
	• Taut (due to shrinkage), tenting		• Debris on roof
	• Wrinkles, ridges, fishmouths		• Discoloration
			• Fasteners loose, backing out, corroded
	METAL		• Leaks
			• Leaning parapets, stacks, etc.
	• Asphalt on metal		• Multiple layers
	• Damage, punctures, tears, bent metal		• Old, worn out
	• Debris on roof		• Openings at seams or flashings
	• Failed caulking		• Patched, ponding
	• Fasteners loose, backing out, corroded, missing		• Polystyrene touching PVC
	• Leaks		• Surface cracks, orange peeling
	• Open, loose seams		• Taut (due to shrinkage)
	• Patched, ponding		• Wrinkling, ridges, fishmouths
	• Rust		

LOCATION	FLASHINGS	LOCATION	
	• Caulking, sealant dried out or cracked		
	• Clamps or termination bars loose		
	• Counter flashings not let into m asonry		
	• Damaged, loose, bent		
	• Drain or scuppers missing, clogged, ineffective		
	• Fasteners loose, rust, missing		
	• Incompatible materials		
	• Leaks		
	• Membrane stretched		
	• Missing, too short		
	• Old, worn out		
	• Open at seams or ends		
	• Patched		
	• Ponding on wall flashings (horizontal parts)		
	• Pitch pockets not filled		
	• Rust		
	• Sagging or slipping (base flashings)		
	• Skylight curb missing or too short		
	• Skylight not well secured		

STRUCTURE			
LOCATION	RAFTERS OR TRUSSES	LOCATION	SHEATHING
	• Fire damage		• Buckled
	• Insects		• Delaminated
	• Mechanical damage		• Sag
	• Rafter spread		
	• Ridge sag		
	• Rot		
	• Sagging		
	• Split		
	• Weak framing at openings		

ELECTRICAL			
LOCATION	SERVICE DROPS OR SERVICE LATERALS	LOCATION	SERVICE CONDUCTORS OR SERVICE ENTRANCE WIRES
	• Branches, vines interfering with wires		• Conduit or cable covered by siding
	• Damaged, frayed wires		• Conduit or cable damaged
	• Excessive height		• Conduit or cable not weather-tight
	• Height over decks, balconies and pools		• Drip loop too low (touching roof)
	• Height over driveways		• Mast bent
	• Height over roadways		• Mast loose
	• Height over roofs		• Mast not weather-tight
	• Height over walking areas		• Mast rotted
	• Inadequate window or door clearance		• Mast rusted
	• Poor connection to service conductors		• Masthead not weather-tight
			• No drip loop
			• No masthead
			• Wires too close to roof

CHIMNEYS AND VENTS			
LOCATION	MASONRY CHIMNEYS	LOCATION	METAL CHIMNEYS OR VENTS
	• Abandoned openings for flue connections		• Adjacent chimneys with staggered height
	• Ash pit door too close to combustibles, loose or missing		• Cap missing, obstructed or wrong type
	• Cap cracked		• Chimney not well supported
	• Cap missing		• Chimney walls rusting or pitting
	• Chimney extender rusted		• Creosote buildup
	• Chimney extender stuck		• Excessive offset from vertical
	• Chimney too short above roof		• Inadequate chimney height above roof
	• Cracking		• Inadequate combustible clearances
	• Creosote build-up		• Inadequate fire stopping
	• Draft inducer fan inoperative		• Inadequate total chimney height
	• Efflorescence		• Not continuous through roof
	• Excessive offset from vertical (30%)		• Not labeled for application
	• Fire stopping missing or incomplete		• Sections not well secured
	• Flue or vent connector obstructed		• Too many appliances on one flue
	• Improper slope on cap		
	• Inadequate combustible clearance		
	• Loose, missing or deteriorated masonry		
	• Loose, missing or deteriorated mortar		
	• No capillary break on cap		
	• No chimney liner		
	• No drip edge on cap		
	• Pulling away from house		
	• Settling or leaning		
	• Spalling		
	• Too many appliances on one flue		
	• Total chimney height too short		
	• Vent connectors extending into chimney		
	• Vent connectors loose at chimney		

AIR CONDITIONING AND HEAT PUMPS			
LOCATION	CENTRAL AIR CONDITIONING CAPACITY	LOCATION	REFRIGERANT LINES
	• Oversized		• Damaged
	• Undersized		• Leaking
			• Lines too warm or too cold
	COMPRESSORS		• Lines touching each other
			• Low points or improper slope in lines
	• Electric wires too small		• Missing insulation
	• Excess electric current draw		
	• Excess noise or vibration		CONDENSER FANS
	• Inadequate cooling		
	• Inoperative		• Corrosion
	• Missing electrical shutoff		• Dirty
	• Out of level		• Excess noise, vibration
	• Running continuously		• Inoperative
	• Short cycling		• Mechanical damage
	• Wrong fuse or breaker size		• Obstructed airflow
	AIR COOLED CONDENSER COILS		
	• Clothes dryer or water heater exhaust too close		
	• Corrosion		
	• Damaged		
	• Dirty		

LOCATION	EVAPORATIVE COOLERS	LOCATION	OUTDOOR COILS
	• Cabinet, ducts not weather-tight		• Clothes dryer or water heater exhaust too close
	• Cabinet too close to grade		• Corrosion
	• Clogged pads		• Damaged
	• Duct problems		• Dirty
	• Electrical problems		• Iced up
	• Excess noise or vibration		• Poor location
	• Leaking		
	• Louvers obstructed		OUTDOOR FANS
	• Missing, dirty air filter		
	• No air gap on water supply		• Corrosion
	• No water		• Dirty
	• Poor support for pump and water system		• Excess noise or vibration
	• Pump or fan inoperative		• Inoperative
	• Rust, mold and mildew		• Mechanical damage
			• Obstructed airflow
	HEAT PUMP CAPACITY		
			REFRIGERANT LINES
	• Oversized for cooling		
	• Undersized for heating		• Damaged
			• Leaking
	COMPRESSORS		• Lines too warm or too cold
			• Lines touching each other
	• Electric wires too small		• Low points or improper slope in lines
	• Excess electric current draw		• Missing insulation
	• Excess noise or vibration		
	• Inadequate cooling		
	• Inoperative in heating or cooling mode		
	• Missing electric shutoff		
	• Out of level		
	• Running continuously		
	• Short cycling		
	• Wrong fuse or breaker size		

PLUMBING			
LOCATION	PLUMBING VENTING SYSTEMS	LOCATION	
	• Ineffective		
	• Missing		
	• Too close to grade		
	• Too close to openings		
	• Too close to property line		
	• Too short or too tall		
	• Vent too small diameter (frost closure)		

GUTTERS, DOWNSPOUTS AND DRAINS			
LOCATION	GUTTERS	LOCATION	FLAT ROOF DRAINS
	• Improper slope		• Clogged
	• Leaking or clogged		• Drains not at low spots
	• Loose or damaged		• Leaking
	• Missing		• Scuppers missing
	• Rusted		• Too few drains
	• Undersized		• Undersized
	DOWNSPOUTS		
	• Clogged		
	• Damaged		
	• Downspouts discharging below grade		
	• Downspouts discharging onto roofs		
	• Downspouts discharging onto the ground		
	• Leaking		
	• Missing		
	• Too few		
	• Undersized		

INSULATION			
LOCATION	ROOF VENTING	LOCATION	
	• Inadequate		
	• Missing		
	• Obstructed or damaged		

► 2. EXTERIOR – FIELD CHECKLIST

DESCRIPTION

Items that need to be described to meet ASHI® Standards:

WALL CLADDING MATERIALS

- ☐ Brick
- ☐ Stone
- ☐ Concrete block
- ☐ Poured concrete
- ☐ Stucco
- ☐ Wood siding
- ☐ Plywood hardboard or OSB siding
- ☐ Metal
- ☐ Vinyl
- ☐ Fiber cement
- ☐ Clay and slate
- ☐ Asphalt shingles
- ☐ Insulbrick

Location Legend N = North   S = South   E = East   W = West
1 =1st Floor   2 = 2nd Floor   3 = 3rd Floor   B= Basement   CS = CrawlSpace

STRUCTURE			
LOCATION	FOUNDATIONS	LOCATION	WOOD FRAME WALLS
	• Basement lowered (suspect)		• Bottom plates have poor bearing
	• Bowed, bulging or leaning		• Excess holes or notches
	• Cold joints		• Leaning, bowing, buckling or racking
	• Cracks		• Lintels sagging
	• Crushed		• Mechanical or fire damage
	• Foundations too short		• Poor nailing
	• Foundations too thin		• Rot or insect damage
	• Hollow masonry units installed on their sides		• Sheathing missing or ineffective
	• Honeycombing		•Top plates weak or sagging
	• Large trees close to building (suspect)		•Wood too close to soil
	• Lateral movement		
	• Lateral support poor		ARCHES
	• Mechanically damaged		
	• Mortar deteriorating or missing		• Cracked
	• Not well secured		• Dropped, rotating or leaning
	• Pilasters moving		• Efflorescence
	• Prior repairs		• Masonry deterioration or missing
	• Rot or wood/soil contact		• Masonry units moving
	• Spalling, crumbling or broken material		• Missing
	• Steep slope, unstable soil		• Mortar deterioration or missing
			• Prior repairs
	SOLID MASONRY WALLS		
			LINTELS
	• Bowing, leaning or bulging		• End bearing poor
	• Cracks		• Mechanical damage or fire damage
	• Efflorescence		• Missing
	• Excess corbeling		• Rot or insect damage
	• Foundations weak or missing		• Rotating or leaning
	• Hollow units on their sides		• Rust
	• Lateral support is suspect		• Sagging or undersized
	• Masonry deteriorating or spalling		•Wood supporting masonry
	• Masonry too close to soil		
	• Mortar deteriorating or missing		
	• Prior repairs		
	•Wavy masonry		
	MASONRY VENEER WALLS		
	• Bowing, leaning or bulging		
	• Cracks		
	• Efflorescence		
	• Excess corbeling		
	• Flashing at weep holes missing or ineffective		
	• Foundations weak or missing		
	• Hollow units on their sides		
	• Lintels sagging, rusting		
	• Masonry deteriorating or spalling		
	• Masonry or wood too close to the soil		
	• Mortar deteriorating or missing		
	• Prior repairs		
	•Wavy masonry		
	•Weep holes missing or ineffective		

ELECTRICAL			
LOCATION	SERVICE DROP OR SERVICE LATERALS	LOCATION	SYSTEM GROUNDING
	• Branches or vines interfering with wires		• Box not bonded to ground
	• Damaged, frayed wires		• Connections not accessible
	• Excessive height		• Corroded ground wire
	• Height over decks, balconies and pools		• Ground rod cut
	• Height over driveways		• Missing
	• Height over roadways		• Neutral bonded to ground wire downstream of service box
	• Height over roofs		• Neutral not bonded to ground at box
	• Height over walking areas		• No jumper for meters and valves
	• Inadequate window or door clearance		• No ground for subpanel
	• Poor connection to service conductors		• Poor connections
			• Spliced ground wire
	SERVICE CONDUCTORS OR SERVICE ENTRANCE WIRES		• Undersized ground wire
			• Wire attached to abandoned pipe
	• Conduit or cable damaged		• Wire attached to plastic pipe
	• Conduit or cable covered by siding		
	• Conduit or cable not weather-tight		DISTRIBUTION PANELS
	• Drip loop too low (touching roof)		
	• Mast rusted		• Circuits not labeled
	• Mast bent		• Damaged panel or components
	• Mast rotted		• Double taps
	• Mast loose		• Fuse holder loose or broken
	• Mast not weather-tight		• Fused neutrals
	• Masthead not weather-tight		• Fuses loose
	• No masthead		• Fuses or breakers too big
	• No drip loop		• Fuses bypassed
	• Wires too close to roof		• Inappropriate mounting surface
			• Loose breakers
	SERVICE BOXES		• Loose or missing door
			• Loose panel
	• Box rating too small		• Multi-wire circuit on same bus
	• Box location		• Neutral and ground wires bonded at subpanel
	• Box not weather-tight		• No fuses or breakers for subpanel and feeder
	• Damaged parts		• No links for multi-wire circuits
	• Fused neutral		• Not rated for aluminum
	• Fuses upstream of disconnect switch		• Obsolete
	• Illegal taps		• Openings in panel
	• Inappropriate mounting surface		• Overheating
	• Multiple disconnects		• Panel crowded
	• Neutral wire bypasses service box		• Panel upside-down
	• Not well secured		• Poor access
	• Obsolete service box		• Rust or water in panel
	• Overheating		• Subpanel not grounded
	• Poor access		• Too many breakers
	• Poor connections		• Undersized panel
	• Rust		• Wrong breaker for panel
	• Service entrance wires exposed in house		• Wrong fuses or breakers for subpanel and feeder
	• Single main disconnect		
	• Unprotected openings		
	• Wrong fuse or breaker size		

LOCATION	OUTDOOR WIRING	LOCATION	
	• Buried wire		
	• Extension cords powering exterior outlets		
	• Garage door opener connected to extension cord		
	• Indoor wire used outdoors		
	• Not suitable for outdoor use		
	• Solid wire run overhead		
	• Wires not well secured to walls		
	• Wires too close to grade		
	• Wires run on roof surfaces		
	• Wires through gutters or downspouts		

HEATING			
LOCATION	GAS METER	LOCATION	MASONRY CHIMNEYS
	• Gas shut off and locked		• Abandoned openings for flue connections
	• Ice		• Ash pit door too close to combustibles, loose or missing
	• Leaks		• Cap missing or cracked
	• Mechanical damage		• Chimney extender rusted or stuck
	• Poor access		• Chimney too short above roof
	• Poor location		• Cracking
	• Rusting		• Creosote build-up
	• Undersized		• Draft inducer fan inoperative
			• Efflorescence
	GAS PIPING		• Excessive offset from vertical (30%)
			• Fire stopping missing or incomplete
	• Improper connections		• Flue or vent connector obstructed
	• Inadequate support		• Improper slope on cap
	• Inappropriate materials		• Inadequate combustible clearance
	• Leaks		• Loose, missing or deteriorated mortar
	• Missing shut off valves		• Loose, missing or deteriorated masonry
	• No drip leg		• No capillary break on cap
	• Piping in chimney or duct system		• No chimney liner
	• Plastic pipe exposed above grade		• No drip edge on cap
	• Rusting		• Pulling away from house
			• Settling or leaning
	FURNACES, BOILERS AND WATER HEATERS – MID- AND HIGH-EFFICIENCY		• Spalling
			• Too many appliances on one flue
	• Poor vent location, arrangement		• Total chimney height too short
			• Vent connectors extending into chimney
	OIL TANKS		• Vent connectors loose at chimney
	• Empty		METAL CHIMNEYS OR VENTS
	• Leakage		
	• Not suitable for outdoor use		• Adjacent chimneys with staggered height
	• Rusting		• Cap missing, obstructed or wrong type
	• Underground		• Missing caps
	• Unsafe location		• Chimney walls rusting or pitting
			• Chimney not well supported
	FILL AND VENT PIPES		• Creosote build-up
			• Excessive offset from vertical
	• Abandoned		• Inadequate combustible clearances
	• Damaged or corroded		• Inadequate fire stopping
	• Leak		• Inadequate total chimney height
			• Inadequate chimney height above roof
			• Not continuous through roof
			• Not labeled for application
			• Sections not well secured
			• Too many appliances on one flue

AIR CONDITIONING AND HEAT PUMPS			
LOCATION	CENTRAL AIR CONDITIONING CAPACITY	LOCATION	COMPRESSORS
	• Oversized		• Electric wires too small
	• Undersized		• Excess electric current draw
			• Excess noise or vibration
	COMPRESSORS		• Inadequate cooling
			• Inoperative in heating or cooling mode
	• Electric wires too small		• Missing electric shutoff
	• Excess electric current draw		• Out of level
	• Excess noise or vibration		• Running continuously
	• Inadequate cooling		• Short cycling
	• Inoperative		•Wrong fuse or breaker size
	• Missing electrical shutoff		
	• Out of level		OUTDOOR COILS
	• Running continuously		
	• Short cycling		• Clothes dryer or water heater exhaust too close
	•Wrong fuse or breaker size		• Corrosion
			• Damaged
	AIR COOLED CONDENSER COILS		• Dirty
			• Iced up
	• Clothes dryer or water heater exhaust too close		• Poor location
	• Corrosion		OUTDOOR FANS
	• Damaged		
	• Dirty		• Corrosion
			• Dirty
	REFRIGERANT LINES		• Excess noise or vibration
			• Inoperative
	• Damaged		• Mechanical damage
	• Leaking		• Obstructed airflow
	• Lines too warm or too cold		
	• Lines touching each other		REFRIGERANT LINES
	• Low points or improper slope in lines		
	• Missing insulation		• Damaged
			• Leaking
	EVAPORATIVE COOLERS		• Line touching each other
			• Lines too warm or too cold
	• Cabinet or ducts not weather-tight		• Low points or improper slope in lines
	• Cabinet too close to grade		• Missing insulation
	• Clogged pads		
	• Duct problems		HEAT PUMP CAPACITY
	• Electrical problems		
	• Excess noise or vibration		• Oversized for cooling
	• Leaking		• Undersized for heating
	• Louvers obstructed		
	• Missing, dirty air filter		
	• No water		
	• No air gap on water supply		
	• Poor support for pump and water system		
	• Pump or fan inoperative		
	• Rust, mold and mildew		

PLUMBING			
LOCATION	WATER SUPPLY PUMPS	LOCATION	SUMP PUMPS
	• Damaged		• Debris in the sump, clogged sump
	• Excessive noise or vibration		• Discharge pipe problems
	• Frozen		• Excess noise or vibration
	• Inoperative		• Inoperative, poorly secured or rusted
	• Leak		• Lid missing, rotted or not secure
	• Lost prime		• Short cycling or running continuously
	• Overheating		• Sump damaged
	• Running continuously		
	• Rust		HOSE BIBBS
	• Short cycling		
	• Wiring problems		• Damage
			• Leaks or drips
	PRESSURE TANKS		• Loose
			• No backflow preventer
	• Condensation		• Pipe frozen or split
	• Leaking		• Poor slope on frost-free bibb
	• Rust		• Stiff or inoperative
	• Tank wobbling or unstable		
	• Waterlogged		REGULATORS
	WATER SERVICE PIPES		• Leaking
			• Missing
	• Freezing		• No bypass or relief valve
	• Leaking		• Poor location
	• Low pressure		• Rust
	• Mechanical damage		• Set wrong
	SHUT OFF VALVES		SUPPLY PIPING
	• Damaged handle		• Combustible piping
	• Exposed to mechanical damage		• Excess pressure
	• Inoperable, inaccessible, buried		• Excessive noise
	• Leaking		• Leaking
	• Missing or cannot be located		• Non-standard material
	• Partly closed		• Poor support
	• Rusted		• Poor pressure or flow
			• Rust
			• Split, damaged, crimped
			• Suspect connections on polybutylene

WALLS			
LOCATION	GENERAL	LOCATION	METAL AND VINYL SIDING
	• Exposed foundations — cracked or spalled		• Buckled or wavy
	• Insulation problems		• Discolored
	• Planters and gardens against walls		• Flashing and caulking defects
	• Too close to grade or wood/soil contact		• Loose
	• Vines		• Mechanical damage
	• Water penetration		• Metal siding not grounded
			• Rust
	BRICK, STONE AND CONCRETE		• Too close to grade
	• Bowing walls		CEMENT-BASED SIDING (Fiber-cement, Asbestos Cement)
	• Cracking		
	• Efflorescence		• Loose
	• Mechanical damage		• Mechanical damage
	• Missing, ineffective weep holes or flashings		• Missing paint or caulking
	• Mortar deterioration		• Nailing problems
	• Spalling		• Too close to grade
	• Too close to grade		
			CLAY AND SLATE SHINGLES
	STUCCO AND EIFS (SYNTHETIC STUCCO)		
			• Broken
	• Bulging		• Damage
	• Cracking		• Flashing or joint defects
	• Crumbling		• Loose or missing pieces
	• Incompatible flashings		• Missing or loose
	• Loose		• Paint or stain needed
	• Mechanical damage		• Rot
	• Moisture penetration		• Too close to grade
	• No drip screed		• Vents missing or ineffective
	• Rusted lath or trim		
	• Too close to grade		ASPHALT SHINGLES AND INSUL-BRICK
	WOOD SIDING (Board, Shakes And Shingles)		
			• Aging
	• Loose		• Loose, missing or torn tabs
	• Paint or stain – needed		• Too close to grade
	• Rot		
	• Splitting		SOFFITS AND FASCIA
	• Too close to grade		• Damage
	• Warping		• Loose or missing pieces
			• Paint or stain needed
	PLYWOOD, HARDBOARD AND OSB		• Rot
			• Vents missing, ineffective
	• Buckling and cracking		
	• Delamination		TRIM FLASHINGS AND CAULKING
	• Inner-Seal®		
	• Loose		• Caulking missing or ineffective
	• Mechanical damage		• Flashings incomplete or ineffective
	• Rot		• Flashings missing
	• Swelling		• Loose
	• Too close to grade		• Rot
			• Rust

PORCHES, DECKS AND BALCONIES				
LOCATION	STEPS AND LANDINGS	LOCATION	BEAMS	
	• Carpet over wood steps or landing		• End support inadequate	
	• Landings missing or undersized		• Rot, insect damage, wood/soil contact	
	• Masonry or concrete spalling or cracking		• Rotation	
	• Rot		• Sag	
	• Stair rise too big or not uniform			
	• Stair run too small or not uniform		JOISTS	
	• Steps slope			
	• Steps or landings settling or heaving		• Cantilevered joist problems	
	• Steps spring, loose or sagging		• End bearing inadequate	
	•Tread widths too small or not uniform		• Fastener problems	
	•Wood/soil contact		• Ledgerboard problems	
			• Rot, insect damage or wood/soil contact	
	HANDRAILS AND GUARDS		• Rotation	
			• Sag (undersized, overspanned, damaged, overloaded)	
	• Loose			
	• Missing		FLOORS	
	• Rot			
	• Spindles missing, too far apart, climbable		• Carpet	
			• Concrete cracked or spalled	
	COLUMNS		• No step up into house	
			• Paint or stain needed	
	• Leaning, settled, heaved		• Poor quality materials	
	• Rot, insect damage		• Rot, insect damage or wood/soil contact	
	• Rust		• Rust	
	• Spalling, cracked or damaged		• Sag	
	•Wood/soil contact			
			SKIRTING	
	ROOF STRUCTURES			
			• Fastener problems	
	• Mechanical damage		• Mechanical damage	
	• Rot, insect damage		• Paint or stain needed	
	• Settlement or other movement		• Rot, insect damage or wood/soil contact	

93

OTHER EXTERIOR			
LOCATION	BASEMENT STAIRWELLS	LOCATION	WINDOW WELLS
	• Cover inoperable		• Damaged
	• Door threshold missing, too low, not watertight		• Drains –
	• Drains missing, clogged or undersized		– Missing
	• Frost damage		– Not connected
	• Guard and handrail problems		– Broken
	• Insect damage		– Obstructed
	• Leaking		• Missing
	• Paint or stain needed		• Rot or wood/soil contact
	• Rot		• Rust
	• Rust		
	• Step and landing problems		WALKS AND DRIVEWAYS
	• Walls cracking, leaning, bowing or spalling		• Cracked or damaged surfaces
			• Improper slope or drainage
	LOT GRADING		• Uneven (trip hazard)
	• Clogged catch basins		GROUNDS
	• Improper slope		
	• Porous material		• Disturbed ground
	• Soil erosion		• Trees or shrubs too close to house
	GUTTERS		PATIOS
	• Improper slope		• Retaining walls –
	• Leaking or clogged		– Cracks
	• Loose or damaged		– Bulging
	• Missing		– Bowing
	• Rusted		– Drainage system missing
	• Undersized		– Leaning
			– Deteriorated mortar
	DOWNSPOUTS		– Spalling
			– Settlement or shifting
	• Clogged		– Rot or insect damage
	• Damaged		• Slip hazards
	• Downspouts discharging onto roofs		• Slope toward house
	• Downspouts discharging onto the ground		• Trip hazards
	• Downspouts discharging below grade		
	• Leaking		GUARDRAILS AND HANDRAILS
	• Missing		
	• Too few		• Damage at bottom
	• Undersized		• Missing or ineffective
			• Missing
	FLAT ROOF DRAINS		• Rust
			• Too low
	• Clogged		• Weak
	• Drains not at low spots		
	• Leaking		RETAINING WALLS
	• Scuppers missing		
	• Too few drains		• Bowing
	• Undersized		• Cracking
			• Drainage system missing
	COLUMNS		• Leaning
			• Mortar – deteriorated, missing
	• Cracking		• Rot or insect damage
	• Heaving		• Rusting
	• Leaning		• Settling or shifting
	• Rusting		• Spalling
	• Settling		
	• Spalling		

INSULATION			
LOCATION	FOUNDATION	LOCATION	FLOORS OVER UNHEATED AREAS
	• Exterior insulation not protected at top		• Evidence insulation has been added
	• Exterior insulation not suitable for use below grade		•Too little insulation (usually difficult) to tell
	WALLS		
	• Evidence insulation has been added		

WINDOWS, SKYLIGHTS AND SOLARIUMS			
LOCATION	GENERAL	LOCATION	SASHES
	• Air leaks		• Inoperable
	• Lintels sagging or missing		• Loose fit
	•Water leaks		• Poor weatherstrip
			• Rot
	FRAMES		• Rust
			• Sash coming apart
	• Deformation		• Stiff
	• Drain holes blocked or missing		
	• Installed backwards		GLASS (GLAZING)
	• Racked		
	• Rot		• Broken
	• Rust		• Cracked
			• Excess condensation
	EXTERIOR DRIP CAPS		• Loose
			• Lost seal on double or triple glazing
	• Ineffective		• Missing
	• Missing		
			STORMS AND SCREENS
	EXTERIOR TRIM		
			• Loose
	• Caulking or flashing missing, deteriorated, loose, rusting or incomplete		• Missing
	• Damaged, cracked or loose		• Rusted
	• Inadequate sill projection		•Torn or holes
	• Missing		
	• No drip edge		SKYLIGHTS AND SOLARIUMS
	• Paint or stain needed		
	• Putty (glazing compound) cracked, missing, loose or deteriorated		• Evidence of ice dams
	• Rot		• Special glazing not provided (more than 15 inches off vertical)
	• Rust		
	• Sills with reverse slope		
	•Vines		

DOORS			
LOCATION	GENERAL	LOCATION	GLASS (GLAZING)
	• Air leaks		• Broken
	• Lintels sagging or missing		• Cracked
	• Water leaks		• Excess condensation
			• Loose
	DOORS AND FRAMES		• Lost seal on double or triple glazing
			• Missing
	• Damaged		
	• Dark paint on metal exposed to sun		STORMS AND SCREENS
	• Deformation		
	• Delaminated		• Loose
	• Drain holes blocked or missing		• Missing
	• Installed backwards		• Rusted
	• Loose or poor fit		• Torn or holes
	• Plastic trim on metal door behind storm		
	• Racked		EXHAUST FANS
	• Rot		
	• Rust		• Clothes dryer vented outside?
			• Inadequate backflow prevention (flap)
	EXTERIOR DRIP CAPS		• Poor termination location
			• Weather hood missing or loose
	• Ineffective		
	• Missing		HEAT RECOVERY VENTILATORS
	EXTERIOR TRIM		• Inadequate backflow prevention on exhaust (flap)
	• Caulking or flashing missing, deteriorated, loose, rusting or incomplete		• Inadequate screening on inlet
	• Damaged, cracked or loose		• Poor termination or inlet location
	• Inadequate sill projection		• Termination or inlet points not found
	• Missing		• Weather hood loose
	• No drip edge		• Weather hood damaged
	• Paint or stain needed		• Weather hood missing
	• Putty (glazing compound) cracked, missing, loose or deteriorating		
	• Rot		
	• Rust		
	• Sill too low		
	• Sill not well supported		
	• Sills with reverse slope		

► 3. GARAGE/CARPORT – FIELD CHECKLIST

Location Legend   N = North   S = South   E = East   W = West

LOCATION	GARAGE FLOORS	LOCATION	FIRE SAFETY
	• Broken		• Exposed combustible insulation
	• Cracked, settled or heaved		• Fireproofing or gasproofing ineffective
	• Drainage problems		
	• Structural garage floors (specialized inspection needed)		**WINDOWS – GENERAL**
			• Air leaks
	FOOTINGS AND FOUNDATIONS		• Lintels sagging or missing
			• Water leaks
	• Cracked		
	• Heaved		FRAMES
	• Missing		
	• Settled		• Deformation
	• Spalling		• Drain holes blocked or missing
			• Installed backwards
	MASONRY WALLS		• Racked
			• Rot
	• Bowing or bulging		• Rust
	• Cracked		
	• Leaning		EXTERIOR DRIP CAPS
	• Mechanical damage		• Ineffective
	• Mortar deterioration		• Missing
	• Spalling		
			EXTERIOR TRIM
	WOOD FRAME WALLS AND ROOFS		
			• Caulking or flashing missing, deteriorated, loose, rusting or incomplete
	• Leaning or racking		• Damaged, cracked or loose
	• Mechanical damage		• Inadequate sill projection
	• Paint or stain needed		• Missing
	• Rafter spreading		• No drip edge
	• Rot, insect damage or wood/soil contact		• Paint or stain needed
	• Sagging or bowing		• Putty (glazing compound) cracked, missing, loose or deteriorated
	COLUMNS		• Rot
			• Rust
	• Leaning, settled, heaved		• Sills with reverse slope
	• Rot, insect damage		• Vines
	• Rust		
	• Spalling, cracked or damaged		SASHES
	• Wood/soil contact		
			• Inoperable
	ROOF COVERINGS		• Loose fit
			• Poor weatherstrip
	• Leaks		• Rot
	• Damaged		• Rust
	• Missing		• Sash coming apart
	• Worn		• Stiff
	• Poor flashing details		
			GLASS (GLAZING)
	GUTTERS AND DOWNSPOUTS		
			• Broken
	• Leaking or clogged		• Cracked
	• Loose or damaged		• Excess condensation
	• Missing		• Loose
	• Poor location		• Lost seal on double or triple glazing
	• Poor slope		• Missing
	• Rusted		
	• Undersized		

LOCATION	DOORS – GENERAL	LOCATION	MAN-DOORS
	• Air leaks		• Door not fire rated or exterior type
	• Lintels sagging or missing		• Door not tightfitting and weather-stripped
	• Water leaks		• No self closer
			• No step up into house
	DOORS AND FRAMES		• Opens into bedroom
	• Damaged		VEHICLE DOORS
	• Dark paint on metal exposed to sun		
	• Deformation		• Automatic opener
	• Delaminated		– Inoperative
	• Drain holes blocked or missing		– Fails to auto reverse
	• Installed backwards		– Adjustment needed to open or close limits
	• Loose or poor fit		• Difficult to open or close
	• Plastic trim on metal door behind storm		• Paint or stain needed
	• Racked		• Rot or insect damage
	• Rot		• Rust or denting
	• Rust		
			COMBUSTION APPLIANCES IN GARAGES
	EXTERIOR DRIP CAPS		
			• Too close to floor
	• Ineffective		• Vulnerable to mechanical damage
	• Missing		
			ELECTRICAL WIRING
	EXTERIOR TRIM		
			• Abandoned wire
	• Caulking or flashing missing, deteriorated, loose, rusting or incomplete		• Buried cable
	• Damaged, cracked or loose		• Damaged
	• Inadequate sill projection		• Exposed on walls or ceilings
	• Missing		• Extension cord used as permanent wiring
	• No drip edge		• Extension cords powering exterior outlets
	• Paint or stain needed		• Garage door opener connected to extension cord
	• Putty (glazing compound) cracked, missing, loose or deteriorating		• Improper color coding
	• Rot		• In steel studs without protection
	• Rust		• Indoor cable used outdoors
	• Sill too low		• Loose connections
	• Sill not well supported		• Missing
	• Sills with reverse slope		• Not well secured
			• Open splices
	GLASS (GLAZING)		• Overhead wires not stranded
			• Permanent wiring used as extension cord
	• Broken		• Too close to ducts, pipes, chimneys, etc.
	• Cracked		• Too close to edge of studs or joists
	• Excess condensation		• Undersized wire
	• Loose		• Wires run on roof surfaces
	• Lost seal on double or triple glazing		• Wires through gutters or downspouts
	• Missing		• Wires too close to grade
			• Wrong type
	STORMS AND SCREENS		
			KNOB-AND-TUBE
	• Loose		
	• Missing		• Buried in (combustible) insulation
	• Rusted		• Connections need boxes
	• Torn or holes		• Conventional lights in wet areas
			• Fused neutrals
			• Wire insulation or sheathing brittle

LOCATION	ALUMINUM	LOCATION	OUTLETS
	• Connectors not compatible with aluminum		• Broken pin or blade in slots
	• No grease on stranded wires		• Damaged
	• Overheating		• Dedicated circuits needed
			• Inoperative
	LIGHTS		• Loose
			• No GFI
	• Damaged		• Open hot
	• Inoperative		• Open neutral
	• Isolating links needed on pull chains		• Overheated neutral
	• Loose		• Overheating
	• Not grounded		• Reverse polarity
	• Obsolete		• Ungrounded
	• Overheating		• Within 18 inches of garage floor
			• Worn receptacles
	SWITCHES		• Wrong type
	• Damaged, loose		**HOSE BIBBS**
	• Inoperative, obsolete		
	• No shut off		• Damage
	• Overheated		• Leaks or drips
			• Loose
	JUNCTION BOXES		• No backflow preventer
			• Pipe frozen or split
	• Concealed boxes		• Poor slope on frost-free bibb
	• Cover loose or missing		• Stiff or inoperative
	• Damaged		
	• Missing, loose		
	• Not grounded		
	• Overcrowded		
	• Overheating		

► 4. HEATING – FIELD CHECKLIST

DESCRIPTION

Items that need to be described to meet ASHI® Standards:

ENERGY SOURCE

☐ Gas
☐ Propane
☐ Oil
☐ Electricity
☐ Wood
☐ Coal
☐ _____

HEATING EQUIPMENT AND DISTRIBUTION TYPE

☐ Forced air
☐ Hot water
☐ Steam
☐ Radiant
☐ Combination system
☐ Space heaters
☐ Wall furnace
☐ Floor furnace
☐ Wood stove
☐ _____

Location Legend   N = North   S = South   E = East   W = West
                 1 = 1st Floor   2 = 2nd Floor   3 = 3rd Floor   B = Basement   CS = CrawlSpace

GAS BURNERS AND VENTING			
LOCATION	GAS METERS	LOCATION	HEAT SHIELDS
	• Gas shut off and locked		• Loose
	• Ice		• Missing
	• Leaks		• Rust
	• Mechanical damage		• Scorched
	• Poor access		
	• Poor location		VENTING SYSTEMS
	• Rust		
	• Undersized		• Connector extends too far in chimney
			• Draft hood spillage or backdraft
	GAS PIPING		• Improper material
			• Inadequate combustible clearance
	• Copper tubing not properly labeled		• Poor manifolding
	• Improper connections		• Poor slope
	• Inadequate support		• Poor support
	• Inappropriate materials		• Poor connections
	• Leak		• Rust, dirty, obstructed
	• Missing shut off valves		• Vent connector too long
	• No drip leg		• Vent connector too big or too small
	• Piping in chimney or duct systems		
	• Plastic pipe exposed above grade		MID- AND HIGH-EFFICIENCY GAS FURNACES
	• Rust		
			• Airflow proving switch problems
	COMBUSTION AIR		• Condensate problems
			• Electronic ignition problems
	• Inadequate combustion air		• Excess temperature rise• Heat exchanger problems
	GAS BURNERS		• Induced draft fan problems
			• Poor vent location, arrangement
	• Delayed ignition		• Poor combustion air intake location
	• Dirt or soot		• Spillage switch problems
	• Flame wavers when fan comes on		• Vent damper stuck
	• Gas odor or leak		
	• Inoperative		
	• Poor flame color or pattern		
	• Rust		
	• Scorching		
	• Short cycling		

OIL BURNERS AND VENTING			
LOCATION	OIL TANKS	LOCATION	REFRACTORY/FIRE POT
	• Empty		• Crumbling, cracked, collapsed
	• Leakage		• Saturated
	• Not suitable for outdoor use		
	• Rusting		PRIMARY CONTROLLERS
	• Underground		
	• Unsafe location		• Inoperative
			• Missing
	FILL AND VENT PIPES		• Tripped
	• Abandoned		BAROMETRIC DAMPERS/DRAFT REGULATORS
	• Damaged or corroded		
	• Leak		• Improper location
	• Missing caps		• Inadequate draft air
			• Inoperative
	OIL SUPPLY LINES		• Misadjusted
			• Missing
	• Corrosion, damage, crimped		• Rusting
	• Leak		• Spillage
	• Undersized		
	• Unprotected		VENTING SYSTEMS
	OIL FILTERS		• Improper material
			• Inadequate combustible clearance
	• Dirty		• Poor support
	• Leak		• Poor slope
	• Missing		• Poor connections
			• Poor manifolding
	COMBUSTION AIR		• Poor insertion into chimney
			• Rust, dirty, obstructed
	• Inadequate combustion air		• Vent connector too big, too small
			• Vent connector too long
	BURNERS		
			MID-EFFICIENCY OIL FURNACES
	• Dirty		
	• Incomplete combustion – soot		• Corroded vents
	• Inoperative		• Excess temperature rise
	• Leaking		• Poor vent location, arrangement
	• Short cycling		• Reliability
	• Too close to combustibles		
	• Vibrating, noisy		

WARM AIR FURNACES			
LOCATION	HEAT EXCHANGERS	LOCATION	MECHANICAL AIR FILTERS
	• Cracks, holes or rust		• Dirty
	• Excess temperature rise		• Installed backwards
	• Soot or deposits		• Loose or collapsed
			• Missing
	CABINETS		• Wrong size
	• Combustible clearances		ELECTRONIC AIR CLEANERS
	• Mechanical damage		
	• Missing components		• Damaged cells
	• Obstructed air intake		• Dirty
	• Rust		• Improper orientation
	• Scorching		• Inoperative
			• Mis-wired
	THERMOSTATS		• Missing components
	• Anticipator problems		HUMIDIFIERS
	• Damaged		
	• Dirty		• Clogged pad, mesh or nozzle
	• Loose		• Dirty
	• Not level		• Inoperative motor or solenoid valve
	• Poor adjustment or calibration		• Leaks
	• Poor location		• No duct damper
			• Poor location
	HOUSE AIR FANS (BLOWERS)		
			DUCTS, REGISTERS AND GRILLES
	• Dirty		
	• Fan belt loose, worn, damaged		• Balancing damper adjustment
	• Inoperative		• Dirty, obstructed collapsed
	• Noisy		• Disconnected ducts
	• Overheating		• Excessively long runs, excessive elbows
	• Poorly secured		• Insulation missing, damaged
	• Running continuously		• Leaky joints
	• Rust		• Registers or grilles in garage
	• Too small		• Rust (in-slab ducts)
	• Unbalanced or vibration		• Undersized
			• Weak airflow
	FAN/LIMIT SWITCHES		• Wire or pipes in ducts
	• Improperly wired		COMBINATION SYSTEMS
	• Mechanical damage		
	• Missing cover		• Cabinet problems
	• Rusting or dirty		• Control problems
	• Scorching		• Domestic water too hot
	• Set wrong or defective		• Fan problems
			• Filter problems
			• Inadequate heat for house
			• Inoperative, inefficient pumps
			• Inoperative water heater
			• Leaking, clogged coils
			• Water control problems

HOT WATER BOILERS			
LOCATION	HEAT EXCHANGERS	LOCATION	THERMOSTATS
	• Clogged		• Anticipator problems
	• Excess temperature rise		• Damaged
	• Leaks		• Dirty
	• Rust		• Loose
			• Not level
	CABINETS		• Poor adjustment or calibration
			• Poor location
	• Combustible clearance		
	• Mechanical damage		EXPANSION TANKS
	• Missing components		
	• Obstructed air intake		• Leaks
	• Rust		• Poor discharge location for open tank
	• Scorching		• Poor location for tank
			• Rust
	AIR VENTS		• Too small
			• Waterlogged
	• Inoperative, damaged		
	• Leaking		CIRCULATORS
	• Missing		
	• Obstructed		• Hot
			• Inoperative
	PRIMARY CONTROLS		• Leaks
			• Noisy
	• Inoperative		
	• Set incorrectly		PRESSURE RELIEF VALVES
	PUMP CONTROLS		• Missing
			• No piped extension
			• Pipe too small
	• Inoperative		• Pipe threaded, capped or corroded at the bottom
	• Set incorrectly		
	ZONE CONTROLS		• Pipe dripping or leaking
			• Poor location
	• Inoperative		• Set wrong
	• Leaking		• Wrong size
	OUTDOOR AIR THERMOSTATS		HIGH TEMPERATURE LIMIT SWITCHES
	• Inoperative		• Defective, not wired correctly
			• Missing
	FLOW CONTROL VALVES		• Set too high
	• Inoperative		LOW WATER CUTOUTS
	• Leaks		
			• Inoperative
	ISOLATING VALVES		• Leaking
	• Inoperative		BACKFLOW PREVENTERS
	• Leaks		
	• Rust		• Installed backwards
			• Leaking
			• Missing

LOCATION	PRESSURE REDUCING VALVES	LOCATION	MID- AND HIGH-EFFICIENCY BOILERS (ADDITIONAL PROBLEMS)
	• Inoperative		• Cabinet problems
	• Installed backwards		• Combustion air and venting problems
	• Leaking		• Condensate handling problems
	• Missing		• Fuel supply and burner problems
	• Set too low		• Heat exchanger problems
			• Ignition problems
	PIPES		• Induced draft and forced draft fan problems
	• Crimped		• Safety and operating control problems
	• Leaks		
	• No insulation		RADIANT HEATING
	• Poor support		
	• Rust		• Balancing valve problems
	•Too small		• Bleed valve problems
			• Cool rooms or parts of rooms – inoperative?
	RADIATORS, CONVECTORS AND BASEBOARDS		• Leak
			TANKLESS COILS
	• Balancing valve problems		
	• Bleed valve problems		• Leak
	• Cold		• Rust
	• Damaged baseboard fins		• Poor hot water pressure or flow (clogged?)
	• Leaks		•Tempering valve – missing, set wrong, defective
	• Missing		
	• Obstructed airflow		
	• Poor location		
	• Rust		
	•Too small (cool rooms)		

STEAM BOILERS			
LOCATION	HEAT EXCHANGERS	LOCATION	EQUALIZERS
	• Clogged		• Clogged
	• Leaks		• Connected to boiler at wrong location (beyond Scope)
	• Rust		• Missing
			• Too small
	CABINETS		
			ZONE CONTROLS
	• Combustible clearance		
	• Mechanical damage		• Inoperative
	• Missing components		• Leaking
	• Obstructed air intake		
	• Rust		ISOLATING VALVES
	• Scorching		
			• Inoperative
	THERMOSTATS		• Leaks
			• Rust
	• Anticipator problems		
	• Damaged		DISTRIBUTION PIPES AND RADIATORS
	• Dirty		
	• Loose		• Air vents –
	• Not level		– Missing
	• Poor adjustment or calibration		– Obstructed
	• Poor location		– Leak
			– Stuck open, closed
	AIR VENTS		– Damaged
			– Poor location
	• Inoperative or damaged		• Clogged
	• Leak		• Improper slope
	• Missing		• Leaking
	• Obstructed		• Low spots
	• Poor location		• Radiators won't warm up
	• Stuck open or closed		
			STEAM TRAPS
	LOW WATER CUT-OUTS		
			• Damaged
	• Inoperative		• Leaking
	• Leaking		• Missing
			• Stuck open or closed
	WATER GAUGE LEVELS		
			CONDENSATE AND BOILER FEED PUMPS
	• Dirty		
	• Leaking		• Air vent on receiver blocked
			• Automatic water feed problem (boiler feed pump)
	PRESSURETROLS		• Check valve stuck open or closed
			• Check valve missing
	• Blocked		• Float adjustment problem
	• Inoperative		• Improper pump discharge pressure
	• Set too high		• Inoperative
	• Set too low		
			GENERAL OPERATING PROBLEMS
	HARTFORD LOOPS		
			• Boiler generates too little heat
	• Clogged		• Water level fluctuates during operation
	• Lacking a close nipple		• Water level not visible
	• Missing		
	• Too small		
	• Too low		

CHIMNEYS AND VENTS			
LOCATION	MASONRY CHIMNEYS	LOCATION	METAL CHIMNEYS OR VENTS
	• Abandoned openings for flue connections		• Adjacent chimneys with staggered height
	• Ash pit door too close to combustibles, loose or missing		• Cap missing, obstructed or wrong type
	• Cap missing or cracked		• Chimney walls rusting or pitting
	• Chimney extender rusted or stuck		• Chimney not well supported
	• Chimney too short above roof		• Creosote build-up
	• Cracking		• Excessive offset from vertical
	• Creosote build-up		• Inadequate combustible clearances
	• Draft inducer fan inoperative		• Inadequate fire stopping
	• Efflorescence		• Inadequate total chimney height
	• Excessive offset from vertical (30%)		• Inadequate chimney height above roof
	• Fire stopping missing or incomplete		• Not continuous through roof
	• Flue or vent connector obstructed		• Not labeled for application
	• Improper slope on cap		• Sections not well secured
	• Inadequate combustible clearance		• Too many appliances on one flue
	• Loose, missing or deteriorated mortar		
	• Loose, missing or deteriorated masonry		
	• No capillary break on cap		
	• No chimney liner		
	• No drip edge on cap		
	• Pulling away from house		
	• Settling or leaning		
	• Spalling		
	• Too many appliances on one flue		
	• Total chimney height too short		
	• Vent connectors extending into chimney		
	• Vent connectors loose at chimney		

WOOD FURNACES				
LOCATION	CABINETS	LOCATION	VENTING SYSTEMS	
	• Combustible clearances		• Creosote deposits	
	• Mechanical damage		• Extends too far into chimney	
	• Missing components		• Improper material (galvanized)	
	• Not listed or certified		• Inadequate combustible clearance	
	• Obstructed air intakes		• Poor support	
	• Rust		• Poor slope	
	• Scorching		• Poor connection to chimney	
			• Poor manifolding	
	COMBUSTION AIR		• Poor connections	
			• Rust	
	• Inadequate combustion air		• Too long	
			• Too big or too small	
	COMBUSTION AIR DAMPERS			
			THERMOSTATS	
	• Inoperative valve or motor			
	• Poor adjustment		• Anticipator problems	
	• Running continuously		• Damaged	
	• Warped or stuck		• Dirty	
			• Loose	
	FORCED DRAFT COMBUSTION FANS		• Not level	
			• Poor adjustment, calibration	
	• Inoperative		• Poor location	
	• Noisy or vibrating			
			HOUSE AIR FANS (BLOWERS)	
	COMBUSTION CHAMBERS			
			• Dirty	
	• Deteriorated brick		• Fan belt loose, worn or damaged	
	• Dirty combustion chamber		• Inoperative	
	• Poor door seal		• Noisy	
	• Warped door		• Overheating	
	• Warped or cracked metal firebox		• Poorly secured	
	• Warped grate		• Rust	
			• Too small	
	HEAT EXCHANGERS		• Unbalanced or vibration	
	• Cracks or holes		FAN CONTROLS	
	• Rust			
	• Soot or creosote deposits		• Dirty	
			• Improperly wired	
	BAROMETRIC DAMPERS		• Mechanical damage	
			• Missing cover	
	• Inadequate draft air		• Rusting	
	• Inoperative		• Scorching	
	• Missing		• Set wrong or defective	
	• Poorly adjusted			
	• Rusting		HIGH TEMPERATURE LIMIT SWITCHES	
	• Spillage			
			• Missing	
			• Set wrong	

LOCATION	DUCT SYSTEMS	LOCATION	
	• Add-on furnace not downstream from other		
	• Combustible clearances		
	• Combustible return ducts		
	• Dirty ducts		
	• Disconnected ducts		
	• Ducts obstructed or collapsed		
	• Leaks		
	• No air or weak airflow		
	• Poor register location		
	• Registers obstructed, painted shut or damaged		
	• Registers or grills in garages		
	• Rust		
	• Too few return grills		
	• Uninsulated ducts		
	• Wire or pipe in ducts		

WOOD BOILERS			
LOCATION	CABINETS	LOCATION	HEAT EXCHANGERS
	• Combustible clearances		• Cracks or holes
	• Mechanical damage		• Rust
	• Missing components		• Soot or creosote deposits
	• Not listed or certified		
	• Obstructed air intakes		BAROMETRIC DAMPERS
	• Rust		
	• Scorching		• Inadequate draft air
			• Inoperative
	COMBUSTION AIR		• Missing
			• Poorly adjusted
	• Inadequate combustion air		• Rusting
			• Spillage
	COMBUSTION AIR DAMPERS		
			VENTING SYSTEMS
	• Inoperative valve or motor		
	• Poor adjustment		• Creosote deposits
	• Warped or stuck		• Extends too far into chimney
			• Improper material (galvanized)
	FORCED DRAFT COMBUSTION FANS		• Inadequate combustible clearance
			• Poor support
	• Inoperative		• Poor slope
	• Noisy or vibrating		• Poor connection to chimney
			• Poor manifolding
	COMBUSTION CHAMBERS		• Poor connections
			• Rust
	• Deteriorated brick		• Too long
	• Dirty combustion chamber		• Too big or too small
	• Poor door seal		
	• Warped door		PUMP CONTROLS
	• Warped or cracked metal firebox		
	• Warped grate		• Inoperative
			• Set incorrectly

LOCATION	ZONE CONTROLS	LOCATION	THERMOSTATS
	• Inoperative		• Anticipator problems
	• Leaking		• Damaged
			• Dirty
	OUTDOOR AIR THERMOSTATS		• Loose
			• Not level
	• Inoperative		• Poor adjustment or calibration
			• Poor location
	FLOW CONTROL VALVES		
			AIR VENTS
	• Inoperative		
	• Leaks		• Inoperative
			• Leaking
	ISOLATING VALVES		• Missing
	• Inoperative		PRIMARY CONTROLS
	• Leaks		
	• Rust		• Inoperative
			• Set incorrectly
	EXPANSION TANKS		
			BACKFLOW PREVENTERS
	• Leaks		
	• Poor discharge location for open tank		• Installed backwards
	• Poor location for tank		• Leaking
	• Rust		• Missing
	• Too small		
	• Waterlogged		PRESSURE REDUCING VALVES
	CIRCULATORS		• Inoperative
			• Installed backwards
	• Hot		• Leaking
	• Inoperative		• Missing
	• Leaks		• Set too low
	• Noisy		
			PIPES
	PRESSURE RELIEF VALVES		
			• Crimped
	• Missing		• Leaks
	• No piped extension		• No insulation
	• Pipe too small		• Poor support
	• Pipe threaded, capped or corroded at bottom		• Rust
	• Pipe dripping or leaking		• Too small
	• Poor location		
	• Set wrong		RADIATORS, CONVECTORS AND BASEBOARDS
	• Wrong size		
			• Balancing valve problems
			• Damaged baseboard fins
			• Leaks
			• Missing
			• Obstructed airflow
			• Poor location
			• Rust
			• Too small

LOCATION	CABINETS	LOCATION	VENTING SYSTEMS
	WOOD STOVES		
	• Door gasket – loose, missing, brittle or incomplete		• Creosote deposits
	• Door loose, warped or poorly fit		• Excess length
	• Leakage		• Goes through walls or closets
	• Unsteady or not well secured		• Heat reclaimer installed
	• Warped, cracked or gaps		• Inadequate combustible clearance
			• Multiple appliances connected to chimney
	COMBUSTION CHAMBERS		• No expansion provision
			• Pieces poorly connected
	• Catalytic combuster clogged		• Poor slope
	• Combustible clearances		• Poor connection to chimney
	– Floor		• Seams on bottom
	– Side and rear walls		• Too many elbows
	– Front walls		• Wrong material
	– Ceiling		
	• Creosote deposits		
	• Firebrick cracked, crumbling or incomplete		
	• Owner's manual missing		
	• Warped, cracked or creosote deposit		

LOCATION	FOOTINGS AND FOUNDATIONS	LOCATION	DAMPERS
	WOOD BURNING FIREPLACES		
	• Cracked		• Damper or frame rusted
	• Deteriorating concrete, masonry or mortar		• Frame loose
	• Heaved		• Inoperative
	• Leakage		• Missing
	• Settled		• Obstructed
			• Too low
	HEARTHS		• Undersized
	• Evidence of overheating		THROATS, SMOKE SHELVES & SMOKE CHAMBERS
	• Gaps or cracks		
	• Inappropriate material		• Debris
	• Settled		• Excess slope
	• Too thin		• Missing
	• Too small		• Rust (metal firebox)
	• Wood forms not removed		• Uneven slope
			• Walls not smooth
	FIREBOXES		• Wood forms not removed
	• Cracked masonry or refractory		FACES OR BREASTS
	• Designed for coal		
	• Deteriorated, missing or loose masonry or mortar		• Combustible clearances
	• Draft suspect		• Cracked
	• Inappropriate materials		• Evidence of overheating
	• Lintels rusted, sagging or loose		• Loose
	• Rust out, burn out, buckled or cracked metal firebox		• Settled (gap at wall)
	• Too shallow		• Too thick

LOCATION	ASHPITS	LOCATION	GLASS DOORS
	• Ash dump missing		• Cracked or broken glass
	• Cleanout door too close to combustibles		• Frame warped
	• Cleanout door missing		• Frame rust
	• Floor below cleanout door		• Inappropriate installation
	• Wood forms not removed		• Inoperative
	OUTDOOR COMBUSTION AIR SYSTEMS		HEAT CIRCULATORS
			• Fan inoperative
	• Damper stuck		• Obstructed intakes or outlets
	• Damper missing		
	• Disconnected		GAS IGNITERS
	• Hood and screen at firebox missing, damaged or loose		
	• Inadequate combustible clearance		• Gas leak
	• Inappropriate material		• Inadequate seal at firebox wall or floor
	• Intake not weather-tight		• Inadequate combustible clearance
	• Intake not screened		• Pipe rusted
	• Intake poor location		• Pipe obstructed
	• Rust		
	• Uninsulated		

ELECTRIC HEATING			
LOCATION	WIRING	LOCATION	
	• Aluminum wires used without compatible connectors		
	• Fuses or breakers too big		
	• Fuses or breakers bypassed		
	• Fuses or breakers loose		
	• Fuses or breakers missing		
	• Loose connections		
	• Multi-wire circuits on the same bus		
	• No links for 240 volt circuits		
	• No grease on stranded aluminum wires		
	• Open splices		
	• Wire not well secured		
	• Wire damaged		
	• Wire overheating		
	• Wire running through steel studs without protection		
	• Wires too close to ducts, pipes or chimneys		
	• Wires exposed on walls or ceilings		
	• Wires exposed in attics		
	• Wires under carpet		
	• Wires too small		
	• Wires too close to edge of studs or joists		
	• Wrong breaker for panel		

SPACE HEATERS			
LOCATION		LOCATION	
	• 120 volt heaters installed on 240 volt circuits or vice versa		
	• Damaged or rusted heaters		
	• Dirty or bent fins on heaters		
	• Electrical receptacles above heaters		
	• Fans – noisy, inoperative, loose or dirty		
	• Inoperative heaters		
	• Loose or missing covers		
	• Missing or too few heaters		
	• Obstructed heaters		
	•Thermostat overloaded		

ELECTRIC FURNACES			
LOCATION	GENERAL	LOCATION	MECHANICAL AIR FILTERS
	• Excess temperature rise		• Dirty
	• Inadequate heat		• Installed backwards
	• Individual elements, sequencers or relays inoperative		• Loose or collapsed
			• Missing
	CABINETS		•Wrong size
	• Mechanical damage		ELECTRONIC AIR CLEANERS
	• Missing components		
	• Obstructed air intake		• Damaged cells
	• Rust		• Dirty
			• Improper orientation
	THERMOSTATS		• Inoperative
			• Missing components
	• Anticipator		• Miswired
	• Damaged		
	• Dirty		HUMIDIFIERS
	• Loose		
	• Not level		• Clogged pad, mesh or nozzle
	• Poor adjustment or calibration		• Dirty
	• Poor location		• Inoperative motor or solenoid valve
			• Leaks
	BLOWERS		• No duct damper
			• Poor location
	• Dirty		
	• Fan belt loose, worn or damaged		DUCTS, REGISTERS AND GRILLES
	• Inoperative		
	• Noisy		• Balancing damper adjustment
	• Overheating		• Dirty, obstructed or collapsed ducts
	• Poorly secured		• Disconnected ducts
	• Running continuously		• Excessive elbows
	• Rust		• Excessively long runs
	•Too small		• Leaky joints
	• Unbalanced or vibration		• Undersized
			•Weak airflow
	FAN/LIMIT SWITCHES		
	• Improperly wired		
	• Mechanical damage		
	• Missing cover		
	• Rusting or dirty		
	• Scorching		
	• Set wrong or defective		

ELECTRIC BOILERS				
LOCATION	GENERAL	LOCATION	PRESSURE RELIEF VALVES	
	• Excess temperature rise		• Missing	
	• Inadequate heat		• No piped extension	
	• Individual elements, sequencers or relays inoperative		• Pipe too small	
			• Pipe threaded, capped or corroded at bottom	
	CABINETS		• Pipe dripping or leaking	
			• Poor location	
	• Combustion clearance		• Set wrong	
	• Mechanical damage		• Wrong size	
	• Missing components			
	• Not well secured		HIGH TEMPERATURE LIMIT SWITCHES	
	• Obstructed air intake			
	• Rust		• Defective or not wired correctly	
	• Scorching		• Missing	
			• Set too high	
	AIR VENTS			
			LOW WATER CUT-OUTS	
	• Inoperative			
	• Leaking		• Inoperative	
	• Missing		• Leaking	
	PUMP CONTROLS		BACKFLOW PREVENTERS	
	• Inoperative		• Installed backwards	
	• Set incorrectly		• Leaking	
			• Missing	
	ZONE CONTROLS			
			PRESSURE REDUCING VALVES	
	• Inoperative			
	• Leaking		• Inoperative	
			• Installed backwards	
	FLOW CONTROL VALVES		• Leaking	
			• Missing	
	• Inoperative		• Set too low	
	• Leaking			
			CIRCULATOR PUMPS	
	ISOLATING VALVES			
			• Hot	
	• Inoperative		• Inoperative	
	• Leaking		• Leaking	
	• Rust		• Noisy	
	THERMOSTATS		PIPES	
	• Anticipator		• Crimped	
	• Damaged		• Leaks	
	• Dirty		• No insulation	
	• Loose		• Poor support	
	• Not level		• Rust	
	• Poor adjustment or calibration		• Too small	
	• Poor location			
			RADIATORS, CONVECTORS AND BASEBOARDS	
	EXPANSION TANKS			
			• Balancing valve problems	
	• Leaking		• Bleed valve problems	
	• Rust		• Damaged baseboard fins	
	• Too small		• Leaks	
	• Waterlogged		• Missing	
			• Obstructed airflow	
			• Poor location	
			• Rust	
			• Too small	
			• Won't warm up	

RADIANT HEAT			
LOCATION	GENERAL	LOCATION	THERMOSTATS
	• Inadequate heat		• Anticipator problems
			• Damaged
			• Loose
			• Not level
			• Poor adjustment or calibration
			• Poor location

WALL AND FLOOR FURNACES, ROOM HEATERS & GAS FIREPLACES			
LOCATION	HEAT EXCHANGERS	LOCATION	FAN/LIMIT SWITCHES
	• Cracks, holes or rust		• Improperly wired
	• Soot or deposits		• Mechanical damage
			• Missing cover
	CABINETS		• Rusting or dirty
			• Scorching
	• Combustible clearances		• Set wrong or defective
	• Mechanical damage		
	• Missing components		ITEMS SPECIFIC TO WALL FURNACES
	• Obstructed air intake		
	• Rust		• Ducts added
	• Scorching		• Not listed, certified or approved
			• Unvented furnace in bedroom or bathroom
	THERMOSTATS		• Unvented furnace
	• Anticipator		ITEMS SPECIFIC TO FLOOR FURNACES
	• Damaged		
	• Dirty		• Cap missing or damaged
	• Loose		• Firebox cracked or rusted
	• Not level		• Not permitted
	• Poor adjustment or calibration		• Not listed, certified or approved
	• Poor location		• Restricted airflow causing overheating
			• Thermostat remote
	BLOWERS		
			ITEMS SPECIFIC TO ROOM HEATERS (SPACE HEATERS)
	• Dirty		
	• Fan belt loose, worn or damaged		• Fireplace damper not fixed open
	• Inoperative		• Not labeled for use in a fireplace
	• Noisy		• Unvented
	• Overheating		
	• Poorly secured		ITEMS SPECIFIC TO GAS FIREPLACES AND GAS LOGS
	• Running continuously		
	• Rust		• Damper in existing fireplace not fixed open
	• Too small		• Glass door problem
	• Unbalanced or vibration		• Not suitable for use in a bedroom or bathroom
			• Unvented (may be acceptable)

► 5. AIR CONDITIONING AND HEAT PUMPS – FIELD CHECKLIST

DESCRIPTION

Items that need to be described to meet ASHI® Standards:

ENERGY SOURCE

☐ Electricity
☐ Gas
☐ _____

COOLING EQUIPMENT TYPE

☐ Air
☐ Water
☐ Earth
☐ _____

Location Legend   N = North   S = South   E = East   W = West
    1 =1st Floor   2 = 2nd Floor   3 = 3rd Floor   B= Basement   CS = CrawlSpace

AIR CONDITIONING				
LOCATION	CAPACITY		LOCATION	REFRIGERANT LINES
	• Oversized			• Damaged
	• Undersized			• Leak
				• Lines too warm or too cold
	COMPRESSORS			• Lines touching each other
				• Low points or improper slope in lines
	• Electric wires too small			• Missing insulation
	• Excess electric current draw			
	• Excess noise or vibration			EXPANSION DEVICES
	• Inadequate cooling			
	• Inoperative			• Capillary tube crimped, disconnected, leaking
	• Missing electrical shutoff			•Thermostatic expansion valve loose, clogged, sticking
	• Out of level			
	• Running continuously			CONDENSER FANS
	• Short cycling			
	•Wrong fuse or breaker size			• Corrosion
				• Dirty
	AIR COOLED CONDENSER COILS			• Excess noise or vibration
				• Inoperative
	• Clothes dryer or water heater exhaust too close			• Mechanical damage
	• Corrosion			• Obstructed airflow
	• Damaged			
	• Dirty			EVAPORATOR FANS
	WATER COOLED CONDENSER COILS			• Corrosion
				• Damage
	• Cooled by pool water			• Dirty
	• Leak			• Dirty or missing filter
	• No water			• Excess noise or vibration
	• No backflow preventer			• Inoperative
				• Misadjustment of belt or pulleys
	EVAPORATOR COILS			• Undersized
	• Corrosion			DUCT SYSTEMS
	• Damage			
	• Dirty			• Dirty
	• Frost			• Disconnected or leaking
	• No access to coil			• Humidifier damper missing
	•Temperature split too low			• Incomplete
	•Temperature split too high			• Obstructed or collapsed
	•Top of coil dry			• Poor support
				• Poor balancing
	CONDENSATE SYSTEMS			• Supply or return registers – obstructed
	• Dirt in pan			• Supply or return registers – poor location
	• Inappropriate pan slope			• Supply or return registers – too few
	• No float switch			• Undersized
	• No auxiliary pan			•Weak airflow
	• Pan not well secured			
	• Pan cracked			DUCT INSULATION
	• Pan leaking or overflowing			
	• Rust or holes in pan			• Incomplete
				• Missing

LOCATION	DUCT VAPOR BARRIERS	LOCATION	CONDENSATE PUMPS
	• Damaged		• Inoperative
	• Missing		• Leaking
			• Poor wiring
	CONDENSATE DRAIN LINES		
			THERMOSTATS
	• Blocked or crimped		
	• Disconnected, missing		• Damaged
	• Improper discharge point		• Dirty
	• Leaking, damaged, split		• Inoperative
	• No trap		• Loose
			• Not level
			• Poor adjustment or calibration
			• Poor location

LOCATION	EVAPORATIVE COOLERS	LOCATION	
	• Cabinet or ducts not weather-tight		
	• Cabinet too close to grade		
	• Clogged pads		
	• Duct problems		
	• Electrical problems		
	• Excess noise or vibration		
	• Leaking		
	• Louvers obstructed		
	• Missing or dirty air filter		
	• No water		
	• No air gap on water supply		
	• Poor support for pump and water system		
	• Pump or fan inoperative		
	• Rust, mold and mildew		

LOCATION	WHOLE HOUSE FANS	LOCATION	
	• Excess noise or vibration		
	• Inadequate attic venting		
	• Inoperative		

HEAT PUMPS			
LOCATION	CAPACITY	LOCATION	OUTDOOR COILS
	• Oversized for cooling		• Clothes dryer or water heater exhaust too close
	• Undersized for heating		• Corrosion
			• Damaged
	COMPRESSORS		• Dirty
			• Iced up
	• Electric wires too small		• Poor location
	• Excess electric current draw		
	• Excess noise or vibration		INDOOR COILS
	• Inadequate cooling		
	• Inoperative in heating or cooling mode		• Corrosion
	• Missing electrical shutoff		• Damage
	• Out of level		• Dirty
	• Running continuously		• Frost
	• Short cycling		• No access to coil
	• Wrong fuse or breaker size		• Temperature split too low
			• Temperature split too high
			• Top of coil dry in cooling mode

LOCATION	CONDENSATE SYSTEMS	LOCATION	DUCT VAPOR BARRIERS
	• Dirt in pan		• Damaged
	• Inappropriate pan slope		• Missing
	• No float switch		
	• No auxiliary pan		CONDENSATE DRAIN LINES
	• Pan not well secured		
	• Pan cracked		• Blocked or crimped
	• Pan leaking or overflowing		• Disconnected or missing
	• Rust or holes in pan		• Improper discharge point
			• Leaking, damaged, split
	EXPANSION DEVICES		• No trap
	• Capillary tube crimped, disconnected, leaking		CONDENSATE PUMPS
	• Thermostatic expansion valve loose, clogged, sticking		• Inoperative
			• Leaking
	OUTDOOR FANS		• Poor wiring
	• Corrosion		REFRIGERANT LINES
	• Dirty		
	• Excess noise or vibration		• Damaged
	• Inoperative		• Leaking
	• Mechanical damage		• Lines too warm or too cold
	• Obstructed airflow		• Lines touching each other
			• Low points or improper slope in lines
	INDOOR FANS		• Missing insulation
	• Corrosion		THERMOSTATS
	• Damage		
	• Dirty		• Damaged
	• Dirty or missing filter		• Dirty
	• Excess noise or vibration		• Inoperative
	• Inoperative		• Loose
	• Misadjustment of belt or pulleys		• Not level
	• Undersized		• Poor adjustment or calibration
			• Poor location
	DUCT SYSTEMS		
			BACKUP HEAT
	• Dirty		
	• Disconnected or leaking		• Missing
	• Humidifier damper missing		• Inoperative
	• Incomplete		• Poor location
	• Obstructed or collapsed		• Runs continuously
	• Poor support		
	• Poor balancing		DUCT INSULATION
	• Supply or return registers —		
	– Too few		• Incomplete
	– Poor location		• Missing
	– Obstructed		
	• Undersized for cooling		
	• Weak airflow		

► 6. PLUMBING – FIELD CHECKLIST

DESCRIPTION

Items that need to be described to meet ASHI® Standards:

WATER SUPPLY MATERIALS

☐ Copper
☐ Galvanized steel
☐ Lead
☐ Plastic
☐ Brass
☐ _____
☐ Not visible

DRAIN, WASTE AND VENT PIPING MATERIALS

☐ Galvanized steel
☐ Plastic
☐ Copper
☐ Cast iron
☐ Lead
☐ _____
☐ Not visible

WATER HEATING EQUIPMENT

☐ Gas
☐ Electric
☐ Oil
☐ _____
☐ Tankless
☐ Combination system

Location Legend   N = North   S = South   E = East   W = West
   1 =1st Floor   2 = 2nd Floor   3 = 3rd Floor   B= Basement   CS = CrawlSpace

SUPPLY PLUMBING				
LOCATION	WATER SUPPLY PUMPS	LOCATION	PRESSURE REGULATORS	
	• Damaged		• Leaking	
	• Excessive noise or vibration		• Missing	
	• Frozen		• No bypass or relief valve	
	• Inoperative		• Poor location	
	• Leak		• Rust	
	• Lost prime		• Set wrong	
	• Overheating			
	• Running continuously		SUPPLY PIPING IN HOUSES	
	• Rust			
	• Short cycling		• Combustible piping	
	• Wiring problems		• Cross connections	
			• Excess pressure	
	PRESSURE TANKS		• Excessive noise	
			• Leak	
	• Condensation		• Non-standard material	
	• Leaking		• Poor pressure or flow	
	• Rust		• Poor support	
	• Tank wobbling or unstable		• Rust	
	• Waterlogged		• Split, damaged, crimped	
			• Suspect connections on polybutylene	
	WATER SERVICE PIPES			
			SHUT OFF VALVES	
	• Freezing			
	• Leaking		• Damaged handle	
	• Low pressure		• Exposed to mechanical damage	
	• Mechanical damage		• Inoperable, inaccessible, buried	
			• Leaking	
			• Missing or cannot be located	
			• Partly closed	
			• Rusted	

WATER HEATERS				
GAS BURNERS AND VENTING				
LOCATION	GAS METERS	LOCATION	COMBUSTION AIR	
	• Gas shut off and locked		• Inadequate combustion air	
	• Ice			
	• Leak		GAS BURNERS	
	• Mechanical damage			
	• Poor access		• Delayed ignition	
	• Poor location		• Dirt or soot	
	• Rust		• Gas odor or leak	
	• Undersized		• Inoperative	
			• Poor flame color or pattern	
	GAS PIPING		• Rust	
			• Scorching	
	• Copper tubing not properly labeled		• Short cycling	
	• Improper connections			
	• Inadequate support		HEAT SHIELDS	
	• Inappropriate materials			
	• Leak		• Loose	
	• Missing shut off valves		• Rusted	
	• No drip leg		• Missing	
	• Piping in chimney or duct system		• Scorched	
	• Plastic pipe exposed above-grade			
	• Rust			

LOCATION	VENTING SYSTEMS	LOCATION	
	• Improper material		
	• Inadequate combustible clearance		
	• Poor support		
	• Poor connections		
	• Poor manifolding		
	• Poor slope		
	• Rust, dirty, obstructed		
	• Spillage or backdraft at the draft hood		
	• Too long		
	• Vent connector extends too far into chimney		
	• Vent connector too small, too big for water heater		

OIL BURNER AND VENTING			
LOCATION	OIL STORAGE TANKS	LOCATION	OIL BURNERS AND REFRACTORIES
	• Empty		• Dirt or soot
	• Leak		• Excess noise or vibration
	• Not suitable for outdoor use		• Incomplete combustion
	• Poor location		• Inoperative
	• Rust		• Leak
	• Underground		• Poor flame color pattern
			• Refractory problems
	FILL AND VENT PIPES		• Rust
			• Scorching
	• Abandoned		• Too close to combustibles
	• Damaged or corroded		
	• Leak		PRIMARY CONTROLLER
	• Missing caps		
			• Inoperative
	OIL SUPPLY LINES		• Missing
			• Tripped
	• Corrosion, mechanical damage, crimped		BAROMETRIC DAMPERS/DRAFT REGULATORS
	• Leak		
	• Undersized		• Improper location
	• Unprotected		• Inadequate draft air
			• Inoperative
	OIL FILTERS		• Misadjusted
			• Missing (often not needed)
	• Dirty		• Rust
	• Leak		• Spillage
	• Missing		
	COMBUSTION AIR		
	• Inadequate		

LOCATION	VENTING SYSTEMS	LOCATION	
	• Improper material		
	• Inadequate combustible clearance		
	• Loose connections		
	• Poor support		
	• Poor slope		
	• Poor insertion into chimney		
	• Poor manifolding		
	• Rust, dirty, obstructed		
	• Too small or too big		
	• Too long		

CONVENTIONAL TANK TYPE WATER HEATERS			
LOCATION		LOCATION	CIRCULATING PUMPS
	• Baffle collapsed or missing (gas or oil)		• Improper arrangement
	• Damaged tank		• Inoperative
	• Drain valve problems		• Leak
	• Gas burner cover or roll out shield missing, damaged, rust		• Overheating or excess noise or vibration
	• Hot and cold piping reversed		
	• Inadequate combustible clearance		
	• Inadequate capacity or recovery rate		
	• Inoperative		
	• Insulation obstructing combustion air or draft hood (gas or oil)		
	• Leak		
	• Low water pressure and flow		
	• No isolating valve		
	• Noisy water heater		
	• Poor location –		
	– Bedrooms		
	– Bathrooms		
	– Closets		
	• Propane water heater in low area		
	• Rust		
	• Tank wobbly or not stable		
	• Temperature/pressure relief valve problems		

COMBINATION HEATING SYSTEMS			
LOCATION		LOCATION	
	• No hot water or inadequate hot water		
	• Tempering valve missing, set improperly		
	• Water too hot		

TANKLESS COILS			
	• Leak		
	• Poor hot water pressure or flow (clogged?)		
	• Rust		
	• Tempering valve —		
	– Defective		
	– Missing		
	– Set wrong		

	WASTE PLUMBING		
LOCATION	DRAIN PIPING MATERIALS	LOCATION	FLOOR DRAINS
	• Clean-outs missing or inaccessible		• Backup
	• Clogged		• Downspout connection upstream of trap
	• Clothes washer drain connections		• Grate missing, rusted or obstructed
	• Combustible piping		• Missing
	• Cross connections		• No trap
	• Defective ABS piping		• No primer or poor primer arrangement
	• Dishwasher drain connections		• Poor location
	• Exposed to mechanical damage		
	• Freezing		VENTING SYSTEMS
	• Galvanized steel pipe buried in soil		
	• Improper condensate drain connections		• Automatic air vents
	• Leak		• Ineffective
	• Noisy		• Island venting problems
	• Nonstandard materials and patches		• Missing
	• Pipe size reduced downstream		• Poor vent pipe arrangements
	• Poor slope		• Too small or too long
	• Poor support		• Vent termination problems
	• Poor manifolding of drain piping		
	• Rust		LAUNDRY TUB PUMPS
	• Split, damaged, crimped pipe		
	• Undersized		• Clogged
	• Welded steel piping		• Discharge pipe problems
			• Electrical problems
	TRAPS		• Excess noise or vibration
			• Inoperative
	• Clogged		• Missing
	• Double trapping		• Short cycling or running continuously
	• Freezing		
	• Leak		SUMP PUMPS
	• Missing		
	• No clean out provision		• Debris in the sump, clogged sump
	• Nonstandard shape or material		• Discharge pipe problems
	• Split, rusted or damaged		• Electrical problems
	• Tailpiece (fixture outlet pipe) too long		• Excess noise or vibration
	• Trap primer – possible cross connection		• Inoperative, poorly secured or rust
	• Trap primer missing		• Lid missing, rotted or not secure
	• Trap arm too long or too short		• Missing
	• Traps too small or too big		• Short cycling or running continuously
	• Wrong type		• Sump damaged
	SEWAGE EJECTOR PUMPS		
	• Alarm sounding		
	• Discharge pipe problems		
	• Electrical problems		
	• Inoperative		
	• Missing, rusting or inoperative union, check valve or gate		
	• No vent		
	• Odor		
	• Short cycling or running continuously		

FIXTURES AND FAUCETS			
LOCATION	BASINS, SINKS AND LAUNDRY TUBS	LOCATION	SHOWER STALLS
	• Cross connections		• Entrance problems
	• Leak		• Leak
	• Loose		• Pooling water on the floor
	• Not level		• Rust
	• Overflows missing, leak, rust or inappropriate		• Sill and threshold problems
	• Rust		• Slow drains
	• Slow drains		• Too small
	• Surface defects		
			BIDETS
	FAUCETS		
			• Cracked, broken bowl
	• Cross connections		• Cross connections
	• Drip, leak		• Floor damage suspected
	• Hot and cold reversed		• Loose
	• Loose		• Slow drains
	• Noisy		• Spray or rim wash diverter inoperative
	• Obstructed aerator		• Surface defects
	• Shower diverter inoperative or defective		
	• Stiff or inoperative		BATHTUBS
	HOSE BIBBS		• Cross connections
			• Leak
	• Damage		• Loose or unstable
	• Leaks or drips		• Overflow leaking, disconnected or rust
	• Loose		• Rust
	• No backflow preventer		• Slow drains
	• Pipe frozen or split		• Surface defects
	• Poor slope on frost-free bibb		
	• Stiff or inoperative		TUB AND SHOWER STALL ENCLOSURES
	TOILETS		• Leak
			• Loose, broken or missing tile
	• Broken or cracked tank lids, bowls or seats		• Electrical problems at the enclosure
	• Connected to the hot water system		• Not smooth, impervious or water resistant
	• Cross connection		
	• Crowded		WHIRLPOOL BATHS
	• Floor damage suspected		
	• Flush mechanism inoperative		• Cross connections
	• Lazy flush		• Dirty water from the jets
	• Leaks		• Diverter inoperative
	• Loose		• Electrical switch or receptacles too close to tub
	• Obstructed		• Excess pump noise or vibration
	• Odor around toilet		• Leak
	• Running continuously		• No pump access
	• Shutoff valve missing or inoperative		• No GFCI
	• Surface defects		• Not level
			• Odor
			• Pump doesn't run
			• Suction cover missing, loose, suspect
			• Surface defects

► 7. ELECTRICAL – FIELD CHECKLIST

DESCRIPTION

Items that need to be described to meet ASHI® Standards:

SERVICE AMPERAGE

_____ Amps

VOLTAGE

☐ 240
☐ _____

SERVICE ENTRY CONDUCTOR MATERIALS

☐ Copper
☐ Aluminum
☐ _____

SERVICE TYPE

☐ Overhead
☐ Underground

LOCATION OF MAIN SERVICE BOX

_____

LOCATION OF DISTRIBUTION PANELS

_____

_____

_____

ALUMINUM BRANCH CIRCUIT WIRING NOTED

☐ Yes
☐ No

Location Legend   N = North   S = South   E = East   W = West

1 =1st Floor   2 = 2nd Floor   3 = 3rd Floor   B= Basement   CS = CrawlSpace

SERVICE DROPS AND SERVICE ENTRANCES				
LOCATION	SERVICE DROPS OR SERVICE LATERALS	LOCATION	SERVICE SIZE	
	• Branches, vines interfering with wires		• Fuse, breaker size in service box	
	• Damaged, frayed wires		• Inadequate service size	
	• Excessive height		• Marginal service size	
	• Height over roofs		• Rating of service box	
	• Height over walking areas		• Service conductor size	
	• Height over roadways			
	• Height over driveways			
	• Height over decks, balconies and pools			
	• Inadequate window or door clearance			
	• Poor connection to service conductors			
	SERVICE CONDUCTORS OR SERVICE ENTRANCE WIRES			
	• Conduit or cable damaged			
	• Conduit or cable covered by siding			
	• Conduit or cable not weather-tight			
	• Drip loop too low (touching roof)			
	• Mast rust			
	• Mast bent			
	• Mast rot			
	• Mast loose			
	• Mast not weather-tight			
	• Masthead not weather-tight			
	• No masthead			
	• No drip loop			
	• Wires too close to roof			

SERVICES BOXES, GROUNDING AND PANELS			
LOCATION	SERVICE BOXES	LOCATION	DISTRIBUTION PANELS
	• Box rating too small		• Circuits not labeled
	• Box location		• Damaged panel or components
	• Box not weather-tight		• Double taps
	• Damaged parts		• Fuse holder loose or broken
	• Fused neutral		• Fused neutrals
	• Fuses upstream of disconnect switch		• Fuses loose
	• Illegal taps		• Fuses or breakers too big
	• Inappropriate mounting surface		• Fuses bypassed
	• Multiple disconnects		• Inappropriate mounting surface
	• Neutral wire bypasses service box		• Loose breakers
	• Not well secured		• Loose or missing door
	• Obsolete service box		• Loose panel
	• Overheating		• Multi-wire circuit on same bus
	• Poor access		• Neutral and ground wires bonded at subpanel
	• Poor connections		• No fuses or breakers for subpanel and feeder
	• Rust		• No links for multi-wire circuits
	• Service entrance wires exposed in house		• Not rated for aluminum
	• Single main disconnect		• Obsolete
	• Unprotected openings		• Openings in panel
	• Wrong fuse or breaker size		• Overheating
			• Panel crowded
	SYSTEM GROUNDING		• Panel upside-down
			• Poor access
	• Box not bonded to ground		• Rust or water in panel
	• Connections not accessible		• Subpanel not grounded
	• Corroded ground wire		• Too many breakers
	• Ground rod cut		• Undersized panel
	• Missing		• Wrong breaker for panel
	• Neutral bonded to ground wire downstream of service box		• Wrong fuses or breakers for subpanel and feeder
	• Neutral not bonded to ground at box		
	• No jumper for meters and valves		WIRES
	• No ground for subpanel		
	• Poor connections		• Abandoned wires in panel
	• Spliced ground wire		• Damaged
	• Undersized ground wire		• Loose connections
	• Wire attached to plastic pipe		• Not well secured
	• Wire attached to abandoned pipe		• Overheating
			• Sheathing not removed
			• Wire crossing bus connections

DISTRIBUTION SYSTEMS			
LOCATION	WIRING	LOCATION	LIGHTS
	• Abandoned wire		• Damaged
	• Buried cable		• Heat lamps over doors
	• Damaged		• Improper closet lighting
	• Exposed on walls or ceilings		• Improper potlights
	• Exposed in attics		• Inoperative
	• Extension cord used as permanent wiring		• Isolating links needed on pull chains
	• Improper color coding		• Loose
	• In steel studs without protection		• Not grounded
	• Indoor cable used outdoors		• Obsolete
	• Loose connections		• Overheating
	• Missing		• Poor stairway lighting
	• Not well secured		
	• Open splices		SWITCHES
	• Overhead wires not stranded		
	• Permanent wiring used as extension cord		• Damaged, loose, rust
	• Too close to ducts, pipes, chimneys, etc.		• Faulty 3-way dimmer switch
	• Too close to edge of studs or joists		• Inoperative, obsolete
	• Under carpets		• No shut off
	• Undersized wire		• Overheated
	• Wrong type		• Poor location in bathroom
			• Poor garbage disposal switch location
	KNOB-AND-TUBE		• Poor location at furnace
	• Buried in insulation		JUNCTION BOXES
	• Connections need boxes		
	• Conventional lights in wet areas		• Concealed boxes
	• Fused neutrals		• Cover loose or missing
	• Wire insulation or sheathing brittle		• Damaged, rust
			• Missing, loose
	ALUMINUM		• Not grounded
			• Overcrowded
	• Connectors not compatible with aluminum		• Overheating
	• No grease on stranded wires		OUTLETS
	• Overheating		
			• Above electric baseboard heaters
	OUTDOOR WIRING		• Broken pin or blade in slots
			• Damaged
	• Buried wire		• Dedicated circuits needed
	• Extension cords powering exterior outlets		• In floors or countertops
	• Garage door opener connected to extension cord		• Inoperative
	• Indoor wire used outdoors		• Loose
	• Not suitable for use		• No GFI
	• Solid wire run overhead		• Open neutral
	• Wires not well secured to walls		• Open hot
	• Wires too close to grade		• Overheated neutral
	• Wires run on roof surfaces		• Overheating
	• Wires through gutters or downspouts		• Reverse polarity
			• Too close to bathtubs
			• Too few outlets
			• Too far from basin
			• Ungrounded
			• Within 18 inches of garage floor
			• Worn receptacles
			• Wrong type

▶ 8. STRUCTURE – FIELD CHECKLIST

DESCRIPTION

Items that need to be described to meet ASHI® Standards:

FOUNDATIONS

- ☐ Poured concrete
- ☐ Masonry block
- ☐ Stone
- ☐ Brick
- ☐ Clay tile
- ☐ Piers and grade beams
- ☐ Piers or Piles
- ☐ Wood
- ☐ Not visible/none

CONFIGURATION

- ☐ Basement
- ☐ Crawlspace
- ☐ Slab-on-grade

FLOOR STRUCTURE

- ☐ Joists
- ☐ Trusses
- ☐ Concrete
- ☐ Not visible

COLUMNS

- ☐ Brick
- ☐ Masonry block
- ☐ Concrete
- ☐ Steel
- ☐ Wood
- ☐ Not visible

WALL STRUCTURE

☐ Masonry
☐ Wood frame
☐ Wood frame brick veneer
☐ _____
☐ Not visible

CEILING STRUCTURE

☐ Joists
☐ Trusses
☐ Rafters
☐ Not visible

Location Legend   N = North   S = South   E = East   W = West
    1 =1st Floor   2 = 2nd Floor   3 = 3rd Floor   B= Basement   CS = CrawlSpace

FOUNDATIONS			
LOCATION		LOCATION	
	• Basement lowered (suspect)		
	• Bowed, bulging or leaning		
	• Cold joints		
	• Cracks		
	• Crushed		
	• Foundations too short		
	• Foundations too thin		
	• Hollow masonry units installed on their sides		
	• Honeycombing		
	• Insect or fire damage		
	• Large trees close to building (suspect)		
	• Lateral support poor		
	• Lateral movement		
	• Mechanically damaged		
	• Mortar deteriorating or missing		
	• Not well secured		
	• Pilasters moving		
	• Prior repairs		
	• Rot or wood/soil contact		
	• Spalling, crumbling or broken material		
	• Steep slope or unstable soil		

FLOORS			
LOCATION	SILLS	LOCATION	BEAMS
	• Anchor nuts missing		• Concentrated loads
	• Anchor washers missing		• Inadequate lateral support
	• Anchor bolts too short		• Missing beams or sections of beams
	• Anchor bolts not secure in foundation		• Notches or holes
	• Anchor bolts missing		• Poor bearing, crushed or loose shims
	• Anchor nuts not tightened		• Poor connections of built-up components
	• Anchors not centered in sill		• Prior repairs
	• At or below grade level		• Rot, insect or fire damage
	• Crushed		• Rotated or twisted beams
	• Gaps under sills		• Rust
	• Missing		• Sag
	• Rot, insect or fire damage		• Weak connections to joists
	• Sill split at anchor bolts		• Weak connections to columns
	COLUMNS OR PIERS		JOISTS
	• Buckling		• Concentrated loads
	• Crushed		• Inappropriate notching or holes
	• Heaved		• Ineffective blocking, bracing or bridging
	• Leaning		• Missing
	• Mechanical damage		• No blocking, bracing or bridging
	• Missing		• Poor end bearing, joist hanger connections
	• Missing footing?		• Prior repairs
	• Mortar deterioration		• Rot, insect or fire damage
	• Poorly secured at top or bottom		• Sag or springy
	• Prior repairs		• Split or damaged
	• Rot, insect or fire damage		• Weak cantilevers
	• Settled		• Weak mortise and tenon joints
	• Spalling concrete or brick		• Weak openings (stairs, chimneys, etc.)

LOCATION	SUBFLOORING	LOCATION	CONCRETE SLABS
	• Concentrated loads		• Cracked
	• Cracking ceramic tiles		• Heaved
	• Damaged or cut		• Hollow below slab
	• Plywood in wrong orientation		• Rusted re-bar
	• Poor fastening (nailing, screwing, gluing)		• Settled
	• Poor end support or cantilevered		• Shaling
	• Prior repairs		• Spalling
	• Rot, insect or fire damage		
	• Sag or springy		
	• Squeaks		
	• Swollen waferboard		

WALLS			
LOCATION	SOLID MASONRY WALLS	LOCATION	WOOD FRAME WALLS
	• Bowing, leaning or bulging		• Bottom plates have poor bearing
	• Cracks		• Excess holes or notches
	• Efflorescence		• Firestopping missing
	• Excess corbeling		• Girts missing
	• Foundations weak or missing		• Leaning, bowing, buckling or racking
	• Hollow units on their sides		• Lintels sagging
	• Lateral support is suspect		• Mechanical damage
	• Masonry deteriorating or spalling		• Offset excessive
	• Masonry too close to soil		• Poor nailing
	• Mortar deteriorating or missing		• Rot, fire or insect damage
	• Prior repairs		• Sheathing missing or ineffective
	• Wavy masonry		• Top plates weak or sagging
			• Wood too close to soil
	MASONRY VENEER WALLS		
			ARCHES
	• Bowing, leaning or bulging		
	• Cracks		• Cracked
	• Efflorescence		• Dropped, rotating or leaning
	• Excess corbeling		• Efflorescence
	• Flashing at weep holes missing or ineffective		• Masonry deterioration or missing
	• Foundations weak or missing		• Masonry units moving
	• Hollow units on their sides		• Missing
	• Lintels sagging, rusting		• Mortar deterioration or missing
	• Masonry or wood too close to the soil		• Prior repairs
	• Masonry deteriorating or spalling		
	• Mortar deteriorating or missing		LINTELS
	• Prior repairs		
	• Wavy masonry		• End bearing poor
	• Weep holes missing or ineffective		• Mechanical damage
			• Missing
			• Rot, fire or insect damage
			• Rotating or leaning
			• Rust
			• Sagging or undersized
			• Wood supporting masonry

ROOF FRAMING				
LOCATION	RAFTERS	LOCATION	TRUSSES	
	• Bearing on ridge board		• Buckled webs	
	• Concentrated loads		• Endbearing	
	• Endbearing not adequate		• Mechanical damage	
	• Mechanical damage		• Missing webs	
	• Rafter spread		• Modified (improperly)	
	• Ridge sag		• Notches, holes	
	• Rot, insect or fire damage		• Rot, insect or fire damage	
	• Sagging		• Sag	
	• Spliced		• Truss uplift	
	• Split		• Weak connections	
	• Too small or overspanned			
	• Warped		SHEATHING	
	• Weak framing at openings			
	• Weak connections		• Buckled	
			• Delaminated	
	COLLAR TIES		• FRT deterioration	
			• Mold, mildew	
	• Buckling		• Rot, insect or fire damage	
	• Loose or poor connections		• Sag	
	• Mechanical damage		• Too thin	
	• Missing			
	• Need lateral bracing		I JOISTS	
	• Rot, insect or fire damage			
			• Birds' mouths	
	KNEE WALLS/PURLINS		• No ridge beams	
			• Notched	
	• Buckling		• Rot, insect or fire damage	
	• Mechanical damage		• Toe bearing or endbearing inadequate	
	• Poor connections		• Weak connections	
	• Purlins installed on side			
	• Purlins sagging			
	• Removed, needed			
	• Rot, insect or fire damage			
	• Single top plate, sag			

► 9. KITCHENS AND LAUNDRY ROOMS – FIELD CHECKLIST

Location Legend	N = North	S = South	E = East	W = West
	1 =1st Floor	2 = 2nd Floor	3 = 3rd Floor	B= Basement

ELECTRICAL				
LOCATION	WIRING	LOCATION	OUTLETS	
	• Abandoned wire		• Above electric baseboard heaters	
	• Damaged		• Broken pin or blade in slots	
	• Exposed on walls or ceilings		• Damaged	
	• Extension cord used as permanent wiring		• Dedicated circuits needed	
	• Improper color coding		• In floors or countertops	
	• In steel studs without protection		• Inoperative	
	• Loose connections		• Loose	
	• Missing		• No GFI	
	• Not well secured		• Open hot	
	• Open splices		• Open neutral	
	• Permanent wiring used as extension cord		• Overheated neutral	
	•Too close to ducts, pipes, chimneys, etc.		• Overheating	
	•Too close to edge of studs or joists		• Reverse polarity	
	• Under carpets		•Too few outlets	
	• Undersized wire		• Ungrounded	
	•Wrong type		•Worn receptacles	
			•Wrong type	
	KNOB-AND-TUBE			
			LIGHTS	
	• Connections need boxes			
	•Wire insulation or sheathing brittle		• Damaged	
			• Improper potlights	
	ALUMINUM		• Inadequate	
			• Inoperative	
	• Connectors not compatible with aluminum		• Isolating links needed on pull chains	
	• No grease on stranded wires		• Loose	
	• Overheating		• Not grounded	
			• Obsolete	
	JUNCTION BOXES		• Overheating	
			• Poor stairway lighting	
	• Concealed boxes			
	• Cover loose or missing		SWITCHES	
	• Damaged			
	• Missing, loose		• Damaged, loose	
	• Not grounded		• Faulty 3-way dimmer switch	
	• Overcrowded		• Inoperative, obsolete	
	• Overheating		• No shut off for dimmer switch	
			• Overheated	
			• Poor garbage disposal switch location	

HEATING			
LOCATION	DUCTS, REGISTERS AND GRILLES	LOCATION	STEAM DISTRIBUTION PIPES AND RADIATORS
	• Weak airflow		• Air vent –
	• Disconnected ducts		– Leak
	• Dirty, obstructed collapsed		– Missing
	• Leaky joints		– Obstructed
	• Excessively long runs, excessive elbows		– Poor location
	• Undersized		• Clogged
	• Balancing damper adjustment		• Improper slope
	• Rust (in-slab ducts)		• Leaking
	• Wires or pipes in ducts		• Low spots
			• Radiators won't warm up
	HOT WATER RADIATORS, CONVECTORS AND BASEBOARDS		• Traps –
			– Missing
	• Balancing valve problems		– Leak
	• Bleed valve problems		– Stuck open, closed
	• Cold		– Damage
	• Damaged baseboard fins		– Inoperative
	• Leak		
	• Missing		ELECTRIC SPACE HEATERS
	• Obstructed airflow		
	• Poor location		• 120 volt heaters installed on 240 volt circuits or vice versa
	• Rust		• Damaged or rusted
	• Too small (room cool)		• Dirty or bent fins
			• Electrical receptacles above heaters
	HOT WATER RADIANT HEATING		• Fans – noisy, inoperative, loose or dirty
			• Inoperative
	• Leaks		• Loose or missing covers
	• Cool rooms or parts of rooms		• Missing or too few heaters
	• Balancing valve problems		• Obstructed
	• Bleed valve problems		• Thermostat overloaded

PLUMBING			
LOCATION	SUPPLY PIPING IN HOUSES	LOCATION	VENTING SYSTEMS
	• Combustible piping		• Automatic air vents
	• Cross connections		• Ineffective
	• Excess pressure		• Island venting problems
	• Excessive noise		• Missing
	• Leak		• Poor vent pipe arrangements
	• Non-standard material		• Too small or too long
	• Poor pressure or flow		• Vent termination problems
	• Poor support		
	• Rust		SINKS
	• Split, damaged, crimped		
	• Suspect connections on polybutylene		• Cross connections
			• Leaks
	DRAIN PIPING MATERIALS		• Loose
			• Not level
	• Clean-outs missing or inaccessible		• Overflows inappropriate
	• Clogged		• Rust
	• Clotheswasher drain connection		• Slow drains
	• Combustible piping		• Surface defects
	• Cross connections		
	• Defective ABS piping		FAUCETS
	• Dishwasher drain connections		
	• Exposed to mechanical damage		• Cross connections
	• Freezing		• Drips, leaks
	• Leak		• Hot and cold reversed
	• Noisy		• Loose
	• Nonstandard materials and patches		• Noisy
	• Pipe size reduced downstream		• Obstructed aerator
	• Poor manifolding of drain piping		• Stiff or inoperative
	• Poor support		
	• Poor slope		LAUNDRY TUB PUMPS
	• Rust		
	• Split, damaged, crimped pipe		• Clogged
	• Undersized		• Discharge pipe problems
	• Welded steel piping		• Electrical problems
			• Excess noise or vibration
	TRAPS		• Inoperative
			• Missing
	• Clogged		• Short cycling or running continuously
	• Double trapping		
	• Freezing		SUMP PUMPS
	• Leak		
	• Missing		• Debris in the sump, clogged sump
	• No clean out provision		• Discharge pipe problems
	• Nonstandard shape or material		• Electrical problems
	• Split, rusted or damaged		• Excess noise or vibration
	• Tailpiece (fixture outlet pipe) too long		• Inoperative, poorly secured or rusted
	• Trap primer – possible cross connection		• Lid missing, rotted or not secure
	• Trap primer missing		• Short cycling or running continuously
	• Trap arm too long or too short		• Sump damaged
	• Traps too small or too big		
	• Wrong type		

FANS AND VENTILATION			
LOCATION	EXHAUST FANS	LOCATION	HEAT RECOVERY VENTILATORS
	• Clothes dryer vented outside?		• Exhaust grille in kitchen missing grease filter
	• Cover missing		• Grease filter dirty
	• Damaged		
	• Disconnected		
	• Ducts leaky		
	• Inadequate air movement		
	• Inadequate backflow prevention (flap)		
	• Inoperative		
	• Missing		
	• Noisy		
	• Not insulated in unconditioned space		
	• Poor termination location		
	• Termination point not found		
	• Weather hood missing or loose		
	• Wiring unsafe		

FLOORS			
LOCATION	GENERAL	LOCATION	CARPET ON FLOORS
	• Absorbent materials in wet areas		• Buckled
	• Loose or missing pieces		• Lifted at seams or edges
	• Mechanical damage		• Odors
	• Trip hazard		• Rot
	• Water damage		• Stains
	CONCRETE FLOORS		RESILIENT FLOORING
	• Cracked		• Lifted seams
	• Efflorescence		• Open seams
	• Heaved		• Split
	• Hollow below		
	• Rusted re-bar		CERAMIC TILE, STONE, MARBLE, ETC.
	• Settled		
	• Shaling, spalling		• Grout missing
	• Slopes away from drain		• Grout loose
	• Water on floor		• Stains on tiles
			• Tiles missing
	SUBFLOORING		• Tiles worn
			• Tiles broken
	• Concentrated loads		• Tiles cracked
	• Damaged or cut		
	• Plywood in wrong orientation		WOOD FLOORS
	• Poor fastening (nailing, screwing, gluing)		
	• Poor end support, cantilevered		• Buckled
	• Prior repairs		• Exposed tongues
	• Rot, insect or fire damage		• Rot
	• Sag or springy		• Squeaks
	• Squeaks		• Stained
	• Swollen waferboard		• Warped

WALLS				
LOCATION	GENERAL		LOCATION	MASONRY OR CONCRETE WALLS
	• Cracks			• Efflorescence
	• Inappropriate finishes in wet areas			• Mortar missing or deteriorated
	• Mechanical damage			• Spalling
	• Truss uplift			
	• Water damage			INSULATION
	PLASTER OR DRYWALL			• Air/vapor barrier – missing, incomplete, wrong location
	• Bulging			• Mold, mildew, rot
	• Crumbling or powdery			• Sagging or voids
	• Loose or missing			• Too little
	• Nail pops			
	• Poor joints			
	• Shadow effect			
	WOOD WALLS			
	• Cracked, split or broken			
	• Loose			
	• Rot			

CEILINGS				
LOCATION	GENERAL		LOCATION	WOOD CEILINGS
	• Cracked, loose or missing sections			• Broken, cracked or split
	• Mechanical damage			• Buckled
	• Stains			• Loose
	• Truss uplift			• Rot
	• Water damage			
				METAL CEILINGS
	PLASTER/DRYWALL CEILINGS			
				• Rust or loose
	• Crumbly or powdery			
	• Nail pops			
	• Poor joints			
	• Sag			
	• Shadow effect			
	• Textured ceilings in poor locations			

TRIM				
LOCATION			LOCATION	
	• Loose			
	• Mechanical damage			
	• Missing			
	• Rot			
	• Water damage			

COUNTERTOPS			
LOCATION		LOCATION	
	• Burned, cut or worn		
	• Damaged, stained		
	• Entire top loose		
	• Grout loose or missing		
	• Loose or missing pieces		
	• Rotted substrate		
	• Rust		
	• Tiles loose, missing, cracked, stained or broken		

CABINETS			
LOCATION		LOCATION	
	• Broken or cracked glass		
	• Defective hardware		
	• Doors or drawers missing or loose		
	• Drawers – missing or defective stops		
	• Not well secured to wall		
	• Other pieces missing or loose		
	• Rot		
	• Rust on medicine cabinets		
	• Shelves not well supported		
	• Stained, worn, damaged		
	• Stiff or inoperative		
	• Water damage		

WINDOWS			
LOCATION	GENERAL	LOCATION	EXTERIOR TRIM
	• Air leaks		• Caulking or flashing missing, deteriorated, loose, rusting or incomplete
	• Lintels sagging or missing		• Damaged, cracked or loose
	• Water leaks		• Inadequate sill projection
			• Missing
	FRAMES		• No drip edge
			• Paint or stain needed
	• Deformation		• Putty (glazing compound) cracked, missing, loose or deteriorated
	• Drain holes blocked or missing		• Rot
	• Installed backwards		• Rust
	• Racked		• Sills with reverse slope
	• Rot		
	• Rust		SASHES
	EXTERIOR DRIP CAPS		• Inoperable
			• Loose fit
	• Ineffective		• Poor weatherstrip
	• Missing		• Rot
			• Rust
			• Sash coming apart
			• Stiff
			• Won't stay open

LOCATION	INTERIOR TRIM	LOCATION	LOCATION
	• Cracked		• Sills too low on stairs or landing
	• Loose		
	• Missing		STORMS AND SCREENS
	• Poor fit		
	• Rot		• Loose
	• Stained		• Missing
			• Rusted
	GLASS (GLAZING)		• Torn or holes
	• Broken		MEANS OF EGRESS
	• Cracked		
	• Excess condensation		• Missing
	• Loose		• Too small
	• Lost seal on double or triple glazing		
	• Missing		
	HARDWARE		
	• Broken		
	• Inoperable		
	• Loose		
	• Missing		
	• Rusted		

	SKYLIGHTS AND SOLARIUMS		
LOCATION		LOCATION	
	• Evidence of ice dams		
	• Leak		
	• Special glazing not provided (more than 15% off vertical)		

	DOORS		
LOCATION	GENERAL	LOCATION	EXTERIOR DRIP CAPS
	• Air leaks		• Ineffective
	• Lintels sagging or missing		• Missing
	• Water leaks		
			EXTERIOR TRIM
	DOORS AND FRAMES		
			• Caulking or flashing missing, deteriorated, loose, rusting or incomplete
	• Damaged		• Damaged, cracked or loose
	• Dark paint on metal exposed to sun		• Inadequate sill projection
	• Deformation		• Missing
	• Delaminated		• No drip edge
	• Drain holes blocked or missing		• Paint or stain needed
	• Inoperable		• Putty (glazing compound) cracked, missing, loose or deteriorating
	• Installed backwards		• Rot
	• Loose or poor fit		• Rust
	• Plastic trim on metal door behind storm		• Sill not well supported
	• Racked		• Sill too low
	• Rot		• Sills with reverse sloe
	• Rust		
	• Stiff		
	• Swings open or closed by itself		

141

LOCATION	INTERIOR TRIM	LOCATION	STORMS AND SCREENS
	• Cracked		• Loose
	• Doorstops missing or ineffective		• Missing
	• Floor stained below		• Rusted
	• Guides and stops missing or damaged		•Torn or holes
	• Loose		
	• Missing		GARAGE DOORS
	• Poorly fit		
	• Rot		• No self-closer
	• Stained		• No 6 inch step down into garage
			• Not weatherstripped
	GLASS (GLAZING)		• Not fire rated or exterior type
			• Opens to bedroom
	• Broken		
	• Cracked		HARDWARE
	• Excess condensation		
	• Loose		• Broken
	• Lost seal on double or triple glazing		• Hinges on exterior
	• Missing		• Ineffective
			• Inoperable
			• Loose
			• Missing
			• Rusted

► 10. BATHROOMS/WASHROOMS – FIELD CHECKLIST

Location Legend	N = North	S = South	E = East	W = West	
	1 =1st Floor	2 = 2nd Floor	3 = 3rd Floor	B= Basement	CS = CrawlSpace

ELECTRICAL				
LOCATION	WIRING	LOCATION	OUTLETS	
	• Abandoned wire		• Above electric baseboard heaters	
	• Damaged		• Broken pin or blade in slots	
	• Exposed on walls or ceilings		• Damaged	
	• Extension cord used as permanent wiring		• Dedicated circuits needed	
	• Improper color coding		• In floors or countertops	
	• In steel studs without protection		• Inoperative	
	• Loose connections		• Loose	
	• Missing		• No GFI	
	• Not well secured		• Open hot	
	• Open splices		• Open neutral	
	• Permanent wiring used as extension cord		• Overheated neutral	
	•Too close to ducts, pipes, chimneys, etc.		• Overheating	
	•Too close to edge of studs or joists		• Reverse polarity	
	• Under carpets		•Too few outlets	
	• Undersized wire		•Too close to bathtubs	
	•Wrong type		•Too far from basin	
			• Ungrounded	
	KNOB-AND-TUBE		•Worn receptacles	
			•Wrong type	
	• Connections need boxes			
	• Conventional lights in wet areas		LIGHTS	
	•Wire insulation or sheathing brittle			
			• Damaged	
	ALUMINUM		• Heat lamps over doors	
			• Improper potlights	
	• Connectors not compatible with aluminum		• Inadequate	
	• No grease on stranded wires		• Inoperative	
	• Overheating		• Isolating links needed on pull chains	
			• Loose	
	JUNCTION BOXES		• Not grounded	
			• Obsolete	
	• Concealed boxes		• Overheating	
	• Cover loose or missing			
	• Damaged		SWITCHES	
	• Missing, loose			
	• Not grounded		• Damaged, loose	
	• Overcrowded		• Inoperative, obsolete	
	• Overheating		• No shut off	
			• Overheated	
			• Poor location in bathroom	

	HEATING		
LOCATION	DUCTS, REGISTERS AND GRILLES	LOCATION	STEAM DISTRIBUTION PIPES AND RADIATORS
	• Balancing damper adjustment		• Air vent –
	• Dirty, obstructed collapsed		– Leak
	• Disconnected ducts		– Missing
	• Excessively long runs, excessive elbows		– Obstructed
	• Leaky joints		– Poor location
	• Rust (in-slab ducts)		• Clogged
	• Undersized		• Improper slope
	• Weak airflow		• Leaking
	• Wires or pipes in ducts		• Low spots
			• Radiators won't warm up
	HOT WATER RADIATORS, CONVECTORS AND BASEBOARDS		• Traps –
			– Missing
	• Balancing valve problems		– Leak
	• Bleed valve problems		– Stuck open, closed
	• Cold		– Damage
	• Damaged baseboard fins		– Inoperative
	• Leak		
	• Missing		ELECTRIC SPACE HEATERS
	• Obstructed airflow		
	• Poor location		• 120 volt heaters installed on 240 volt circuits or vice versa
	• Rust		• Damaged or rusted
	• Too small (room cool)		• Dirty or bent fins
			• Electrical receptacles above heaters
	RADIANT HEATING		• Fans – noisy, inoperative, loose or dirty
			• Inoperative
	• Balancing valve problems		• Loose or missing covers
	• Bleed valve problems		• Missing or too few heaters
	• Cool rooms or parts of rooms		• Obstructed
	• Leaks		• Thermostat overloaded

	PLUMBING		
LOCATION	SUPPLY PIPING IN HOUSES	LOCATION	DRAIN PIPING MATERIALS
	• Leak		• Clean-outs missing or inaccessible
	• Poor pressure or flow		• Clogged
	• Rust		• Combustible piping
	• Split, damaged, crimped		• Cross connections
	• Poor support		• Defective ABS piping
	• Cross connections		• Exposed to mechanical damage
	• Excess pressure		• Freezing
	• Excessive noise		• Leak
	• Combustible piping		• Noisy
	• Suspect connections on polybutylene		• Nonstandard materials and patches
	• Non-standard material		• Pipe size reduced downstream
			• Poor support
			• Poor slope
			• Poor manifolding of drain piping
			• Rust
			• Split, damaged, crimped pipe
			• Undersized
			• Welded steel piping

LOCATION	TRAPS	LOCATION	TOILETS
	• Clogged		• Broken tank lids or seats
	• Double trapping		• Connected to the hot water system
	• Freezing		• Cross connection
	• Leak		• Crowded
	• Missing		• Floor damage suspected
	• No clean out provision		• Flush mechanism inoperative
	• Nonstandard shape or material		• Lazy flush
	• Split, rusted or damaged		• Leaks
	• Tailpiece (fixture outlet pipe) too long		• Loose
	• Trap primer – possible cross connection		• Obstructed
	• Trap primer missing		• Odor around toilet
	• Trap arm too long or too short		• Running continuously
	• Traps too small or too big		• Shutoff valve missing or inoperative
	• Wrong type		• Surface defects
	SEWAGE EJECTOR PUMPS		SHOWER STALLS
	• Alarm sounding		• Entrance problems
	• Discharge pipe problems		• Leaks
	• Electrical problems		• Pooling water on the floor
	• Inoperative		• Rust
	• Missing, rusting or inoperative union, check valve or gate		• Sill and threshold problems
	• No vent		• Slow drains
	• Odor		• Too small
	• Short cycling or running continuously		
			BIDETS
	VENTING SYSTEMS		
			• Cross connections
	• Automatic air vents		• Floor damage suspected
	• Ineffective		• Loose
	• Missing		• Slow drains
	• Poor vent pipe arrangements		• Spray or rim wash diverter inoperative
	• Too small or too long		• Surface defects
	BASINS		BATHTUBS
	• Cross connections		• Cross connections
	• Leaks		• Leaks
	• Loose		• Loose or unstable
	• Not level		• Overflow leaking, disconnected or rusting
	• Overflows missing		• Rust
	• Rust		• Slow drains
	• Slow drains		• Surface defects
	• Surface defects		
			TUB AND SHOWER STALL ENCLOSURES
	FAUCETS		
			• Electrical problems at the enclosure
	• Cross connections		• Leaks
	• Drips, leaks		• Loose, broken or missing tile
	• Hot and cold reversed		
	• Loose		WHIRLPOOL BATHS
	• Noisy		• Cross connections
	• Obstructed aerator		• Dirty water from the jets
	• Shower diverter inoperative or defective		• Diverter inoperative
	• Stiff or inoperative		• Electrical switch or receptacles too close to tub
			• Excess pump noise or vibration
			• Leaks
			• No pump access
			• No GFCI
			• Not level
			• Odor
			• Pump doesn't run
			• Suction cover missing, loose, suspect
			• Surface defects

EXHAUST FANS			
LOCATION		LOCATION	
	• Cover missing		
	• Damaged		
	• Disconnected		
	• Ducts leaky		
	• Inadequate backflow prevention (flap)		
	• Inadequate air movement		
	• Inoperative		
	• Missing		
	• Noisy		
	• Not insulated in unconditioned space		
	• Poor termination location		
	• Termination point not found		
	• Weather hood missing or loose		
	• Wiring unsafe		

FLOORS			
LOCATION	GENERAL	LOCATION	WOOD FLOORS
	• Absorbent materials in wet areas		• Buckled
	• Loose or missing pieces		• Exposed tongues
	• Mechanical damage		• Rot
	• Trip hazard		• Squeaks
	• Water damage		• Stained
			• Warped
	CONCRETE FLOORS		
			CARPET ON FLOORS
	• Cracked		
	• Efflorescence		• Buckled
	• Heaved		• Lifted at seams or edges
	• Hollow below		• Odors
	• Rusted re-bar		• Rot
	• Settled		• Stains
	• Shaling, spalling		
	• Slopes away from drain		RESILIENT FLOORING
	• Water on floor		
			• Lifted seams
	SUBFLOORING		• Open seams
			• Split
	• Concentrated loads		
	• Cracking ceramic tiles		CERAMIC TILE, STONE, MARBLE, ETC.
	• Damaged or cut		
	• Plywood in wrong orientation		• Grout missing
	• Poor fastening (nailing, screwing, gluing)		• Grout loose
	• Poor end support, cantilevered		• Stains on tiles
	• Prior repairs		• Tiles missing
	• Rot, insect or fire damage		• Tiles worn
	• Sag or springy		• Tiles broken
	• Squeaks		• Tiles cracked
	• Swollen waferboard		

WALLS				
LOCATION	GENERAL	LOCATION	MASONRY OR CONCRETE WALLS	
	• Water damage		• Efflorescence	
	• Cracks		• Mortar missing or deteriorated	
	• Mechanical damage		• Spalling	
	• Inappropriate finishes in wet areas			
	• Truss uplift		INSULATION	
	PLASTER OR DRYWALL		• Too little	
			• Sagging or voids	
	• Bulging		• Air/vapor barrier – missing, incomplete, wrong location	
	• Crumbling or powdery		• Mold, mildew, rot	
	• Loose or missing			
	• Nail pops			
	• Poor joints			
	• Shadow effect			
	WOOD WALLS			
	• Buckled			
	• Cracked, split or broken			
	• Loose			
	• Rot			
	• Stained			

CEILINGS				
LOCATION	GENERAL	LOCATION	WOOD CEILINGS	
	• Cracked, loose or missing sections		• Broken, cracked or split	
	• Mechanical damage		• Buckled	
	• Stains		• Loose	
	• Truss uplift		• Rot	
	• Water damage			
			METAL	
	PLASTER/DRYWALL CEILINGS			
			• Rust or loose	
	• Crumbly or powdery			
	• Nail pops			
	• Poor joints			
	• Sag			
	• Shadow effect			
	• Textured ceilings in poor locations			

TRIM				
LOCATION		LOCATION		
	• Damaged			
	• Loose			
	• Missing			
	• Rot			
	• Water damage			

COUNTERTOPS				
LOCATION		LOCATION		
	• Burned, cut or worn			
	• Damaged			
	• Entire top loose			
	• Grout loose or missing			
	• Loose or missing pieces			
	• Rotted substrate			
	• Rusted metal			
	• Stained			
	•Tiles – loose, missing, cracked, stained, broken			

CABINETS				
LOCATION		LOCATION		
	• Broken or cracked glass			
	• Defective hardware			
	• Doors or drawers missing or loose			
	• Drawers – missing or defective stops			
	• Not well secured to wall			
	• Other pieces missing or loose			
	• Rot			
	• Rust on medicine cabinets			
	• Shelves not well supported			
	• Stained, worn, damaged			
	• Stiff or inoperative			
	•Water damage			

WINDOWS			
LOCATION	GENERAL	LOCATION	EXTERIOR TRIM
	• Air leaks		• Caulking or flashing missing, deteriorated, loose, rusting or incomplete
	• Lintels sagging or missing		• Damaged, cracked or loose
	•Water leaks		• Inadequate sill projection
			• Missing
	FRAMES		• No drip edge
			• Paint or stain needed
	• Deformation		• Putty (glazing compound) cracked, missing, loose or deteriorated
	• Drain holes blocked or missing		• Rot
	• Installed backwards		• Rust
	• Racked		• Sills with reverse slope
	• Rot		
	• Rust		SASHES
	EXTERIOR DRIP CAPS		• Inoperable
			• Loose fit
	• Ineffective		• Poor weatherstrip
	• Missing		• Rot
			• Rust
			• Sash coming apart
			• Stiff
			•Won't stay open

LOCATION	INTERIOR TRIM	LOCATION	LOCATION
	• Cracked		• Sills too low on stairs or landing
	• Loose		
	• Missing		STORMS AND SCREENS
	• Poor fit		
	• Rot		• Loose
	• Stained		• Missing
			• Rusted
	GLASS (GLAZING)		•Torn or holes
	• Broken		MEANS OF EGRESS
	• Cracked		
	• Excess condensation		• Missing
	• Loose		•Too small
	• Lost seal on double or triple glazing		
	• Missing		
	HARDWARE		
	• Broken		
	• Inoperable		
	• Loose		
	• Missing		
	• Rusted		

SKYLIGHTS AND SOLARIUMS			
LOCATION			
	• Evidence of ice dams		
	• Leak		
	• Special glazing not provided (more than 15% off vertical)		

DOORS			
LOCATION	DOORS AND FRAMES	LOCATION	INTERIOR TRIM
			• Cracked
	• Damaged		• Doorstops missing or ineffective
	• Delaminated		• Guides and stops missing or damaged
	• Inoperable		• Loose
	• Loose or poor fit		• Missing
	• Racked		• Poorly fit
	• Rot		• Rot
	• Rust		• Stained
	• Stiff		
	• Swings open or closed by itself		HARDWARE
			• Broken
			• Ineffective
			• Inoperable
			• Loose
			• Missing
			• Rusted

► 11. ROOM BY ROOM – FIELD CHECKLIST

Location Legend   N = North   S = South   E = East   W = West

                   1 =1st Floor   2 = 2nd Floor   3 = 3rd Floor   B= Basement

ELECTRICAL			
LOCATION	WIRING	LOCATION	OUTLETS
	• Abandoned wire		• Above electric baseboard heaters
	• Damaged		• Broken pin or blade in slots
	• Exposed on walls or ceilings		• Damaged
	• Extension cord used as permanent wiring		• Dedicated circuits needed
	• Improper color coding		• In floors or countertops
	• In steel studs without protection		• Inoperative
	• Loose connections		• Loose
	• Missing		• No GFI
	• Not well secured		• Open hot
	• Open splices		• Open neutral
	• Permanent wiring used as extension cord		• Overheated neutral
	•Too close to ducts, pipes, chimneys, etc.		• Overheating
	•Too close to edge of studs or joists		• Reverse polarity
	• Under carpets		•Too few outlets
	• Undersized wire		• Ungrounded
	•Wrong type		•Worn receptacles
			•Wrong type
	KNOB-AND-TUBE		
			LIGHTS
	• Connections need boxes		
	• Conventional lights in wet areas		• Damaged
	•Wire insulation or sheathing brittle		• Heat lamps over doors
			• Improper closet lighting
	ALUMINUM		• Improper potlights
			• Inadequate
	• Connectors not compatible with aluminum		• Inoperative
	• No grease on stranded wires		• Isolating links needed on pull chains
	• Overheating		• Loose
			• Not grounded
	JUNCTION BOXES		• Obsolete
			• Overheating
	• Concealed boxes		• Poor stairway lighting
	• Cover loose or missing		
	• Damaged		SWITCHES
	• Missing, loose		• Damaged, loose
	• Not grounded		• Faulty 3-way dimmer switch
	• Overcrowded		• Inoperative, obsolete
	• Overheating		• No shut off for dimmer switch
			• Overheated

HEATING			
LOCATION	DUCTS, REGISTERS AND GRILLES	LOCATION	STEAM, DISTRIBUTION PIPES AND RADIATORS
	• Balancing damper adjustment		• Air vent –
	• Dirty, obstructed collapsed		– Leak
	• Disconnected ducts		– Missing
	• Excessively long runs, excessive elbows		– Obstructed
	• Leaky joints		– Poor location
	• Rust (in-slab ducts)		• Clogged
	• Undersized		• Improper slope
	• Weak airflow		• Leaking
	• Wires or pipes in ducts		• Low spots
			• Radiators won't warm up
	HOT WATER RADIATORS, CONVECTORS AND BASEBOARDS		• Traps –
			– Missing
	• Balancing valve problems		– Leak
	• Bleed valve problems		– Stuck open, closed
	• Cold		– Damage
	• Damaged baseboard fins		– Inoperative
	• Leak		
	• Missing		ELECTRIC SPACE HEATERS
	• Obstructed airflow		
	• Poor location		• 120 volt heaters installed on 240 volt circuits or vice versa
	• Rust		• Damaged or rusted
	• Too small (room cool)		• Dirty or bent fins
			• Electrical receptacles above heaters
	RADIANT HEATING		• Fans – noisy, inoperative, loose or dirty
			• Inoperative
	• Balancing valve problems		• Loose or missing covers
	• Bleed valve problems		• Missing or too few heaters
	• Cool rooms or parts of rooms		• Obstructed
	• Leaks		• Thermostat overloaded

FLOORS			
LOCATION	GENERAL	LOCATION	SUBFLOORING
	• Absorbent materials in wet areas		• Concentrated loads
	• Loose or missing pieces		• Cracking ceramic tiles
	• Mechanical damage		• Damaged or cut
	• Trip hazard		• Plywood in wrong orientation
	• Water damage		• Poor fastening (nailing, screwing, gluing)
			• Poor end support or cantilevered
	CONCRETE FLOORS		• Prior repairs
			• Rot, insect or fire damage
	• Cracked		• Sag or springy
	• Efflorescence		• Squeaks
	• Heaved		• Swollen waferboard
	• Hollow below		
	• Rusted re-bar		WOOD FLOORS
	• Settled		
	• Shaling, spalling		• Buckled
	• Slopes away from drain		• Exposed tongues
	• Water on floor		• Rot
			• Squeaks
			• Stained
			• Warped

LOCATION	CARPET ON FLOORS	LOCATION	CERAMIC TILE, STONE, MARBLE, ETC.
	• Buckled		• Grout missing
	• Lifted at seams or edges		• Grout loose
	• Odors		• Stains on tiles
	• Rot		•Tiles missing
	• Stains		•Tiles worn
			•Tiles broken
	RESILIENT FLOORING		•Tiles cracked
	• Lifted seams		
	• Open seams		
	• Split		

WALLS			
LOCATION	GENERAL	LOCATION	PARTY WALLS
	• Cracks		• Ice dams
	• Inappropriate finishes in wet areas		• Not continuous – penetrated
	• Mechanical damage		• Not continuous – incomplete
	•Truss uplift		
	•Water damage		GARAGE WALLS AND CEILINGS
	PLASTER OR DRYWALL		• Not fireproof
			• Not gastight
	• Bulging		
	• Crumbling or powdery		INSULATION
	• Loose or missing		
	• Nail pops		•Too little
	• Poor joints		• Sagging or voids
	• Shadow effect		• Air/vapor barrier – missing, incomplete, wrong location
	WOOD WALLS		• Mold, mildew, rot
	• Buckled		MASONRY OR CONCRETE WALLS
	• Cracked, split or broken		
	• Loose		• Efflorescence
	• Rot		• Mortar missing or deteriorated
			• Spalling

CEILINGS			
LOCATION	GENERAL	LOCATION	WOOD CEILINGS
	• Cracked, loose or missing sections		• Broken, cracked or split
	• Mechanical damage		• Buckled
	• Stains		• Loose
	•Truss uplift		• Rot
	•Water damage		
			METAL CEILINGS
	PLASTER/DRYWALL CEILINGS		
			• Rust or loose
	• Crumbly or powdery		
	• Nail pops		
	• Poor joints		
	• Sag		
	• Shadow effect		
	•Textured ceilings in poor locations		

TRIM			
LOCATION		LOCATION	
	• Loose		
	• Mechanical damage		
	• Missing		
	• Rot		
	• Water damage		

COUNTERTOPS			
LOCATION		LOCATION	
	• Burned, cut or worn		
	• Damaged		
	• Entire top loose		
	• Grout loose or missing		
	• Loose or missing pieces		
	• Rotted substrate		
	• Rusted metal		
	• Stained		
	•Tiles – loose, missing, cracked, stained, broken		

CABINETS			
LOCATION		LOCATION	
	• Broken or cracked glass		
	• Defective hardware		
	• Doors or drawers missing or loose		
	• Drawers – missing or defective stops		
	• Not well secured to wall		
	• Other pieces missing or loose		
	• Rot		
	• Rust on medicine cabinets		
	• Shelves not well supported		
	• Stained, worn, damaged		
	• Stiff or inoperative		
	•Water damage		

STAIRS			
LOCATION	GENERAL	LOCATION	HANDRAILS
	• Mechanical damage		• Damaged
	• Rot		• Hard to hold
			• Loose
	TREADS		• Missing
			•Too high
	• Excessive nosing		•Too low
	• Excessive span between stringers		
	• Inadequately secured to header		GUARDRAILS
	• Loose		
	• Poorly supported		• Damaged
	• Pulling away from wall or treads		• Loose
	• Rise excessive		• Missing
	• Rise or run not uniform		•Too low
	• Rot at bottom		
	• Sloped		SPINDLES OR BALUSTERS
	• Stringers – too small		
	• Stringers – excessive notching		• Damaged
	• Stringers – too thin		• Easy to climb
	•Thickness inadequate		• Loose
	•Tread width too small		• Missing
	•Winders – too big an angle		•Too far apart
	•Winders – too many		
	•Worn or damaged		FIRE SAFETY
	STAIRWELL		• Drywall missing or incomplete on underside of stairs
	• Headroom inadequate		LIGHTING
	•Too narrow		
			• Missing
	LANDINGS		• Not controlled by three way switch
	• Missing		
	•Too small		

WINDOWS			
LOCATION	GENERAL	LOCATION	EXTERIOR TRIM
	• Air leaks		• Caulking or flashing missing, deteriorated, loose, rusting or incomplete
	• Lintels sagging or missing		• Damaged, cracked or loose
	•Water leaks		• Inadequate sill projection
			• Missing
	FRAMES		• No drip edge
			• Paint or stain needed
	• Deformation		• Putty (glazing compound) cracked, missing, loose or deteriorated
	• Drain holes blocked or missing		• Rot
	• Installed backwards		• Rust
	• Racked		• Sills with reverse slope
	• Rot		
	• Rust		SASHES
	EXTERIOR DRIP CAPS		• Inoperable
			• Loose fit
	• Ineffective		• Poor weatherstrip
	• Missing		• Rot
			• Rust
			• Sash coming apart
			• Stiff
			•Won't stay open

LOCATION	INTERIOR TRIM	LOCATION	LOCATION
	• Cracked		• Sills too low on stairs or landing
	• Loose		
	• Missing		STORMS AND SCREENS
	• Poor fit		
	• Rot		• Loose
	• Stained		• Missing
			• Rusted
	GLASS (GLAZING)		•Torn or holes
	• Broken		MEANS OF EGRESS
	• Cracked		
	• Excess condensation		• Missing
	• Loose		•Too small
	• Lost seal on double or triple glazing		
	• Missing		
	HARDWARE		
	• Broken		
	• Inoperable		
	• Loose		
	• Missing		
	• Rusted		

	SKYLIGHTS AND SOLARIUMS		
LOCATION		LOCATION	
	• Leaks		
	• Evidence of ice dams		
	• Special glazing not provided (more than 15% off vertical)		

	DOORS		
LOCATION	GENERAL	LOCATION	EXTERIOR DRIP CAPS
	• Air leaks		• Ineffective
	• Lintels sagging or missing		• Missing
	•Water leaks		
			EXTERIOR TRIM
	DOORS AND FRAMES		
			• Caulking or flashing missing, deteriorated, loose, rusting or incomplete
	• Damaged		• Damaged, cracked or loose
	• Dark paint on metal exposed to sun		• Inadequate sill projection
	• Deformation		• Missing
	• Delaminated		• No drip edge
	• Drain holes blocked or missing		• Paint or stain needed
	• Inoperable		• Putty (glazing compound) cracked, missing, loose or deteriorating
	• Installed backwards		• Rot
	• Loose or poor fit		• Rust
	• Plastic trim on metal door behind storm		• Sill not well supported
	• Racked		• Sill too low
	• Rot		• Sills with reverse sloe
	• Rust		
	• Stiff		
	• Swings open or closed by itself		

155

LOCATION	INTERIOR TRIM	LOCATION	STORMS AND SCREENS
	• Cracked		• Loose
	• Doorstops missing or ineffective		• Missing
	• Floor stained below		• Rusted
	• Guides and stops missing or damaged		• Torn or holes
	• Loose		
	• Missing		GARAGE DOORS
	• Poorly fit		
	• Rot		• No self-closer
	• Stained		• No six inch step down into garage
			• Not weatherstripped
	GLASS (GLAZING)		• Not fire rated or exterior type
			• Opens to bedroom
	• Broken		
	• Cracked		
	• Excess condensation		
	• Loose		
	• Lost seal on double or triple glazing		
	• Missing		
	HARDWARE		
	• Broken		
	• Hinges on exterior		
	• Ineffective		
	• Inoperable		
	• Loose		
	• Missing		
	• Rusted		
	• Self-closer missing		

WOOD BURNING FIREPLACES			
LOCATION	FOOTINGS & FOUNDATIONS	LOCATION	FIREBOXES
	• Cracked		• Cracked masonry or refractory
	• Deteriorating concrete, masonry or mortar		• Designed for coal
	• Heaved		• Deteriorated, missing or loose masonry or mortar
	• Leakage		• Draft suspect
	• Settled		• Inappropriate materials
			• Lintels rusted, sagging or loose
	HEARTHS		• Rust out, burn out, buckled or cracked metal firebox
	• Evidence of overheating		• Too shallow
	• Gaps or cracks		
	• Inappropriate material		DAMPERS
	• Settled		
	• Too thin		• Damper or frame rusted
	• Too small		• Frame loose
	• Wood forms not removed		• Inoperative
			• Missing
			• Obstructed
			• Too low
			• Undersized

LOCATION	THROATS, SMOKE SHELVES & SMOKE CHAMBERS	LOCATION	GLASS DOORS
	• Debris		• Cracked or broken glass
	• Excess slope		• Frame warped
	• Missing		• Frame rust
	• Rust (metal firebox)		• Inappropriate installation
	• Uneven slope		• Inoperative
	• Walls not smooth		
	• Wood forms not removed		HEAT CIRCULATORS
	FACES OR BREASTS		• Fan inoperative
			• Obstructed intakes or outlets
	• Combustible clearances		
	• Cracked		GAS IGNITERS
	• Evidence of overheating		
	• Loose		• Gas leak
	• Settled (gap at wall)		• Inadequate seal at firebox wall or floor
	• Too thick		• Inadequate combustible clearance
			• Pipe rusted
	ASHPITS		• Pipe obstructed
	• Ash dump missing		
	• Cleanout door too close to combustibles		
	• Cleanout door missing		
	• Floor below cleanout door		
	• Wood forms not removed		
	OUTDOOR COMBUSTION AIR		
	• Damper stuck		
	• Damper missing		
	• Disconnected		
	• Hood and screen at firebox missing, damaged or loose		
	• Inadequate combustible clearance		
	• Inappropriate material		
	• Intake not weather-tight		
	• Intake not screened		
	• Intake poor location		
	• Rust		
	• Uninsulated		

157

	WOOD STOVES		
LOCATION	CABINETS	LOCATION	VENTING SYSTEMS
	• Door gasket – loose, missing, brittle or incomplete		• Creosote deposits
	• Door loose, warped or poorly fit		• Excess length
	• Leakage		• Goes through walls or closets
	• Unsteady or not well secured		• Heat reclaimer installed
	• Warped, cracked or gaps		• Inadequate combustible clearance
			• Multiple appliances connected to chimney
	COMBUSTION CHAMBERS		• No expansion provision
			• Pieces poorly connected
	• Catalytic combuster clogged		• Poor slope
	• Combustible clearances		• Poor connection to chimney
	– Floor		• Seams on bottom
	– Side and rear walls		• Too many elbows
	– Front walls		• Wrong material
	– Ceiling		
	• Creosote deposits		
	• Firebrick cracked, crumbling or incomplete		
	• Owner's manual missing		
	• Warped, cracked or creosote deposit		

	WALL AND FLOOR FURNACES, ROOM HEATERS AND GAS FIREPLACES		
LOCATION	GAS PIPING	LOCATION	HEAT EXCHANGERS
	• Copper pipe not properly labeled		• Cracks, holes or rust
	• Improper connections		• Excess temperature rise
	• Inadequate support		• Soot or deposits
	• Inappropriate materials		
	• Leak		CABINETS
	• Missing shut off valves		
	• No drip leg		• Combustible clearances
	• Piping in chimney or duct system		• Mechanical damage
	• Plastic pipe exposed above-grade		• Missing components
	• Rust		• Obstructed air intake
			• Rust
	COMBUSTION AIR		• Scorching
	• Inadequate		THERMOSTATS
	GAS BURNERS		• Anticipator
	• Delayed ignition		• Damaged
	• Dirt or soot		• Dirty
	• Flame wavers when fan comes on		• Loose
	• Gas odor or leak		• Not level
	• Inoperative		• Poor adjustment or calibration
	• Poor flame color or pattern		• Poor location
	• Rust		
	• Scorching		BLOWERS
	• Short cycling		
			• Dirty
	HEAT SHIELDS		• Fan belt loose, worn or damaged
			• Inoperative
	• Loose		• Noisy
	• Missing		• Overheating
	• Rusted		• Poorly secured
	• Scorching		• Running continuously
			• Rust
			• Too small
			• Unbalanced or vibration

LOCATION	FAN/LIMIT SWITCHES	LOCATION	ITEMS SPECIFIC TO FLOOR FURNACES
	• Improperly wired		• Cap missing or damaged
	• Mechanical damage		• Firebox cracked or rusted
	• Missing cover		• Not permitted
	• Rusting or dirty		• Not listed, certified or approved
	• Scorching		• Restricted airflow causing overheating
	• Set wrong or defective		• Thermostat remote
	VENTING SYSTEMS		ITEMS SPECIFIC TO ROOM HEATERS (SPACE HEATERS)
	• Dirty		• Fireplace damper not fixed open
	• Improper material		• Not labeled for use in a fireplace
	• Inadequate combustible clearance		• Unvented
	• Poor connections		
	• Poor support		ITEMS SPECIFIC TO GAS FIREPLACES AND GAS LOGS
	• Rust		
	• Vent connector wrong size		• Damper in existing fireplace not fixed open
	• Vent offset		• Glass door problem
	• Vent too short		• Not suitable for use in a bedroom or bathroom
			• Vent missing (may be acceptable)
	ITEMS SPECIFIC TO WALL FURNACES		
	• Ducts added		
	• Not listed, certified or approved		
	• Unvented furnace in bedroom or bathroom		
	• Unvented furnace		

► 12. ATTICS – FIELD CHECKLIST

DESCRIPTION

Items that need to be described to meet ASHI® Standards:

METHOD USED TO OBSERVE ATTIC

☐ Attic fully accessed
☐ Inspected from access hatch
☐ No access
☐ _____

INSULATION MATERIALS

☐ Fiberglass
☐ Mineral wool
☐ Cellulose
☐ Vermiculite/perlite
☐ Wood shavings
☐ Plastic/foam board
☐ Sprayed in place
☐ _____

VAPOR RETARDERS

☐ Polyethylene
☐ Kraft paper
☐ Foil
☐ _____

Location Legend   N = North   S = South   E = East   W = West

STRUCTURE			
LOCATION	RAFTERS	LOCATION	TRUSSES
	• Bearing on ridge board		• Buckled webs
	• Concentrated loads		• Endbearing
	• Endbearing not adequate		• Mechanical damage
	• Mechanical damage		• Missing webs
	• Rafter spread		• Modified (improperly)
	• Ridge sag		• Notches, holes
	• Rot, insect or fire damage		• Rot, insect or fire damage
	• Sagging		• Sag
	• Spliced		• Truss uplift
	• Split		• Weak connections
	• Too small or overspanned		
	• Warped		SHEATHING
	• Weak framing at openings		
	• Weak connections		• Buckled
			• Delaminated
	COLLAR TIES		• FRT deterioration
			• Mold, mildew
	• Buckling		• Rot, insect or fire damage
	• Loose or poor connections		• Sag
	• Mechanical damage		• Too thin
	• Missing		
	• Need lateral bracing		I JOISTS
	• Rot, insect or fire damage		
			• Birds mouths
	KNEE WALLS/PURLINS		• No ridge beams
			• Notched
	• Buckling		• Rot, insect or fire damage
	• Mechanical damage		• Toe bearing or endbearing inadequate
	• Poor connections		• Weak connections
	• Purlins installed on side		
	• Purlins sagging		
	• Removed, needed		
	• Rot, insect or fire damage		
	• Single top plate, sag		

ELECTRICAL			
LOCATION	WIRING	LOCATION	LIGHTS
	• Abandoned wire		• Damaged
	• Damaged		• Inoperative
	• Exposed		• Isolating links needed on pull chains
	• Exposed on walls or ceilings		• Loose
	• Extension cord used as permanent wiring		• Not grounded
	• Improper color coding		• Obsolete
	• Loose connections		• Overheating
	• Missing		• Poor stairway lighting
	• Not well secured		
	• Open splices		SWITCHES
	• Permanent wiring used as extension cord		
	• Too close to ducts, pipes, chimneys, etc.		• Damaged, loose
	• Too close to edge of studs or joists		• Overheated
	• Undersized wire		• Inoperative, obsolete
	• Wrong type		
			JUNCTION BOXES
	KNOB-AND-TUBE		
			• Concealed boxes
	• Buried in insulation		• Cover loose or missing
	• Connections need boxes		• Damaged
	• Conventional lights in wet areas		• Missing, loose
	• Wire insulation or sheathing brittle		• Not grounded
			• Overcrowded
	ALUMINUM		• Overheating
	• Connectors not compatible with aluminum		OUTLETS
	• No grease on stranded wires		
	• Overheating		• Broken pin or blade in slots
			• Damaged
			• Inoperative
			• Loose
			• No GFI
			• Open hot
			• Open neutral
			• Overheated neutral
			• Overheating
			• Reverse polarity
			• Ungrounded
			• Worn receptacles
			• Wrong type

HEATING			
LOCATION	EXPANSION TANKS FOR HOT WATER SYSTEMS	LOCATION	METAL CHIMNEYS OR VENTS
	• Leaks		• Chimney walls rusting or pitting
	• Poor discharge location for open tank		• Chimney not well supported
	• Poor location for tank		• Excessive offset from vertical
	• Rust		• Inadequate fire stopping
	• Too small		• Inadequate combustible clearances
	• Waterlogged		• Not continuous through roof
			• Not labeled for application
	MASONRY CHIMNEYS		• Sections not well secured
	• Abandoned openings for flue connections		
	• Cracking		
	• Draft inducer fan inoperative		
	• Efflorescence		
	• Excessive offset from vertical (30%)		
	• Fire stopping missing or incomplete		
	• Flue or vent connector obstructed		
	• Inadequate combustible clearance		
	• Loose, missing or deteriorated masonry		
	• Loose, missing or deteriorated mortar		
	• No chimney liner		
	• Pulling away from house		
	• Settling or leaning		
	• Spalling		
	• Vent connectors loose at chimney		
	• Vent connectors extending into chimney		

AIR CONDITIONING AND HEAT PUMPS			
LOCATION	CENTRAL AIR CONDITIONING CAPACITY	LOCATION	CONDENSATE SYSTEMS
	• Oversized		• Dirt in pan
	• Undersized		• Inappropriate pan slope
			• No float switch
	WATER COOLED CONDENSER COILS		• No auxiliary pan
			• Pan not well secured
	• Cooled by pool water		• Pan cracked
	• Leakage		• Pan leaking or overflowing
	• No water		• Rust or holes in pan
	• No backflow preventer		
			REFRIGERANT LINES
	EVAPORATOR COILS		
			• Damaged
	• Corrosion		• Leaking
	• Damage		• Lines too warm or too cold
	• Dirty		• Lines touching each other
	• Frost		• Low points or improper slope in lines
	• No access to coil		• Missing insulation
	• Temperature split too low		
	• Temperature split too high		
	• Top of coil dry		

LOCATION	EXPANSION DEVICES	LOCATION	COMPRESSORS
	• Capillary tube crimped, disconnected, leaking		• Electric wires too small
	•Thermostatic expansion valve loose, clogged, sticking		• Excess electric current draw
			• Excess noise or vibration
	EVAPORATOR FANS		• Inadequate cooling
			• Inoperative in heating, cooling mode
	• Corrosion		• Missing electrical shutoff
	• Damage		• Out of level
	• Dirty		• Running continuously
	• Dirty or missing filter		• Short cycling
	• Excess noise or vibration		•Wrong fuse or breaker size
	• Inoperative		
	• Misadjustment of belt or pulleys		INDOOR COILS
	• Undersized		
			• Corrosion
	DUCT SYSTEMS		• Damage
			• Dirty
	• Dirty		• Frost
	• Disconnected or leaking		• No access to coil
	• Humidifier damper missing		•Temperature split too low
	• Incomplete		•Temperature split too high
	• Obstructed or collapsed		•Top of coil dry in cooling mode
	• Poor support		
	• Poor balancing		CONDENSATE SYSTEMS
	• Undersized		
	•Weak airflow		• Dirt in pan
			• Inappropriate pan slope
	DUCT INSULATION		• No float switch
			• No auxiliary pan
	• Incomplete		• Pan not well secured
	• Missing		• Pan cracked
			• Pan leaking or overflowing
	DUCT VAPOR BARRIERS		• Rust or holes in pan
	• Damaged		EXPANSION DEVICES
	• Missing		
			• Capillary tube crimped, disconnected, leaking
	CONDENSATE DRAIN LINES		•Thermostatic expansion valve loose, clogged, sticking
	• Blocked or crimped		
	• Disconnected, missing		INDOOR FANS
	• Improper discharge point		
	• Leaking, damaged, split		• Corrosion
	• No trap		• Damage
			• Dirty
	WHOLE HOUSE FANS		• Dirty or missing filter
			• Excess noise or vibration
	• Excess noise, vibration		• Inoperative
	• Inadequate attic venting		• Misadjustment of belt or pulleys
	• Inoperative		• Undersized
	• No insulated cover		
	HEAT PUMP CAPACITY		
	• Oversized for cooling		
	• Undersized for heating		

LOCATION	DUCT SYSTEMS	LOCATION	CONDENSATE DRAIN LINES
	• Dirty		• Blocked or crimped
	• Disconnected or leaking		• Disconnected, missing
	• Humidifier damper missing		• Improper discharge point
	• Incomplete		• Leaking, damaged, split
	• Obstructed or collapsed		• No trap
	• Poor support		
	• Poor balancing		REFRIGERANT LINES
	• Supply or return registers – too few		
	• Undersized for cooling		• Damaged
	• Weak airflow		• Leaking
			• Lines too warm or too cold
	DUCT INSULATIONS		• Lines touching each other
			• Low points or improper slope in lines
	• Incomplete		• Missing insulation
	• Missing		
			BACKUP HEAT
	DUCT VAPOR BARRIERS		
			• Inoperative
	• Damaged		• Missing
	• Missing		• Poor location
			• Runs continuously

PLUMBING			
LOCATION	VENTING SYSTEMS	LOCATION	
	• Ineffective		
	• Missing		
	• Poor vent pipe arrangements		
	• Too small or too long		
	• Vent termination problems		

ATTIC ACCESS			
LOCATION	HATCH	LOCATION	PULL-DOWN STAIRS
	• Inaccessible		• Dangerous to lower or raise
	• Missing		• Not insulated
	• Not weatherstripped		• Not weatherstripped
	• Not insulated		• Unsafe to climb
	ATTIC STAIRCASES		
	• Excessive rise on steps		
	• Handrails or guardrails missing or unsafe		
	• Headroom inadequate		
	• Inadequate insulation		
	• Inadequate run and tread width		
	• Inadequate weatherstripping		
	• Lighting missing or ineffective		
	• Treads sloped or not uniform		
	• Treads loose or broken		

LOCATION	INSULATION	LOCATION	ROOF VENTING
	• Air/vapor barrier wrong location		• Inadequate
	• Air leakage excessive		• Missing
	• Air/vapor barrier incomplete		• Obstructed
	• Air/vapor barrier missing		• Snow or wet spots below roof vents
	• Combustible insulation too close to masonry chimney		
	• Compressed		TURBINE VENTS
	• Covering recessed lights		
	• Gaps or voids		• Noisy
	• Inadequate in knee wall areas		• Seized
	• Inadequate at skylights and light wells		
	• Insulation too close to metal chimney		POWER VENTS
	• Missing at dropped ceilings		
	• Too little		• Inoperative in summer
	• Wet		• Operating in winter
			• Poor wiring

EXHAUST FANS			
LOCATION		LOCATION	PARTY WALLS
	• Cover missing		• Ice dams
	• Damaged		• Not continuous – incomplete, penetrated
	• Disconnected		
	• Ducts leaky		
	• Inadequate air movement		
	• Inoperative		
	• Missing		
	• Noisy		
	• Not insulated in unconditioned space		
	• Poor termination location		
	• Termination point not found		
	• Wiring unsafe		

► 13. UNFINISHED BASEMENTS – FIELD CHECKLIST

Note: Electrical, Heating, Air Conditioning and Plumbing systems are inspected separately.

Items that need to be described to meet ASHI® Standards:

INSULATION MATERIALS

☐ Fiberglass
☐ Mineral wool
☐ Cellulose
☐ Vermiculite/perlite
☐ Wood shavings
☐ Plastic/foam board
☐ Sprayed in place
☐ _____

VAPOR RETARDERS

☐ Polyethylene
☐ Kraft paper
☐ Foil
☐ _____

Location Legend   N = North   S = South   E = East   W = West

WET BASEMENTS			
LOCATION		LOCATION	
	• Auxiliary power for sump pump		
	• Cold pours in concrete walls		
	• Crumbling plaster, drywall or concrete walls		
	• Damaged storage		
	• Dampness on floor or walls		
	• Dehumidifier in basement		
	• Drainage membrane		
	• Efflorescence		
	• Floor drain at high spot		
	• Floor patched around perimeter (drainage tile system?)		
	• Floor drain missing		
	• Honeycombing in concrete		
	• Loose floor tiles		
	• Mildew		
	• Mold		
	• New dampproofing material		
	• Odors		
	• Peeling paint		
	• Peripheral drain		
	• Poor gutters and downspouts (control of roof water)		
	• Poor grading (control of surface water)		
	• Recent exterior excavation		
	• Rot		
	• Rust		
	• Spare pump on hand		
	• Stains		
	• Storage kept off floor		
	• Sump pump operating continuously		
	• Sump full		
	• Trough at wall/floor intersection		
	• Wall cracks with water stains		
	• Water marks		
	• Water on floor		

CONCRETE FLOOR SLABS			
LOCATION		LOCATION	
	• Cracked		
	• Heaved		
	• Hollow below slab		
	• Rusted re-bar		
	• Settled		
	• Shaling		
	• Spalling		

STAIRS				
LOCATION	GENERAL	LOCATION	LANDINGS	
	• Mechanical damage		• Missing	
	• Poor lighting		•Too small	
	• Rot			
			HANDRAILS	
	TREADS			
			• Damaged	
	• Excessive nosing		• Hard to hold	
	• Excessive span between stringers		• Loose	
	• Inadequately secured to header		• Missing	
	• Loose		•Too high	
	• Poorly supported		•Too low	
	• Pulling away from wall or treads			
	• Rise excessive		GUARDRAILS	
	• Rise or run not uniform			
	• Rot at bottom		• Damaged	
	• Sloped		• Loose• Missing	
	• Stringers – too small		•Too low	
	• Stringers – excessive notching			
	• Stringers – too thin		SPINDLES OR BALUSTERS	
	•Thickness inadequate			
	•Tread width too small		• Damaged	
	•Winders – too big an angle		• Easy to climb	
	•Winders – too many		• Loose	
	•Worn or damaged		• Missing	
			•Too far apart	
	STAIRWELL			
			FIRE SAFETY	
	• Headroom inadequate			
	•Too narrow		• Drywall missing or incomplete on underside of stairs	

WINDOWS				
LOCATION	GENERAL	LOCATION	INTERIOR TRIM	
	• Air leaks		• Cracked	
	• Lintels sagging or missing		• Loose	
	• Water leaks		• Missing	
			• Poor fit	
	FRAMES		• Rot	
			• Stained	
	• Deformation			
	• Drain holes blocked or missing		GLASS (GLAZING)	
	• Installed backwards			
	• Racked		• Broken	
	• Rot		• Cracked	
	• Rust		• Excess condensation	
			• Loose	
	EXTERIOR DRIP CAPS		• Lost seal on double or triple glazing	
			• Missing	
	• Ineffective			
	• Missing		HARDWARE	
	EXTERIOR TRIM		• Broken	
			• Inoperable	
	• Caulking or flashing missing, deteriorated, loose, rusting or incomplete		• Loose	
	• Damaged, cracked or loose		• Missing	
	• Inadequate sill projection		• Rusted	
	• Missing			
	• No drip edge		LOCATION	
	• Paint or stain needed			
	• Putty (glazing compound) cracked, missing, loose or deteriorated		• Sills too low on stairs or landing	
	• Rot		STORMS AND SCREENS	
	• Rust			
	• Sills with reverse slope		• Loose	
			• Missing	
	SASHES		• Rusted	
			• Torn or holes	
	• Inoperable			
	• Loose fit		MEANS OF EGRESS	
	• Poor weatherstrip			
	• Rot		• Missing	
	• Rust		• Too small	
	• Sash coming apart			
	• Stiff			
	• Won't stay open			

DOORS			
LOCATION	GENERAL	LOCATION	INTERIOR TRIM
	• Air leaks		• Cracked
	• Lintels sagging or missing		• Doorstops missing or ineffective
	• Water leaks		• Floor stained below
			• Guides and stops missing or damaged
	DOORS AND FRAMES		• Loose
			• Missing
	• Damaged		• Poorly fit
	• Dark paint on metal exposed to sun		• Rot
	• Deformation		• Stained
	• Delaminated		
	• Drain holes blocked or missing		GLASS (GLAZING)
	• Inoperable		
	• Installed backwards		• Broken
	• Loose or poor fit		• Cracked
	• Plastic trim on metal door behind storm		• Excess condensation
	• Racked		• Loose
	• Rot		• Lost seal on double or triple glazing
	• Rust		• Missing
	• Stiff		
	• Swings open or closed by itself		HARDWARE
	EXTERIOR DRIP CAP		• Broken
			• Hinges on exterior
	• Ineffective		• Ineffective
	• Missing		• Inoperable
			• Loose
	EXTERIOR TRIM		• Missing
			• Rusted
	• Caulking or flashing missing, deteriorated, loose, rusting or incomplete		• Self-closer missing
	• Damaged, cracked or loose		STORMS AND SCREENS
	• Inadequate sill projection		
	• Missing		• Loose
	• No drip edge		• Missing
	• Paint or stain needed		• Rusted
	• Putty (glazing compound) cracked, missing, loose or deteriorating		• Torn or holes
	• Rot		
	• Rust		
	• Sill not well supported		
	• Sill too low		
	• Sills with reverse sloe		

INSULATION			
LOCATION		LOCATION	
	• Air/vapor barrier missing, incomplete or in wrong location		
	• Exposed combustible insulation		
	• Incomplete		
	• Missing at rim joists		
	• No moisture barrier on basement walls		
	• No moisture barrier on earth floor		
	• Sagging, loose or voids		
	• Too little		

HEAT RECOVERY VENTILATORS				
LOCATION	DUCTS	LOCATION	CONTROLS	
	• Cold-side ducts not insulated		• HRV not interlocked with furnace fan	
	• Damaged		• Ventilation fan switch not labeled	
	• Leaky		• Ventilation fan switch not found	
	• Missing			
	• Poor termination or inlet location		FILTERS	
	• Termination or inlet points not found			
			• Dirty	
	WEATHER HOODS		• Missing	
	• Inadequate backflow prevention on exhaust (flap)		HEAT EXCHANGER CORES	
	• Inadequate screening on inlet		• Dirty	
	• Missing, damaged, loose		• Missing	
	DUCTS AND GRILLES			
	• Balancing dampers missing			
	• Duct vapor barrier missing, damaged or incomplete			
	• Exhaust grilles missing			
	• Flow measuring stations missing			
	• Obstructed			
	• Poor location			
	• Warm-side fresh air duct not properly connected to furnace duct			

FLOOR DRAINS			
LOCATION		LOCATION	
	• Backup		
	• Downspout connection upstream of trap		
	• Grate missing, rusted or obstructed		
	• Missing		
	• No trap		
	• No primer or poor primer arrangement		
	• Poor location		

SUMP PUMPS			
LOCATION		LOCATION	
	• Debris in the sump, clogged sump		
	• Discharge pipe problems		
	• Electrical problems		
	• Excess noise or vibration		
	• Inoperative, poorly secured or rust		
	• Lid missing, rotted or not secure		
	• Missing		
	• Short cycling or running continuously		
	• Sump damaged		

SEWAGE EJECTOR PUMPS			
LOCATION		LOCATION	
	• Alarm sounding		
	• Discharge pipe problems		
	• Electrical problems		
	• Inoperative		
	• Missing, rusting or inoperative union, check valve or gate		
	• No vent		
	• Odor		
	• Short cycling or running continuously		

LAUNDRY TUB PUMPS			
LOCATION		LOCATION	
	• Clogged		
	• Discharge pipe problems		
	• Electrical problems		
	• Excess noise or vibration		
	• Inoperative		
	• Missing		
	• Short cycling or running continuously		

► 14. CRAWLSPACES – FIELD CHECKLIST

DESCRIPTION

Items that need to be described to meet ASHI® Standards:

METHOD USED TO OBSERVE CRAWLSPACE

☐ Access gained
☐ Inspected from access hatch
☐ No access
☐ _____

INSULATION MATERIALS

☐ Fiberglass
☐ Mineral wool
☐ Cellulose
☐ Vermiculite/perlite
☐ Wood shavings
☐ Plastic/foam board
☐ Sprayed in place
☐ _____

VAPOR RETARDERS

☐ Polyethylene
☐ Kraft paper
☐ Foil
☐ _____

Location Legend   N = North   S = South   E = East   W = West
                    1 =1st Floor   2 = 2nd Floor   3 = 3rd Floor   B= Basement   CS = CrawlSpace

	WET CRAWLSPACES		
LOCATION		LOCATION	
	• Auxiliary power for sump pump		
	• Cold pours in concrete walls		
	• Crumbling plaster, drywall or concrete walls		
	• Damaged storage		
	• Dampness on floor or walls		
	• Dehumidifier in crawlspace		
	• Drainage membrane		
	• Efflorescence		
	• Floor drain at high spot		
	• Floor patched around perimeter (drainage tile system?)		
	• Floor drain missing		
	• Honeycombing in concrete		
	• Loose floor tiles		
	• Mildew		
	• Mold		
	• New dampproofing material		
	• Odors		
	• Peeling paint		
	• Peripheral drain		
	• Poor gutters and downspouts (control of roof water)		
	• Poor grading (control of surface water)		
	• Recent exterior excavation		
	• Rot		
	• Rust		
	• Spare pump on hand		
	• Stains		
	• Storage kept off floor		
	• Sump pump operating continuously		
	• Sump full		
	• Trough at wall/floor intersection		
	• Wall cracks with water stains		
	• Water marks		
	• Water on floor		

STRUCTURE			
LOCATION	FOUNDATIONS	LOCATION	BEAMS
	• Bowed, bulging or leaning		• Concentrated loads
	• Cold joints		• Inadequate lateral support
	• Cracks		• Missing beams or sections of beams
	• Crushed		• Notches or holes
	• Foundations too short		• Poor bearing, crushed or loose shims
	• Foundations too thin		• Poor connections of built-up components
	• Hollow masonry units installed on their sides		• Prior repairs
	• Honeycombing		• Rot, insect or fire damage
	• Insect or fire damage		• Rotated or twisted beams
	• Large trees close to building (suspect)		• Rust
	• Lateral support poor		• Sag
	• Lateral movement		• Weak connections to joists
	• Mechanically damaged		• Weak connections to columns
	• Mortar deteriorating or missing		
	• Not well secured		JOISTS
	• Pilasters moving		
	• Prior repairs		• Concentrated loads
	• Rot or wood/soil contact		• Inappropriate notching or holes
	• Spalling, crumbling or broken material		• Ineffective blocking, bracing or bridging
	• Steep slope or unstable soil		• Missing
			• No blocking, bracing or bridging
	SILLS		• Poor end bearing, joist hanger connections
	• Anchor nuts missing		• Prior repairs
	• Anchor washers missing		• Rot, insect or fire damage
	• Anchor bolts too short		• Sag or springy
	• Anchor bolts not secure in foundation		• Split or damaged
	• Anchor bolts missing		• Weak cantilevers
	• Anchor nuts not tightened		• Weak mortise and tenon joints
	• Anchors not centered in sill		• Weak openings (stairs, chimneys, etc.)
	• At or below grade level		
	• Crushed		SUBFLOORING
	• Gaps under sills		
	• Missing		• Concentrated loads
	• Rot, insect or fire damage		• Cracking ceramic tiles
	• Sill split at anchor bolts		• Damaged or cut
			• Plywood in wrong orientation
	COLUMNS OR PIERS		• Poor fastening (nailing, screwing, gluing)
	• Buckling		• Poor end support or cantilevered
	• Crushed		• Prior repairs
	• Heaved		• Rot, insect or fire damage
	• Leaning		• Sag or springy
	• Mechanical damage		• Squeaks
	• Missing		• Swollen waferboard
	• Missing footing?		
	• Mortar deterioration		CONCRETE SLABS
	• Poorly secured at top or bottom		
	• Prior repairs		• Cracked
	• Rot, insect or fire damage		• Heaved
	• Settled		• Hollow below slab
	• Spalling concrete or brick		• Rusted re-bar
			• Settled
			• Shaling
			• Spalling

ELECTRICAL			
LOCATION	WIRING	LOCATION	SWITCHES
	• Abandoned wire		• Damaged, loose
	• Damaged		• Inoperative, obsolete
	• Exposed on walls or ceilings		• Overheated
	• Extension cord used as permanent wiring		
	• Improper color coding		JUNCTION BOXES
	• Loose connections		
	• Missing		• Concealed boxes
	• Not well secured		• Cover loose or missing
	• Open splices		• Damaged
	• Permanent wiring used as extension cord		• Missing, loose
	• Too close to edge of studs or joists		• Not grounded
	• Too close to ducts, pipes, chimneys, etc.		• Overcrowded
	• Undersized wire		• Overheating
	• Wrong type		
			OUTLETS
	KNOB-AND-TUBE		
			• Broken pin or blade in slots
	• Connections need boxes		• Damaged
	• Conventional lights in wet areas		• Inoperative
	• Wire insulation or sheathing brittle		• Loose
			• No GFI
	ALUMINUM		• Open hot
			• Open neutral
	• Connectors not compatible with aluminum		• Overheated neutral
	• No grease on stranded wires		• Overheating
	• Overheating		• Reverse polarity
			• Ungrounded
	LIGHTS		• Worn receptacles
			• Wrong type
	• Damaged		
	• Inoperative		
	• Isolating links needed on pull chains		
	• Loose		
	• Not grounded		
	• Obsolete		
	• Overheating		

PLUMBING				
LOCATION	SUPPLY PIPING IN HOUSES	LOCATION	SUMP PUMPS	
	• Combustible piping		• Debris in the sump, clogged sump	
	• Excessive noise		• Discharge pipe problems	
	• Leaking		• Excess noise or vibration	
	• Non-standard material		• Inoperative, poorly secured or rusted	
	• Poor support		• Lid missing, rotted or not secure	
	• Rust		• Short cycling or running continuously	
	• Split, damaged, crimped		• Sump damaged	
	• Suspect connections on polybutylene			
			SEWAGE EJECTOR PUMPS	
	DRAIN PIPING MATERIALS			
			• Alarm sounding	
	• Clean-outs missing or inaccessible		• Discharge pipe problems	
	• Clogged		• Electrical problems	
	• Combustible piping		• Inoperative	
	• Defective ABS piping		• Missing, rusting or inoperative union, check valve or gate	
	• Exposed to mechanical damage		• No vent	
	• Freezing		• Odor	
	• Galvanized steel pipe buried in soil		• Short cycling or running continuously	
	• Improper condensate drain connections			
	• Leaks		TRAPS	
	• Noisy			
	• Nonstandard materials and patches		• Clogged	
	• Pipe size reduced downstream		• Double trapping	
	• Poor manifolding of drain piping		• Freezing	
	• Poor slope		• Leak	
	• Poor support		• Missing	
	• Rust		• No clean out provision	
	• Split, damaged, crimped		• Nonstandard shape or material	
	• Undersized		• Split, rusted or damaged	
	• Welded steel piping		• Tailpiece (fixture outlet pipe) too long	
			• Trap primer – possible cross connection	
			• Trap primer missing	
			• Trap arm too long or too short	
			• Traps too small or too big	
			• Wrong type	

INSULATION			
LOCATION		LOCATION	
	• Air/vapor barrier missing, incomplete or in wrong location		
	• Exposed combustible insulation		
	• Incomplete		
	• Missing at rim joists		
	• No moisture barrier on earth floor		
	• Sagging, loose or voids		
	• Too little		

Communication &
Professional Practice

M O D U L E

FIELD EXERCISE 1

☑ INSTRUCTIONS

This Field Exercise has three parts. Part A concentrates on verbal communication. Part B focuses on report writing. Part C is a variation on the mock inspection you performed earlier in this Module. You'll want to have access to a home for this Field Exercise. Ideally, you'll also have access to a videotape recorder with a tripod. If you don't have a videotape recorder, an audiotape recorder can be used.

What Business Are We In? Many people think that the home inspection profession is technical. In our opinion, it is roughly 50 percent technical and 50 percent a communication business. We think of ourselves as being in the information transfer business. This sounds a lot like education, doesn't it?

Communication Skills Important Everywhere We are talking about communication skills within the scope of home inspection. Communications skills are obviously important everywhere in your life. It's hard to get through life without communicating with people. Many successful home inspectors work hard on their communication skills. Many have benefitted from joining organizations like Toastmasters.

Exercise A

We're going to break this Exercise into two parts. The first part is going to be working by yourself and the second part is going to be in front of an audience. Start by going back to your notes from the previous Field Exercise and gathering your seller introduction, introductory discussion and closing discussion. If you've done the first Exercise properly, you've practiced this presentation in front of a mirror and then in front of a family member or friend. We're going to take this a step further. Your family member and friend may not have perfect communication skills. We're going to ask you to record (either Video or audio) your presentation and analyze it yourself.

Part 1

1. After making sure you can recite the presentations without referring to notes, turn on the recorder and make your presentation of your seller introduction. Pause and gather yourself.
2. Present your introductory discussion to the recorder. Pause and gather yourself.
3. Present your closing discussion to the recorder.
4. Now play back your presentations.
   - Are you surprised at what you see and hear?
   - Does it need practice?
   - Could it be better?
   - Did you build in any obstacles to good communication?
   - Did you use any techniques for improved communication?
   - Did you attempt to use humor? Were you successful?
5. Rehearse your presentations one more time and then record them a second time. Watch or listen to the first recording and then the second.
   - Did you see improvement?
   - In what areas?
   - Do you still have areas to work on?

Part 2

For this part, we'd like you to perform an inspection. Ideally, it would be a different home than the inspection that you conducted in the first Exercise of this Module. Don't worry about the technical accuracy or completeness of the information. Ask the friend or family member to act as your client. Present the inspection using the introductory discussion script you created in the first Field Exercise in this Module. You can just walk quickly through the house in the pattern you have chosen and discuss the house in very general terms with your "client." Excuse yourself and take a few minutes to gather your thoughts. Now present your closing discussion to the "client."

When you are finished, look at the Communication Questionnaire that follows. Have your friend complete the Questionnaire being as honest as he or she can. Where the rankings were low, see if your friend can provide specifics of the perceived problems. Is there something you can do to improve this communication?

This Exercise can be difficult and stressful. So can a home inspection. It's much better to make mistakes and have the opportunity to correct them in a low pressure situation with a friend, than with a paying client.

As you work through individual Modules of this program, you can practice inspecting individual house systems and providing summaries to friends or relatives. It takes practice to become a good presenter of technical information. Simplicity, clarity and conciseness are the keys. This is a skill that you can develop and continue to refine throughout your career. There is always a better, clearer, shorter way to say something. Many clients miss important points the first time. It's very useful if you can present the same information two or three different ways. Since you don't know what kind of filter systems and decoding systems your audience is using, you will have to guess at the most effective way to present information. We use different words to say the same thing to a 20-year-old artist than to a 60-year-old engineer.

Communication Questionnaire

1. The inspector appeared well-prepared.

True						False
1	2	3	4	5	6	7

2. The conversation was not rushed.

1	2	3	4	5	6	7

3. The inspector's purpose was clear to me.

1	2	3	4	5	6	7

4. The inspector's tone of voice was appropriate.

1	2	3	4	5	6	7

5. The inspector had no distracting mannerisms.

1	2	3	4	5	6	7

6. The conversation was well organized.

1	2	3	4	5	6	7

7. The inspector told me about the entire inspection.

1	2	3	4	5	6	7

8. The inspector pinpointed key information.

1	2	3	4	5	6	7

9. The inspector spoke in easily understood terms.

1	2	3	4	5	6	7

10. The inspector asked me if I had any questions.

1	2	3	4	5	6	7

11. The inspector listened to my concerns.

1	2	3	4	5	6	7

12. The report can be summarized in one sentence as follows:

"

"

Exercise B

In this Field Exercise, you will evaluate some excerpts from actual reports. To the right of each report section is a line. Indicate the type of statement that is made. The categories are –

1. Scope
2. Description
3. Condition
4. Cause
5. Implication
6. Recommended action
7. Life expectancy
8. Priority
9. Ballpark cost

Note: Some statements cover more than one category.

1. *We have visually examined the property in accordance with the Standards of Practice of the American Society of Home Inspectors.* _____

2. *The inspection is not technically exhaustive, nor is this a code compliance inspection.* _____

3. *Cosmetic deficiencies have not been addressed.* _____

4. *Replacement of the clay tile roof covering will be necessary within the next three to five years.* _____

5. *Gutters should be cleared of debris and leaks should be repaired.*

   _____

6. *Caulking and weatherstripping of doors and windows should be improved.*

   _____

7. *The heating system is a gas-fired, forced-air furnace.* _____

8. *This heating system is estimated to be 15 years old and its remaining useful life is estimated at 5 to 10 years.* _____

9. *Recent repairs were noted to a crack in the north brick wall.*

   _____

10. *The south concrete block foundation wall is bowing inward. Approximately three inches of movement was noted near its midpoint.*

    _____

11. *The downspouts should be disconnected from the below grade drainage system and redirected to discharge above grade, six feet from the house.*

    _____

12. *The attic insulation has an R-value of approximately 20. Modern homes have an attic insulation value of roughly R-32.* _____

13. *The air conditioning system was operating properly at the time of the inspection.* _____

14. *The forced-air furnace should be serviced promptly.* _____

15. *The furnace was visually inspected.* _____

16. *The gas-fired, forced-air furnace is approximately 13 years old. Rust was noted at the burners.* _____

17. *The furnace fan is noisy. This may indicate a bearing problem. When the fan fails, the house will be without heat.* _____

18. *No heating source was noted in the master bedroom.* _____

19. *The majority of the heat exchanger could not be inspected.* _____

20. *The furnace is estimated to have 5 to 10 years of life remaining.* _____

21. *Investigating and correcting the cause of the rust at the burners should not be delayed.* _____

22. *The cost of the heating system improvements are noted to be $300 to $500.* _____

23. *The electrical service is 100-amp, 240-volt provided by overhead copper wiring.* _____

24. *The overfusing should be corrected immediately to reduce the threat of fire.* _____

25. *A stain was noted near the center of the master bedroom ceiling.* _____

26. *Aluminum wiring was noted in the circuits supplying the family room. No deficiencies were noted in the installation.* _____

27. *The electrical outlets should be replaced with those specifically designed for use with aluminum wiring. Alternatively, specialized connectors compatible with aluminum and copper wiring should be employed.* _____

28. *The supply plumbing is copper. Waste plumbing is a combination of copper and plastic.* _____

29. *Two cracks were noted on the north side of the foundation wall. The cracks are approximately $1\frac{1}{8}$ inch wide and extend vertically from the basement floor to the top of the foundation.* _____

30. *The horizontal cracking in the foundation wall approximately four feet above the basement floor on the west side of the building is the result of exterior pressure on the wall, probably from frost.* _____

31. *The unevenness of the living room floor is the result of crowned joists and no remedial action is considered necessary.*

32. *No warranty or guarantee is expressed or implied as a result of this inspection.* _____

33. *This report was intended for the use of the named client. No usage by a third party is anticipated.* _____

34. *No inspection or comment is offered with respect to termites or environmental concerns.* _____

35. Structure

   a. ☐ Concrete block foundations
   b. ☐ Brick foundations
   c. ☐ No structural defects observed
   d. ☐ Walls out of plumb
   e. ☐ Poured concrete foundations
   f. ☐ Foundations not visible
   g. ☐ Cracks noted in walls
   h. ☐ Deterioration noted to wall

36. *The lead waste plumbing under the second floor bathroom should be replaced with copper or plastic.* _____

37 *The structure is in good condition. (Risky statement!)* _____

38. *There are no leaks in the plumbing system. (Another risky one!)* _____

39. *An exhaust fan should be added in the main bathroom.* _____

40. *The leaking gutters may cause basement leakage and should be replaced promptly.* _____

41. *The missing ground wire on the electrical service entrance is a safety hazard which should be corrected promptly.*

42. *The chimney height should be extended to improve draft and reduce the risk of fire caused by flying brands.* _____

43. *A railing should be added on the main staircase.* _____

44. *The deteriorated chimneys should be repaired or replaced, as necessary. This is a safety hazard.* _____

45. *All exterior wood trim should be painted or stained and caulked as necessary. This work is typically required every four to six years.* _____

46. *The electrical service should be upgraded to 200 amps.* _____

47. *The cost is estimated at $1,200 to $1,800.* _____

48. *All exterior walls are plumb and square.* (Risky statement!)

_____

49. *The floor joists are typically two inches by eight inches, spaced 16 inches on center and span approximately 11 feet.* _____

50. *Telescopic steel posts should be provided in the basement to support the main beam (cost approximately $300 each).* _____

Answers are provided on the next page.

Answers:

1. *We have visually examined the property in accordance with the Standards of Practice of the American Society of Home Inspectors.* **Scope**

2. *The inspection is not technically exhaustive, nor is this a code compliance inspection.* **Limitation**

3. *Cosmetic deficiencies have not been addressed.* **Limitation**

4. *Replacement of the clay tile roof covering will be necessary within the next three to five years.* **Recommended action** and **life expectancy**

5. Gutters should be cleared of debris and leaks should be repaired. Recommended action

6. *Caulking and weatherstripping of doors and windows should be improved.* **Recommended action**

7. *The heating system is a gas-fired, forced-air furnace.* **Description**

8. *This heating system is estimated to be 15 years old and its remaining useful life is estimated at 5 to 10 years.* **Description** and **life expectancy**

9. *Recent repairs were noted to a crack in the north brick wall.* **Description** and **condition**

10. *The south concrete block foundation wall is bowing inward. Approximately three inches of movement was noted near its midpoint.* **Condition**

11. *The downspouts should be disconnected from the below grade drainage system and redirected to discharge above grade, six feet from the house.* **Recommended action**

12. *The attic insulation has an R-value of approximately 20. Modern homes have an attic insulation value of roughly R-32.* **Description** and **condition**

13. *The air conditioning system was operating properly at the time of the inspection.* **Description**

14. *The forced-air furnace should be serviced promptly.* **Recommended action**

15. *The furnace was visually inspected.* **Scope** and/or **limitation**

16. *The gas-fired, forced-air furnace is approximately 13 years old. Rust was noted at the burners.* **Description** and **condition**

17. *The furnace fan is noisy. This may indicate a bearing problem. When the fan fails, the house will be without heat.* **Condition, cause,** and **implication**

18. *No heating source was noted in the master bedroom.* **Condition**

19. *The majority of the heat exchanger could not be inspected.* **Limitation**

20. *The furnace is estimated to have 5 to 10 years of life remaining.* **Life expectancy**

21. *Investigating and correcting the cause of the rust at the burners should not be delayed.* **Recommended action** and **priority**

22. *The cost of the heating system improvements are noted to be $300 to $500.* **Ballpark cost**

23. *The electrical service is 100-amp, 240-volt provided by overhead copper wiring.* **Description**

24. *The overfusing should be corrected immediately to reduce the threat of fire.* **Recommended action** and **implication**

25. *A stain was noted near the center of the master bedroom ceiling.* **Condition** (and its location)

26. *Aluminum wiring was noted in the circuits supplying the family room. No deficiencies were noted in the installation.* **Description** and **condition**

27. *The electrical outlets should be replaced with those specifically designed for use with aluminum wiring. Alternatively, specialized connectors compatible with aluminum and copper wiring should be employed.* **Recommended action**

28. *The supply plumbing is copper. Waste plumbing is a combination of copper and plastic.* **Description**

29. *Two cracks were noted on the north side of the foundation wall. The cracks are approximately $^{11}/_{48}$ inch wide and extend vertically from the basement floor to the top of the foundation.* **Condition**

30. *The horizontal cracking in the foundation wall approximately four feet above the basement floor on the west side of the building is the result of exterior pressure on the wall, probably from frost.* **Condition** and **cause**

31. *The unevenness of the living room floor is the result of crowned joists and no remedial action is considered necessary.* **Condition, cause, recommended action**

32. *No warranty or guarantee is expressed or implied as a result of this inspection.* **Limitation/scope**

33. *This report was intended for the use of the named client. No usage by a third party is anticipated.* **Scope**

34. *No inspection or comment is offered with respect to termites or environmental concerns.* **Scope**

35. Structure

a. ☐ *Concrete block foundations* **Description**
b. ☐ *Brick foundations* **Description**
c. ☐ *No structural defects observed* **Condition**
d. ☐ *Walls out of plumb* **Condition**
e. ☐ *Poured concrete foundations* **Description**
f. ☐ *Foundations not visible* **Limitation**
g. ☐ *Cracks noted in walls* **Condition**
h. ☐ *Deterioration noted to wall* **Condition**

36. *The lead waste plumbing under the second floor bathroom should be replaced with copper or plastic.* **Recommended action**

37 *The structure is in good condition. (Risky statement!)* **Condition**

38. *There are no leaks in the plumbing system. (Another risky one!)* **Condition**

39. *An exhaust fan should be added in the main bathroom.* **Recommended action**

40. *The leaking gutters may cause basement leakage and should be replaced promptly.* **Cause, implication** and **recommended action**

41. *The missing ground wire on the electrical service entrance is a safety hazard which should be corrected promptly.* **Cause, implication** and **recommended action**

42. *The chimney height should be extended to improve draft and reduce the risk of fire caused by flying brands.* **Recommended action** and **implication**

43 *A railing should be added on the main staircase.* **Recommended action**

44. *The deteriorated chimneys should be repaired or replaced, as necessary. This is a safety hazard.* **Recommended action** and **implication**

45. *All exterior wood trim should be painted or stained and caulked as necessary. This work is typically required every four to six years.* **Recommended action** and **life expectancy**

46. *The electrical service should be upgraded to 200 amps.* **Recommended action**

47. *The cost is estimated at $1,200 to $1,800.* **Ballpark cost**

48. *All exterior walls are plumb and square. (Risky statement!)* **Condition**

49. *The floor joists are typically two inches by eight inches, spaced 16 inches on center and span approximately 11 feet.* **Description**

50 *Telescopic steel posts should be provided in the basement to support the main beam (cost approximately $300 each).* **Recommended action** and **cost**

Exercise C

This part of the Exercise is designed to have you evaluate the steps in an inspection and decide which are necessary for you. We're going to ask you to go back and review the step-by-step home inspection in Section 5.0. Look at each item and determine what the implications would be of leaving out this step. Think about your own home inspection activity and determine which of these steps you can safely omit. Any steps you can omit will make your inspection faster and your life easier. One less thing to do is one less thing to remember. As you write down the implications of omitting these steps, it should become apparent to you which are important and which are not.

Step   Implication of Omitting this Step

1. _____

_____

2. _____

_____

3. _____

_____

4. _____

_____

5. _____

_____

6. _____

_____

7. _____

_____

8. _____

_____

9. _____

_____

10. _____
    _____

11. _____
    _____

12. _____
    _____

13. _____
    _____

14. _____
    _____

15. _____
    _____

16. _____
    _____

17. _____
    _____

18. _____
    _____

19. _____
    _____

20. _____
    _____

21. _____
    _____

22. _____
    _____

23. _____

_____

24. _____

_____

25. _____

_____

26. _____

_____

27. _____

_____

28. _____

_____

29. _____

_____

30. _____

_____

31. _____

_____

32. _____

_____

33. _____

_____

34. _____

_____

35. _____

_____

36. _____
    _____

37. _____
    _____

38. _____
    _____

39. _____
    _____

40. _____
    _____

41. _____
    _____

42. _____
    _____

43. _____
    _____

44. _____
    _____

45. _____
    _____

46. _____
    _____

47. _____
    _____

48. _____

_____

49. _____

_____

50. _____

_____

When you have completed the Field Exercise, have a look at the list of Inspection Tools and then you will be ready for the Final Test.

► 7.0 INSPECTION TOOLS

The most important tools that home inspectors have are their eyes, ears, noses, sense of touch and, of course, their brains.

The following tools are also useful. We've broken them down into a basic and optional list. There's nothing magic about this list. Some people will think there are other tools that should be on the basic list, and some will think that some of the basic tools are optional. We offer this simply as a starting point.

BASIC

Binoculars
To look at parts of the home you can't get to.

Flashlight
To look at poorly lit parts of the house and to scan along interior surfaces for irregularities. Flashlights can also be used to tap on siding to determine the substrate. Some inspectors use the end of their flashlight to push open the attic access hatch to avoid getting fingerprints on it.

Spare Flashlight Batteries and Bulbs
To make sure you always have a working flashlight.

Ladder – Step, Extension and/or Foldable
To get to roofs and attics.

Screwdrivers — Assortment
To open electrical panels, remove access hatches and so on.

Carpenter's Awl
To probe wood for rot or insect damage.

Telescopic Mirror – Small
To inspect furnace heat exchangers and other confined areas.

Measuring Tape – 25-Foot-Long, One-Inch-Wide Blade
To measure structural members, roof areas, chimney heights, window sizes, stair risers, etc.

Electrical Circuit Tester
To check that receptacles are wired correctly.

Knife
To probe wood for damage, scrape off paint labels, break paint seals on access hatches, dig paint out of screw slots, etc.

Gloves
To protect hands from hot roofs and irritating insulation.

Coveralls

To keep clothing clean while in attics and crawlspaces. A plastic bag for soiled coveralls is a good idea.

Pliers – We like Channel Lock or Slip Joint

To turn screws where slots are worn or where nuts have been used instead of screws.

Briefcase or Tool Kit

To carry your tools.

OPTIONAL

Tool Belt

To carry tools and keep hands free.

Mask

To avoid inhaling insulation fibers in attics.

Flashlight Belt Loops

This loop attaches to your belt and you can hang your flashlight from it to keep your hands free.

Trouble Light – A Plug-in Light With Extension Cord

To illuminate crawlspaces and other poorly lit areas where a flashlight may not be adequate.

Drop Sheet

To put over clothes in closets and below attic hatches to protect the home from dirt and insulation.

Large Mirror – Six Inches By 10 Inches

To look behind water heaters, furnaces, oil tanks and other spaces that are too small to get into, but not as confined as a furnace heat exchanger.

Wet Wipes, Paper Towels, Towels or Rags

To clean up during and/or after an inspection. We prefer not to use the seller's washroom facilities and hand towels. Towels and rags are also useful for wiping off data plates on heating and cooling equipment so they can be read.

Moisture Meter or Moisture Scanner

To look for elevated moisture levels in suspect areas and to check stains for evidence of moisture.

Voltage Detector

To determine whether wiring is energized.

Ampmeter

To verify correct operation of electric furnace, for example.

Plumb Bob
To measure the amount by which columns or walls are out of plumb.

Mason's Level – Four-Foot Spirit Level
To measure amount by which walls or columns are out of plumb, and floors, walls or ceilings are out of level. Can also be used to measure slope of gutters, waste plumbing pipes or appliances vents.

Extendable Probe
To check for rot in places that cannot be reached from the ground or floor level.

Nut Driver
To remove nuts that may have been used in electrical panels, access covers, etc.

Power Screwdriver
To facilitate removal and replacement of screws from panels, access hatches, etc.

Crescent Wrench
To remove and replace bolts.

Hammer
To pull out and replace nails, sealing, access hatches and so on.

Goggles
To keep insulation and other irritants out of your eyes.

Camera – Polaroid, 35mm, Digital or Video
To record your findings. Note: Some inspectors include photographs of the home in their reports. Some give copies of videotapes to clients.

Carbon Monoxide Sensor
To check for holes in heat exchangers and possible backdraft problems.

Combustible Gas Analyzer
To check for gas leaks, backdraft and holes in heat exchangers.

Compass
To determine which way the house faces. This can be helpful in order to know where prevailing winds or wind-driven rain comes from. Also, if you use the compass points to describe locations of the house in your report, this helps to ensure that you describe the house correctly.

Samples of Various Sizes of Electrical Wire
To help you identify wire sizes in the field.

Wire Gauge
To help you identify wire sizes in the field.

Samples of Various Plumbing Pipe Sizes and Materials
To help identify plumbing pipes in the field.

Magnet

To help differentiate between galvanized steel and copper gutters, galvanized steel and brass piping, etc.

Latex Gloves (Surgical Gloves)

To keep hands clean and avoid getting fingerprints on house components.

Electrical Tape

To make temporary repairs to problems (not recommended by writers, but done by some inspectors).

Thermometer

To check temperature rise and temperature drop across furnace heat exchangers and air conditioning and heat pump coils.

There are other instruments that may be used during home inspections. These are a majority of the common ones.

ANSWERS TO QUICK QUIZZES

Answers to Quick Quiz 1

1. Communication is the transfer of information and comprehension through the use of common symbols.

2. 1. Sender
   2. Receiver
   3. Message
   4. Encoding
   5. Decoding
   6. Feedback
   7. Improving communication
   8. Communication elements
   9. Communication obstacles
   10. Effective listening

3. 1. Sender
   2. Message
   3. Medium
   4. Receiver
   5. Response (feedback)

4. 1. Encoding
   2. Decoding
   3. Noise
   4. Personal filter area

5. a. Sender – the person who has the information and who starts the communication.
   b. Receiver – the person who receives and decodes the message.
   c. The message – what the sender hopes to communicate to the receiver.
   d. Medium – the medium is the form of the message (e.g., fax, telephone, e-mail, face-to-face dialogue)
   e. Encoding – the translation of the sender's ideas and information into a set of symbols
   f. Decoding – the process of translation and interpretation of the message by the receiver
   g. Feedback – the response that the receiver gives the sender after decoding the message
   h. Personal filter areas – include communication barriers, a lack of common experience between the sender and receiver and different frames of reference
   i. Noise – can distort or break down the communications. Noises include a distracting mannerism, odor or article of clothing. Personal discomfort is another kind of noise.

6. 1. Paraverbals (how something was said)
   2. Body language

7. 1. Illustrators
   2. Emblems
   3. Regulators
   4. Adaptors
   5. Affect displays

8. 1. Failure to maintain eye contact
   2. Nervous habits such as biting fingernails or shifting weight
   3. Speaking quickly or mumbling
   4. Sitting while your listeners are standing
   5. Leaning against a wall while talking

9. 1. Different personal filter areas
   2. Credibility of the sender
   3. Jargon
   4. Semantic differences
   5. Proximity of the persons communicating
   6. Information overload
   7. Time constraints
   8. Poor location

10. 1. Use feedback
    2. Provide the message at a rate the receiver can absorb
    3. Ensuring the timing of the message is appropriate
    4. Use simple language
    5. Be empathetic to the receiver
    6. Use repetition
    7. Encourage trust to enhance credibility
    8. Create an effective listening environment

Answers to Quick Quiz 2

1. 1. The Standards require it
   2. To help the client
   3. To control your liability
   4. Marketing tool

2. 1. On site reports
   2. Reports sent after the inspection

3. 1. Checklist
   2. Narrative
   3. Combination

4.
1. Scope/contract
2. Descriptions
3. Conditions or evaluations
4. Causes of conditions
5. Implications of conditions
6. Recommended actions
7. Limitations
8. Life expectancy
9. Priorities
10. Ballpark costs

5.
1. Scope – the inspection was done according to the ASHI® Standards
2. Descriptions – the roofing material is asphalt shingle
3. Conditions or evaluations – the water heater is leaking
4. Causes of conditions – the wet basement is a result of the leaking gutters and downspouts
5. Implications – the uneven stairs are a trip hazard
6. Recommended actions – the 30-amp fuses should be replaced with 15-amp fuses
7. Limitations – No access was gained to the crawlspace
8. Life expectancy – replacement of the roof covering will probably be necessary within the next three to six years
9. Priorities – the open electrical box should be provided with a cover immediately and the service should be upgraded to 200-amps within the next year
10. Ball park – furnace replacement may cost $1,500 – $2,500

6. Descriptions and conditions.

7.
1. Report summary
2. Client questionnaire
3. Maintenance tips
4. Filing systems
5. Life cycle and cost estimates

Answers to Quick Quiz 3

1. People will tell you that you let them down by failing to identify or properly diagnose problems.

2.
1. You were clearly right
2. You were clearly wrong
3. It's difficult to know

3. If a competent inspector under the same circumstances would have found the problem, the claim may have merit.

4. Contractors often indicate that a home inspector should have identified the problem.

5. People tend to believe the most recent information they have heard.

6. 1. Prevention strategies
   2. Response strategies

7. Part 1 – Prevention Strategies
   1. Perform a competent inspection
   2. Adjust client expectations
   3. Describe your scope of work
   4. Define your specific limitations
   5. Keep your comments within your scope of work
   6. Inspect at a consistent depth
   7. Don't report as facts things that you are told
   8. Avoid superficial walk-through inspections
   9. Use a clear and meaningful contract
   10. Tell your clients they should expect things to go wrong

   Part 2 – Response Strategies
   1. Respond as quickly as possible
   2. Don't avoid the issue
   3. Don't argue with the client over the phone
   4. Don't accept as fact anything you are told
   5. Go back to the home
   6. Try to find a resolution that leaves the client satisfied
   7. Follow up as quickly as possible
   8. If there is a problem with the home, acknowledge the problem
   9. Come to a resolution as quickly as possible
   10. Use the "WHEN THINGS GO WRONG" document in your report

8. 1. Office provides you with inspection information
   2. Fill in the buyer's name and address on the contract
   3. Prepare the invoice
   4. Memorize the buyer's names
   5. Memorize the listing agent's and selling agent's names
   6. Locate the inspection address on a map and plan your route
   7. Determine the time you have to leave to arrive at the inspection early
   8. Review your inspection routine
   9. Review your script for your introductory and closing discussions
   10. Review your time goals for the inspection
   11. Check your vehicle
   12. Check your personal condition
   13. Leave the office at the appropriate time
   14. Drive past the home to confirm the address
   15. Drive the neighborhood
   16. Park on the street

17. Turn off your cell phone or pager
18. Make sure you've memorized the names of buyers and agents
19. Get your equipment out of your vehicle
20. Ring the front doorbell with a business card and seller's letter in hand
21. Introduce yourself to the seller and follow your script
22. Take the tools you'll need for your exterior tour
23. Do your exterior tour around the building
24. Smile and look people in the eye as you approach the agents or buyers
25. Introduce yourself
26. If it is an agent or someone else, follow that script
27. If it is the buyer, follow your buyer introductory script
28. Perform your roof inspection
29. Ask the client if everything is in order and complete your introductory discussion
30. Discuss the roof results
31. Start your exterior tour with your clients
32. Establish your technical credibility on the exterior
33. Inspect the garage or carport if you can
34. Summarize the exterior
35. Knock on the door and head inside
36. Discuss with the seller where you'll be going
37. Follow your routine, starting with the heating and cooling system (for example)
38. Check the electrical system and summarize results
39. Check the plumbing system and summarize results
40. Check the structure and summarize results
41. Perform your first interior tour
42. Perform your second interior tour
43. Check the attic and crawlspace
44. Excuse yourself to write your report or complete your notes
45. Let the client know you are going to summarize the report
46. Summarize your report
47. Ask if they have any questions
48. Use your payment script
49. Thank your client, invite them to call anytime and ask them to complete the questionnaire
50. Thank the agents and sellers, say goodbye and leave the property